The ARRL
General Class
License Manual

Edited By:

Larry D. Wolfgang, WR1B

Production Staff:

Joe Shea, Production Assistant: Layout

David Pingree, **N1NAS**, Senior Technical Illustrator:
Technical Illustrations

Steffie Nelson, **KA1IFB**, Proofreader

Jodi Morin, **KA1JPA**, Assistant Production Supervisor: Layout

Paul Lappen, Production Assistant: Layout

Sue Fagan, Graphics Design Supervisor: Cover Design

Michael Daniels, Technical Illustrator: Technical Illustrations

Michelle Bloom, **WB1ENT**, Production Supervisor: Layout

Published By:

The American Radio Relay League, Inc.
Newington, CT 06111-1494

Our cover: Map artwork reproduced with permission from the ARRL Amateur Radio Map of the World, copyright 1998 GeoSystems Global Corp.

Front cover photo: Glenn Swanson, KB1GW, and Peter Budnick, KB1HY, operate W1AW in a contest. (*Photo by Brad Thomas, KC1EX.*)

Back cover photo: Sumner Weisman, W1VIV, enjoys contest operating. (*Photo by Sumner Weisman, W1VIV.*)

Cover design by Sue Fagan.

Contents

FOREWORD

Congratulations! You have selected a wonderful time to earn your General Amateur Radio license. As this book goes to press we are in the early stages of Solar Cycle 23. That means for the next three or four years, worldwide propagation on our HF bands will be improving. Then we can expect several more years of "hot" propagation before the cycle drops off. You will be enjoying the thrill of working DX around the clock. Experience the magic of radio at its best.

Earning the General license will add to your enjoyment of Amateur Radio far beyond the effort required to learn the material in this book and pass your exam. You will gain access to major portions of all our amateur HF bands. You will be permitted to use a wide variety of operating modes on those bands, as well. Go ahead. Accept the challenge to earn your General license and prepare for more Amateur Radio excitement than you can imagine.

For more than 65 years, the ARRL has produced the most widely used, most complete license preparation materials available to prospective radio amateurs. The ARRL offers video study materials and computerized exam review software in addition to printed license manuals. We also offer a full range of Morse code training and practice materials. The ARRL's *Your Introduction to Morse Code* as well as our *Increasing Your Code Speed* series, with sets to take you from *5 to 10 WPM*, from *10 to 15 WPM* and from *15 to 22 WPM*, are now each available as a set of two cassette tapes or two audio CDs. For those who prefer the unlimited practice and code speeds of a computer program, we offer the excellent GGTE *Morse Tutor* and *Morse Tutor Gold* programs for IBM-PC compatible computers.

In this third edition of *The ARRL General Class License Manual* you will find all of the material you need to pass the Element 3B written exam! There is study material to explain every question in the General question pool. Chapter 10 includes detailed information about the FCC RF Safety topic that was added to this question pool.

Chapter 12 is the complete General question pool as released by the Volunteer-Examiner Coordinators' Question Pool Committee in December 1997 for use beginning July 1, 1998. It has been laid out so you can drill yourself on the actual examination questions, to check your understanding of the study material. The answer key is included on the same page as each question, for your convenience. If you do well answering the questions from the pool, you can be confident when you go to take the actual exam.

Of course you aren't studying just to pass a license exam, and we aren't satisfied just to help you pass that exam! We want you to enjoy every aspect of this avocation. That's why we have included Chapter 11, Setting Up Your HF Station. We want to help you get on the air and use those new privileges. The ARRL provides plenty of technical material and operating aids in the many books and supplies that make up our "Radio Amateur's Library." Contact the Publication Sales Office at ARRL Headquarters to request the latest publications catalog or to place an order. (You can reach us by phone — 860-594-0200; by fax — 860-594-0303; by electronic mail — **pubsales@arrl.org**; and now on the World Wide Web — **http://www.arrl.org/**)

This third edition of *The ARRL General Class License Manual* is not just the product of the many ARRL staff members who have helped bring the book to you. Readers of the earlier editions sent comments and suggestions; you can, too. First, use this book to prepare for your exam. Then, write your suggestions (or any corrections you think need to be made) on the Feedback Form at the back of the book, and send the form to us. Your comments and suggestions are important to us. Thanks, and good luck!

David Sumner, K1ZZ
Executive Vice President, ARRL
Newington, Connecticut

HOW TO USE THIS BOOK

To earn a General Amateur Radio license, you will have to know some electronics theory and the rules and regulations governing the Amateur Service, as contained in Part 97 of the FCC Rules. You'll also have to be able to send and receive the international Morse code at a rate of 13 wpm. This book provides a brief description of the Amateur Service, and the General license in particular. Applicants for the General license must pass a 30-question written exam drawn from the Element 3B question pool, as released by the Volunteer-Examiner Coordinators' Question Pool Committee (QPC), and the Element 1B (13 wpm) Morse code exam.

Please note that each class of Amateur Radio license requires that you pass all of the exam elements below that class as well. So if you hold a Novice license, for example, you will also have to pass the Element 3A — Technician — exam. (If you don't already have an Amateur Radio license, you will also have to pass the Element 2 — Novice — exam as well as the Element 3A exam.) Chapter 12 of this book contains the complete Element 3B question pool and multiple-choice answers released by the VEC QPC in December 1997 for use starting July 1, 1998.

At the beginning of each chapter, you will find a list of **Key Words** that appear in that chapter, along with a simple definition for each word or phrase. As you read the text, you will find these words printed in **boldface type** the first time they appear. You may want to refer to the **Key Words** list at the beginning of the chapter when you come to a **boldface** word, to review the definition. After you have studied the material in that chapter, you may also want to review those definitions. Most of the key words are terms that will appear on exam questions, so a quick review of the definitions just before you go to take the test may also be helpful. Appendix C is a glossary of all the key words used in the book. They are arranged in alphabetical order for your convenience as you review before the exam.

The Question Pool

As you study the material, you will be instructed to turn to sections of the questions in Chapter 12. Be sure to use these questions to review your understanding of the material at the suggested times. This breaks the material into bite-sized pieces, and makes it easier for you to learn. Do not try to memorize all of the questions and answers. With over 350 questions, that will be nearly impossible! Instead, by using the questions for review, you will be familiar with them when you take the test, but you will also understand the electronics theory or Rules point behind each question.

Most people learn more easily when they are actively involved in the learning process. Study the text, rather than passively reading it. Use the questions to review your progress rather than just reading the question and looking at the correct answer letter. Fold the answer-key column under at the dashed line down the page before you begin answering questions on that page. Look at the answer key only to verify your answer. This will help you check your progress and ensure you know the answer to each question. If you missed one, go back to the supporting text and review that material. Page numbers are included with each answer letter. These indicate where to turn in the book to find the explanatory text for that question. You may have to read more than one page for the complete explanation. Paper clips make excellent place markers to help you find your spot in the text and question pool.

Other ARRL Study Materials

If you need to learn Morse code, ARRL offers a set of two audio CDs or cassette tapes to teach Morse code: *Your Introduction to Morse Code*. This package introduces each of the required characters one at a time, and drills you on each character as it is introduced. Then the character is used in words and text before proceeding to the next character. After all characters have been introduced, there is plenty of practice at 5 wpm to help you prepare for the Element 1A (5 wpm) exam. ARRL also offers several audio-CD or cassette-tape sets to help you increase your speed: *Increasing Your Code Speed*: *5 to 10 WPM, 10 to 15 WPM* and *15 to 22 WPM*. Each set includes two 74-minute audio CDs or cassette tapes with a variety of practice at gradually increasing speeds over the range for that set. The Morse code is sent using 18-wpm characters, with extra space between characters to slow the overall code speed, for code up to 18 wpm. This same technique is used on ARRL/VEC Morse code exams for 5 and 13 wpm.

For those who prefer a computer program to learn and practice Morse code, ARRL offers the excellent GGTE *Morse Tutor* program for IBM PC and compatible computers.

Even with the tapes or computer program, you'll want to tune in the code-practice sessions transmitted by W1AW, the ARRL Headquarters station. When you are able to copy the code at 15 wpm, you should be ready for your 13 wpm exam! You may find it helpful to listen to the W1AW fast-code-practice sessions as you near your goal. These sessions start at 35 wpm and decrease to 30, 25 and 20 wpm before slowing to the 15 and 13-wpm practice. You can ignore the 35 to 25-wpm practice, and start with the 20-wpm practice and then the 15 and 13-wpm practice. You might also want to try copying the W1AW CW bulletins, which are sent at 18 wpm. (There is a W1AW code-practice schedule on page 8 in the Introduction.) For more information about W1AW or how to order any ARRL publication or set of code tapes, write to ARRL Headquarters, 225 Main St, Newington, CT 06111-1494 or contact us at **http://www.arrl.org/** on the World Wide Web.

WHEN TO USE THIS BOOK

All VECs must cooperate to produce the question pools used for all Amateur Radio license exams. The following schedule describes the expected implementation dates for the next cycle of new question pools:

Pool	*Effective Date*
Novice (Element 2)	July 1, 2001*
Technician (Element 3A)	July 1, 2001*
General (Element 3B)	July 1, 2002*
Advanced (Element 4A)	July 1, 1999
Amateur Extra (Element 4B)	July 1, 2000*

*Tentative date

When the schedule for each new question pool is confirmed, the information will be published in *QST*. New editions of ARRL License Manuals that cover the new question pools will be available before the effective dates of the new pools.

CODE EXAMINATION CREDIT FOR HANDICAPPED PERSONS

Effective February 14, 1991, FCC adopted Rules pertaining to Morse code examinations for handicapped persons. Applicants must have a current FCC amateur license that required a code test. If the license has expired, it must be within the grace period for renewal. Valid licenses include:
•Novice
•Technician Plus
•Technician and a Certificate of Successful Completion of Examination (CSCE)
  for passing Element 1A or 1B
•Technician issued before February 14, 1991
•General
•Advanced

Effective January 1, 1998, all applicants must use a Form 610 dated September 1997 or later in the lower right-hand corner (the latest form as of this printing is dated September 1997.). The back of the form includes the "PHYSICIAN'S CERTIFICATION OF DISABILITY" section, which must be completed and signed by a person licensed to practice in a place where the Amateur Service is regulated by the FCC as a doctor of medicine (MD) or doctor of osteopathy (DO). After the physician signs the Form 610, the applicant must also sign in the same section, granting the physician permission to disclose medical information relevant to the application. The back of the Form 610 also includes a "NOTICE TO PHYSICIAN CERTIFYING TO A DISABILITY," which describes the Morse code exam procedures, including exam accommodations that can be made for handicapped persons.

To obtain a new Form 610, call 800-418-3676. You can also write to: Federal Communications Commission, Forms Distribution Center, 2803 52nd Ave, Hyattsville, MD 20781 (specify "Form 610" on the envelope), or send a business-sized, self-addressed, stamped envelope to: Form 610, ARRL, 225 Main St, Newington, CT 06111-1494. The Form 610 also is available from the FCC's fax on demand service. Call 202-418-0177 and ask for form number 000610. Form 610 also is available via the Internet. The World Wide Web location is: **http://www.fcc.gov/Forms/Form610** or you can receive the form via ftp to: **ftp.fcc.gov/pub/Forms/Form610**.

INTRODUCTION

THE GENERAL LICENSE

Some people prefer to earn the General license as their first "ticket." For those who start out at the Novice, Technician or Technician Plus level, this license provides a giant step in amateur privileges. After all, the General license grants high-power phone privileges on the amateur HF bands.

If you have put off earning your General license because you thought the electronics theory was too difficult, or the 13 wpm Morse code speed was an impossible goal, put those thoughts aside right now! Once you make the commitment to study and learn what it takes to pass the exam, however, you *will* be able to do it. It may take more than one attempt to pass the exam, but many amateurs do pass on their first try. The key is that you must make the commitment, and be willing to study. The ARRL offers Morse code training and practice on audio CDs as well as cassette tapes. If you want a computer program to learn Morse code, the GGTE *Morse Tutor* or *Morse Tutor Gold* is hard to beat. These programs are also available from the ARRL. There is more information about practicing Morse code later in this chapter.

With this book, carefully designed to teach the required electronics theory, operating practices and FCC Rules for your Element 3B General license exam and plenty of Morse code practice, you will soon have that higher class license.

Chapter 1 of this book, Commission's Rules covers those sections of the FCC Part 97 Rules that you will be tested on for your General license. We recommend that you also obtain a copy of *The FCC Rule Book*, published by ARRL, which includes a complete copy of Part 97, along with detailed explanations for *all* the rules governing Amateur Radio.

Chapters 2 through 10 cover the remaining nine subelements for the General license exam. All of the questions in the General question pool are covered in this book. Chapter 11 provides some hints and guidelines for selecting equipment, set-

Figure 1 — A guest operator at ARRL's Hiram Percy Maxim Memorial Station, W1AW, enjoys a Morse code chat (QSO) with another ham.

ting up and operating your HF Amateur Radio station. Chapter 12 contains the complete question pool, with answers, for the General license exam.

Whether you now hold a Novice, Technician or Technician Plus license, or even if you don't yet have any license, you will find the operating privileges available to a General licensee to be worth the time spent learning about your hobby. General operators are allowed to use substantial portions of every amateur high-frequency band. World-wide communication through Morse code and voice operation — as well as modes such as slow-scan TV (SSTV), radioteletype (RTTY) and facsimile (fax) — is available to General licensees.

You can see that the General license allows a wide range of transmitting privileges. It is no wonder that this is one of the most popular license classes in the US. To earn those extra privileges, however, you will have to demonstrate that you know the international Morse code, basic electronic theory, operating practices and FCC Rules and regulations. This book is designed to teach you everything you need to know to qualify for the General Amateur Radio license.

IF YOU'RE A NEWCOMER TO AMATEUR RADIO

Earning an Amateur Radio license, at whatever level, is a special achievement. Nearly $^3/_4$ of a million people in the US call themselves Amateur Radio operators, or hams. We are also part of a much larger global fraternity. Radio amateurs serve the public as a voluntary, noncommercial, communication service. This is especially true during natural disasters or other emergencies. Hams have made

Figure 2 — Once you begin operating on the amateur HF bands, you will soon begin to collect many colorful QSL cards. Many of them will likely be from countries around the world.

many important contributions to the field of electronics and communications, and this tradition continues today. Amateur Radio experimentation is yet another reason many people become part of this self-disciplined group of trained operators, technicians and electronics experts — an asset to any country. Hams pursue their hobby purely for personal enrichment in technical and operating skills, without consideration of any type of payment except the personal satisfaction they feel from a job well done!

Radio signals do not know territorial boundaries, so hams have a unique ability (and responsibility) to enhance international goodwill. Hams become ambassadors of their country every time they put their stations on the air.

Amateur Radio has been around since before World War I, and hams have always been at the forefront of technology. Today, hams operate their own "packet-switched" computer communications networks, relay signals through their own satellites in the OSCAR (Orbiting Satellite Carrying Amateur Radio) series, bounce signals off the moon and use any number of other exotic communication techniques. Amateurs talk from hand-held transceivers through mountaintop repeater stations that can relay their signals to transceivers in other hams' cars or homes. Hams send pictures by television, chat with other hams around the world by voice or tap out messages in Morse code. The "code" represents a distinctive traditional skill, which often proves to be the only way to communicate during an emergency or when signals are weak and interference is present. When emergencies arise, radio amateurs are on the spot to relay information to and from disaster-stricken areas that have lost normal communication lines.

The US government, through the Federal Communications Commission (FCC), grants all US Amateur Radio licenses. This licensing procedure ensures operating skill and electronics knowledge. Without these skills, radio operators might unknowingly cause interference to other services using the radio spectrum because of improperly adjusted equipment or neglected regulations.

Who Can Be a Ham?

The FCC doesn't care how old you are or whether you're a US citizen: If you pass the examination, the Commission will issue you an amateur license. Any person (except the agent of a foreign government) may take the exam, and, if successful, receive an amateur license. It's important to understand that if a citizen of a foreign country receives an amateur license in this manner, he or she is a US Amateur Radio operator. (This should not be confused with a reciprocal permit for alien amateur licensee. A reciprocal permit allows visitors from certain countries who hold valid amateur licenses in their homelands to operate their own stations in the US without having to take an FCC exam.)

Licensing Structure

By examining Table 1, you'll see that there are six US amateur license classes. Each class has its own requirements and privileges. The FCC requires proof of your ability to operate an Amateur Radio station properly. The required knowledge is in line with the privileges of the license you hold. Higher license classes require more knowledge — and offer greater operating privileges. So as you upgrade your license class, you must pass more challenging written examinations. The specific operating privileges for General licensees are shown on the charts in Table 2.

In addition, you must demonstrate an ability to receive international Morse code at 5 wpm for Novice and Technician Plus licenses, 13 wpm for General and Advanced, and 20 wpm for Amateur Extra. It's important to stress that although you may intend to use voice rather than code, this doesn't excuse you from the code test. By international treaty, knowing the international Morse code is a basic requirement for operating on any amateur band below 30 MHz.

The FCC allows Volunteer Examiners to use a variety of procedures to accommodate applicants with various disabilities. In addition, a handicapped individual may be able to receive credit for passing the 13 or 20 wpm Morse code exams if they have passed the 5 wpm exam. A physician must complete the section on the back of Form 610, certifying that the individual has a disability that prevents them from passing a higher-speed code exam even with any special testing provisions. For more information, see the "Code Examination Credit for Handicapped Persons" box before this **Introduction**. If you believe you qualify for special examination procedures or for the code examination credit, contact your local Volunteer Examiners or the Volunteer Examiner Coordinator responsible for the test session you will be attending. You can contact the ARRL/VEC Office, 225 Main Street, Newington, CT 06111-1494 (860-594-0200) for assistance. Ask for more information about the special exam procedures their Volunteer Examiners will use to administer the code exam to you. In any event, you must pass at least the 5 wpm exam for any license except the Technician.

Learning the Morse code is a matter of practice. The ARRL publishes a series of Morse code practice audio CDs and cassette tapes to help you pass the code exams. *Your Introduction to Morse Code* teaches all the characters required by the FCC and gives plenty of practice at 5 wpm. Beyond that is the *Increasing Your Code Speed* series, designed to take you from 5 to 10 wpm, from 10 to 15 wpm and from 15 to 22 wpm. Each set includes two audio CDs or 74-minute cassette tapes

Table 1

Amateur Operator Licenses†

Class	Code Test	Written Examination	Privileges
Novice	5 wpm (Element 1A)	Novice theory and regulations (Element 2)	Telegraphy on 3675-3725, 7100-7150 and 21,100-21,200 kHz with 200 watts PEP output maximum; telegraphy, RTTY and data on 28,100-28,300 kHz and telegraphy and SSB voice on 28,300-28,500 kHz with 200 W PEP max; all amateur modes authorized on 222-225 MHz, 25 W PEP max; all amateur modes authorized on 1270-1295 MHz, 5 W PEP max.
Technician	None	Novice theory and regulations; Technician-level theory and regulations. (Elements 2 and 3A)*	All amateur privileges above 50.0 MHz.
Technician Plus	5 wpm (Element 1A)	Novice theory and regulations; Technician-level theory and regulations. (Elements 2 and 3A)*	All Novice HF privileges in addition to all Technician privileges.
General	13 wpm (Element 1B)	Novice theory and regulations; Technician and General theory and regulations. (Elements 2, 3A and 3B)	All amateur privileges except those reserved for Advanced and Amateur Extra licensees; see Table 2.
Advanced	13 wpm (Element 1B)	All lower exam elements, plus Advanced theory. (Elements 2, 3A, 3B and 4A)	All amateur privileges except those reserved for Amateur Extra licensees; see Table 2.
Amateur Extra	20 wpm (Element 1C)	All lower exam elements; plus Amateur Extra theory (Elements 2, 3A, 3B, 4A and 4B)	All amateur privileges.

†A licensed radio amateur will be required to pass only those elements that are not included in the examination for the amateur license currently held.

*If you hold a valid Technician license issued before March 21, 1987, you also have credit for Element 3B. You must be able to prove your Technician license was issued before March 21, 1987 to claim this credit.

Table 2
Amateur Operating Privileges

US AMATEUR BANDS

December 20, 1994

160 METERS

E,A,G

1800 — 1900 — 2000 kHz

Amateur stations operating at 1900–2000 kHz must not cause harmful interference to the radiolocation service and are afforded no protection from radiolocation operations.

80 METERS

3525, 3675, 3725, 3775, 3850

N,P
G
A
E

3500 — 3750 — 4000 kHz

5167.5 kHz (SSB only): Alaska emergency use only.

40 METERS

7025, 7100, 7150, 7225

N,P
G *
A *
E *

7000 — 7150 — 7300 kHz

* Phone operation is allowed on 7075–7100 kHz in Puerto Rico, US Virgin islands and areas of the Caribbean south of 20 degrees north latitude; and in Hawaii and areas near ITU Region 3, including Alaska.

30 METERS

E,A,G

10,100 — 10,150 kHz

Maximum power on 30 meters is 200 watts PEP output. Amateurs must avoid interference to the fixed service outside the US.

20 METERS

14,025, 14,150, 14,175, 14,225

G
A
E

14,000 — 14,150 — 14,350 kHz

17 METERS

E,A,G

18,068 — 18,110 — 18,168 kHz

15 METERS

21,025, 21,100, 21,200, 21,225, 21,300

N,P
G
A
E

21,000 — 21,200 — 21,450 kHz

12 METERS

E,A,G

24,890 — 24,930 — 24,990 kHz

10 METERS

28,100, 28,500

N,P
E,A,G

28,000 28,300 — 29,700 kHz

Novices and Technician Plus Licensees are limited to 200 watts PEP output on 10 meters.

6 METERS

50.1

E,A,G,P,T

50.0 — 54.0 MHz

2 METERS

144.1

E,A,G,P,T

144.0 — 148.0 MHz

1.25 METERS

E,A,G,P,T,N

222.0 — 225.0 MHz

Novices are limited to 25 watts PEP output from 222 to 225 MHz.

70 CENTIMETERS **

E,A,G,P,T

420.0 — 450.0 MHz

33 CENTIMETERS **

E,A,G,P,T

902.0 — 928.0 MHz

23 CENTIMETERS **

1270   1295

N
E,A,G,P,T

1240 — 1300 MHz

Novices are limited to 5 watts PEP output from 1270 to 1295 MHz.

US AMATEUR POWER LIMITS

At all times, transmitter power should be kept down to that necessary to carry out the desired communications. Power is rated in watts PEP output. Unless otherwise stated, the maximum power output is 1500 W. Power for all license classes is limited to 200 W in the 10,100–10,150 kHz band and in all Novice subbands below 28,100 kHz. Novices and Technicians are restricted to 200 W in the 28,100–28,500 kHz subbands. In addition, Novices are restricted to 25 W in the 222–225 MHz band and 5 W in the 1270–1295 MHz subband.

Operators with Technician class licenses and above may operate on all bands above 50 MHz. For more detailed information see The FCC Rule Book.

KEY

- CW, RTTY and data
- CW, RTTY, data, MCW, test, phone and image
- CW, phone and image
- CW and SSB phone
- CW, RTTY, data, phone, and image
- CW only

E = EXTRA CLASS
A = ADVANCED
G = GENERAL
P = TECHNICIAN PLUS
T = TECHNICIAN
N = NOVICE

** Geographical and power restrictions apply to these bands. See The FCC Rule Book for more information about your area.

Above 23 Centimeters:

All licensees except Novices are authorized all modes on the following frequencies:
2300–2310 MHz
2390–2450 MHz
3300–3500 MHz
5650–5925 MHz
10.0–10.5 GHz
24.0–24.25 GHz
47.0–47.2 GHz
75.5–81.0 GHz
119.98–120.02 GHz
142–149 GHz
241–250 GHz
All above 300 GHz

For band plans and sharing arrangements, see The ARRL Operating Manual or The FCC Rule Book.

and a handy booklet that includes instructions and a transcript of the tapes. *Now You're Talking!*, published by the ARRL, includes an entire chapter dedicated to learning Morse code. The ARRL also publishes *Morse Code: The Essential Language*, which describes much of the history of Morse code and includes plenty of hints on learning and using the code. All of these materials are available from the American Radio Relay League, Newington, CT 06111 and from many local Amateur Radio equipment dealers. The ARRL's Maxim Memorial Station, W1AW, also transmits Morse code practice on a daily schedule.

Code Practice

Besides listening to recorded Morse code practice, some on-the-air operating experience will be a great help in building your code speed. When you are in the middle of a contact via Amateur Radio, and have to copy the code the other station is sending to continue the conversation, your copying ability will improve quickly!

ARRL's Hiram Percy Maxim Memorial Station, W1AW, transmits code practice and information bulletins of interest to all amateurs. These code-practice sessions and Morse code bulletins provide an excellent opportunity for code practice. Table 3 is a W1AW operating schedule. When we change from Standard Time to Daylight Saving Time, the same local times are used.

Station Call Signs

Many years ago, by international agreement, the nations of the world decided to allocate certain call-sign prefixes to each country. This means that if you hear a radio station call sign beginning with K, N or W, for example, you know the station is licensed by the United States. A call sign beginning with the letter G is licensed by Great Britain and a call sign beginning with VE is from Canada. *The ARRL DXCC Countries List* is an operating aid no ham who is active on the HF bands should be without. This booklet, available from the ARRL, includes the common call-sign prefixes used by amateurs in virtually every location in the world. It also includes a check-off list to help keep track of the countries you contact as you work toward collecting QSL cards from 100 or more countries to earn the prestigious DX Century Club award. (DX is ham lingo for distance. On the HF bands, DX is generally taken to mean any country outside the one from which you are operating.)

International Telecommunication Union (ITU) radio regulations outline the basic principles used in forming amateur call signs. According to these regulations, an amateur call sign must be made of one or two characters (either of which may be a numeral) as a prefix, followed by a numeral, and then a suffix of not more than three letters. The prefixes W, K, N and A are used in the United States. (When A is used for a US call sign there are two letters for the prefix, AA through AL.) The continental US is divided into 10 Amateur Radio call districts (sometimes called areas), numbered 0 through 9). Figure 4 is a map showing the US call districts.

All US Amateur Radio call signs issued by the FCC since March 1978 can be categorized into one of four groups, each corresponding to a class, or classes, of license. Call signs are issued systematically by computer at the FCC. In addition, there is a program for "vanity" call signs, in which licensed amateurs may request special call signs. For further information on the FCC's call-sign assignment sys-

Table 3

W1AW's schedule is at the same local time throughout the year. The schedule according to your local time will change if your local time does not have seasonal adjustments that are made at the same time as North American time changes between standard time and daylight time. From the first Sunday in April to the last Sunday in October, UTC = Eastern Time + 4 hours. For the rest of the year, UTC = Eastern Time + 5 hours.

◆ **MORSE CODE TRANSMISSIONS:**

Frequencies are 1.818, 3.5815, 7.0475, 14.0475, 18.0975, 21.0675, 28.0675 and 147.555 MHz.

Slow Code = practice sent at 5, 7½, 10, 13 and 15 wpm.

Fast Code = practice sent at 35, 30, 25, 20, 15, 13 and 10 wpm.

Code practice text is from the pages of *QST*. The source is given at the beginning of each practice session and alternate speeds within each session. For example, "Text is from July 1992 *QST*, pages 9 and 81," indicates that the plain text is from the article on page 9 and mixed number/letter groups are from page 81.

W1AW schedule

Pacific	Mtn	Cent	East	Sun	Mon	Tue	Wed	Thu	Fri	Sat
6 am	7 am	8 am	9 am					Fast Code	Slow Code	
7 am	8 am	9 am	10 am					Code Bulletin		
8 am	9 am	10 am	11 am					Teleprinter Bulletin		
9 am	10 am	11 am	noon							
10 am	11 am	noon	1 pm		Visiting Operator Time					
11 am	noon	1 pm	2 pm							
noon	1 pm	2 pm	3 pm							
1 pm	2 pm	3 pm	4 pm	Slow Code	Fast Code	Slow Code	Fast Code	Slow Code	Fast Code	Slow Code
2 pm	3 pm	4 pm	5 pm	Code Bulletin						
3 pm	4 pm	5 pm	6 pm	Teleprinter Bulletin						
4 pm	5 pm	6 pm	7 pm	Fast Code	Slow Code	Fast Code	Slow Code	Fast Code	Slow Code	Fast Code
5 pm	6 pm	7 pm	8 pm	Code Bulletin						
6 pm	7 pm	8 pm	9 pm	Teleprinter Bulletin						
6^{45} pm	7^{45} pm	8^{45} pm	9^{45} pm	Voice Bulletin						
7 pm	8 pm	9 pm	10 pm	Slow Code	Fast Code	Slow Code	Fast Code	Slow Code	Fast Code	Slow Code
8 pm	9 pm	10 pm	11 pm	Code Bulletin						
9 pm	10 pm	11 pm	Mdnte	Teleprinter Bulletin						
9^{45} pm	10^{45} pm	11^{45} pm	12^{45} am	Voice Bulletin						

Code bulletins are sent at 18 wpm.

W1AW qualifying runs are sent on the same frequencies as the Morse code transmissions. West Coast qualifying runs are transmitted on approximately 3.590 MHz by W6OWP, with K6YR as an alternate. At the beginning of each code practice session, the schedule for the next qualifying run is presented. Underline one minute of the highest speed you copied, certify that your copy was made without aid, and send it to ARRL for grading. Please include your name, call sign (if any) and complete mailing address. Send a 9×12-inch SASE for a certificate, or a business-size SASE for an endorsement.

◆ **TELEPRINTER TRANSMISSIONS:**

Frequencies are 3.625, 7.095, 14.095, 18.1025, 21.095, 28.095 and 147.555 MHz.

Bulletins are sent at 45.45-baud Baudot and 100-baud AMTOR, FEC Mode B. 110-baud ASCII will be sent only as time allows.

On Tuesdays and Saturdays at 6:30 PM Eastern Time, Keplerian elements for many amateur satellites are sent on the regular teleprinter frequencies.

◆ **VOICE TRANSMISSIONS:**

Frequencies are 1.855, 3.99, 7.29, 14.29, 18.16, 21.39, 28.59 and 147.555 MHz.

◆ **MISCELLANEA:**

On Fridays, UTC, a DX bulletin replaces the regular bulletins.

W1AW is open to visitors during normal operating hours: from 1 PM until 1 AM on Mondays, 9 AM until 1 AM Tuesday through Friday, from 1 PM to 1 AM on Saturdays, and from 3:30 PM to 1 AM on Sundays. FCC licensed amateurs may operate the station from 1 to 4 PM Monday through Saturday. Be sure to bring your current FCC amateur license or a photocopy.

In a communication emergency, monitor W1AW for special bulletins as follows: voice on the hour, teleprinter at 15 minutes past the hour, and CW on the half hour.

Headquarters and W1AW are closed on New Year's Day, President's Day, Good Friday, Memorial Day, Independence Day, Labor Day, Thanksgiving and the following Friday, and Christmas Day.

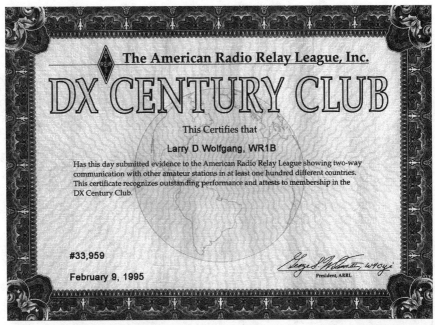

Figure 3 — When you begin collecting DX QSL cards you are working toward the ARRL's prestigious DX Century Club award. When you have collected QSL cards from 100 "DXCC Countries" from around the world you can qualify for this award.

tem, and a table listing the blocks of call signs for each license class as well as information about the vanity call sign system, see the ARRL publication, *The FCC Rule Book*. You can also contact the ARRL/VEC Office for information and forms about the vanity call sign system.

If you already have an amateur call sign, you may keep the same one when you change license class, if you wish. You must check box 4E on the FCC Form 610 to indicate your preference to receive a new call sign when you apply for an exam, change your address or renew your license. (Be careful not to check box 4E if you want to keep your present call sign.) There is also a line for you to place your initials next to box 4E if you do check it.

If you have access to the Internet, you also have a wonderful resource at your fingertips. The FCC's Web site has all kinds of information, including on-line forms that you can complete and submit electronically for a license renewal or vanity call sign. You can also download files to print a copy of the latest forms. Go to **http://www.fcc.gov/** and follow the links for the various information you want.

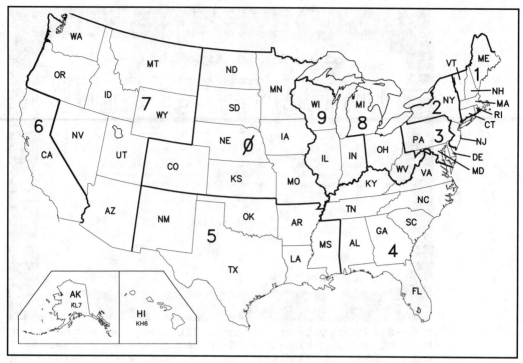

Figure 4 — There are 10 US call areas. Hawaii is part of the sixth call area, and Alaska is part of the seventh.

EARNING A LICENSE

Applying for an Exam: FCC Form 610

Before you can take an FCC exam, you'll have to fill out a Form 610. This form is used as an application for a new license, an upgraded license, a renewal of a license or a modification to a license. In addition, hams who have held a valid license that has expired within the past two years may apply for reinstatement with a Form 610.

Licenses are normally good for 10 years. Your application for a license renewal must be submitted to the FCC no more than 90 days before the license expires. (We recommend you submit the application for renewal between 90 and 60 days before your license expires.) If the FCC receives your renewal application before the license expires, you may continue to operate until your new license arrives, even if it is past the expiration date. If you forget to apply before your license expires, you may still be able to renew your license without taking another exam. There is a two-year grace period, during which you may apply for renewal of your expired license. Use a Form 610 to apply for reinstatement (and your old call sign).

FEDERAL COMMUNICATIONS COMMISSION
1270 FAIRFIELD ROAD
GETTYSBURG, PENNSYLVANIA
17325-7245

Approved by OMB
3060-0003
See instructions for
public burden.

APPLICATION FORM 610 FOR
AMATEUR OPERATOR/PRIMARY STATION LICENSE

SECTION 1 - TO BE COMPLETED BY APPLICANT (See instructions)

1. Print or type last name **DIMOCK**   Suffix   First name **CAROLE**   Middle initial **M**

2. Date of birth **12-21-50** month / day / year

3. Mailing address (Number and street)   **225 MAIN ST.**

3A. Internet Address

City **NewINGTON**   State Code **CT.**   ZIP Code **06111-1494**

4. I HEREBY APPLY FOR (make an X in the appropriate box(es)):

- 4A. ☐ EXAMINATION for a new license
- 4B. ☒ EXAMINATION for upgrade of my operator license class
- 4C. ☐ CHANGE my name on my license to my new name in Item 1. My former name was:

    (Last name) (Suffix) (First name) (MI)

- 4D. ☐ CHANGE my mailing address on my license to my new address in Item 3
- 4E. ☐ CHANGE my station call sign systematically (See instructions) Applicant's Initials _____
- 4F. ☐ RENEWAL of my license

5. Unless you are requesting a new license, attach the original or a photocopy of your license to the back of this Form 610 and complete Items 5A and 5B.

5A. Call sign shown on license **NINAM**

5B. Operator class shown on license **TECH**

6. If you have filed another Form 610 that we have not acted upon, complete Items 6A and 6B.

6A. Purpose of other form

6B. Date filed _____ month day year

WILLFUL FALSE STATEMENTS MADE ON THIS FORM ARE PUNISHABLE BY FINE AND/OR IMPRISONMENT, (U.S. CODE, TITLE 18, SECTION 1001), AND/OR REVOCATION OF ANY STATION LICENSE OR CONSTRUCTION PERMIT (U.S. CODE, TITLE 47, SECTION 312(A)(1)) AND/OR FORFEITURE (U.S. CODE, TITLE 47, SECTION 503).

I certify that:
- all statements and attachments are true, complete, and correct to the best of my knowledge and belief and are made in good faith;
- I am not a representative of a foreign government;
- I waive any claim to the use of any particular frequency regardless of prior use by license or otherwise;
- the station to be licensed will be inaccessible to unauthorized persons;
- the construction of the station would NOT be an action which is likely to have a significant environmental effect (see the Commission's Rules 47 C.F.R. Sections 1.1301-1.1319 and Section 97.13(a);
- I have READ and WILL COMPLY WITH Section 97.13(c) of the Commission's Rules regarding RADIOFREQUENCY (RF) RADIATION SAFETY and the amateur service section of OST/OET Bulletin Number 65.

7. Signature of applicant (Do not print, type, or stamp. Must match name in Item 1.)

✗ **Carole M. Dimock**   **(860) 594-0206**
Daytime Telephone Number

8. Date signed **01-07-98** month day year

SECTION 2 - TO BE COMPLETED BY ALL ADMINISTERING VEs

A. Applicant is qualified for operator license class:

- ☐ NOVICE (Elements 1(A), 1(B), or 1(C) and 2)
- ☐ TECHNICIAN (Elements 2 and 3(A))
- ☐ TECHNICIAN PLUS (Elements 1(A), 1(B), or 1(C), 2 and 3(A))
- ☐ GENERAL (Elements 1(B) or 1(C), 2, 3(A) and 3(B))
- ☐ ADVANCED (Elements 1(B) or 1(C), 2, 3(A), 3(B) and 4(A))
- ☐ AMATEUR EXTRA (Elements 1(C), 2, 3(A), 3(B), 4(A) and 4(B))

B. VEC receipt date:

C. Name of Volunteer-Examiner Coordinator (VEC):

D. Date of VEC coordinated examination session:

E. Examination session location:

I CERTIFY THAT I HAVE COMPLIED WITH THE ADMINISTERING VE REQUIREMENTS IN PART 97 OF THE COMMISSION'S RULES AND WITH THE INSTRUCTIONS PROVIDED BY THE COORDINATING VEC AND THE FCC

	VEs station call sign	VEs signature (must match name)	Date signed
1st VEs name (Print First, MI, Last, Suffix)			
2nd VEs name (Print First, MI, Last, Suffix)			
3rd VEs name (Print First, MI, Last, Suffix)			

FCC Form 610 - Page 1
September 1997

Figure 5—This sample FCC Form 610 shows the sections you should complete before going for your license exam.

If you apply for reinstatement of your expired license under this two-year grace period, you may not operate your station until your new license is issued.

Form 610s showing a date earlier than September 1997 in the lower right corner are no longer valid, and will be returned if you attempt to use one. If you have any old forms, throw them away. (At the time of this writing, there is only one version of the FCC Form 610 that is valid.)

The FCC has a set of detailed instructions for the Form 610. These instructions are printed on a second page that goes with the Form 610. To obtain a new Form 610, call 800-418-3676. You can also write to: Federal Communications Commission, Forms Distribution Center, 2803 52nd Avenue, Hyattsville, MD 20781 (specify "Form 610" on the envelope) or: Form 610, ARRL, 225 Main Street, Newington, CT 06111-1494. (Please include an SASE with your request.)

The Form 610 is also available from the FCC's fax on demand service. Call 202-418-0177 and ask for form number 000610. Form 610 also is available via the Internet. The World Wide Web location is: **http://www.fcc.gov/Forms/Form610**. You can also receive the form via ftp to: **ftp.fcc.gov/pub/Forms/Form610**. Many clubs and Amateur Radio equipment dealers may also have a supply of forms. If you use a form from one of those sources, however, be sure it is the latest version.

Figure 5 shows a sample Form 610. The back of the form is used only for a physician's certification that the applicant has a handicap that makes it impossible for him or her to pass a 13 wpm or 20 wpm Morse code exam. You can ignore the back of the form unless you feel you qualify for such a code exemption. You do need to attach a copy of your current license (if you have one) to the back of the form, however.

Volunteer Examiner Program

All US amateur exams are administered by Volunteer Examiners who are certified by a Volunteer Examiner Coordinator (VEC). Program. *The FCC Rule Book* contains details about the Volunteer Examiner program.

To qualify for a General license you must pass Elements 1B, 2, 3A and 3B. If you already hold a valid Novice license, then you have credit for passing Element 2, and will not have to retake that exam. If you have a Technician license issued after March 21, 1987, and you wish to upgrade to General, you must study the questions in the Element 3B question pool and pass that exam. Finally, if you have a Technician license issued before March 21, 1987, you will be given credit for both Elements 3A and 3B. In that case you only need to pass the 13 wpm Morse code exam, Element 1C to upgrade to General. See Table 1 for details.

The Element 3B exam consists of 30 questions taken from a pool of more than 300. The question pools for all amateur exams are maintained by a Question Pool Committee selected by the Volunteer Examiner Coordinators. The FCC allows Volunteer Examiners to select the questions for an amateur exam, but they must use the questions exactly as they are released by the VEC that coordinates the test session. If you attend a test session coordinated by the ARRL/VEC, your test will be designed by the ARRL/VEC or by a computer program designed by the VEC. The questions and answers will be exactly as they are printed in Chapter 12 of this book.

Finding an Exam Opportunity

To determine where and when an exam will be given, contact the ARRL/VEC Office, or watch for announcements in the Hamfest Calendar and Coming Conventions columns in *QST*. Many local clubs sponsor exams, so they are another good source of information on exam opportunities. ARRL officials such as Directors, Vice Directors and Section Managers receive notices about test sessions in their area. See the latest issue of *QST* for the names and addresses of your local ARRL officials.

To register for an exam, send a completed Form 610 to the Volunteer Examining Team responsible for the exam session if preregistration is required. Otherwise, bring the form to the session. Registration deadlines, and the time and location of the exams, are mentioned prominently in publicity releases about upcoming sessions.

Taking the Exam

By the time examination day rolls around, you should have already prepared yourself. This means getting your schedule, supplies and mental attitude ready. Plan your schedule so you'll get to the examination site with plenty of time to spare. There's no harm in being early. In fact, you might have time to discuss hamming with another applicant, which is a great way to calm pretest nerves. Try not to discuss the material that will be on the examination, as this may make you even more nervous. By this time, it's too late to study anyway!

What supplies will you need? First, be sure you bring your current original Amateur Radio license, if you have one. Bring along several sharpened number 2 pencils and two pens (blue or black ink). Be sure to have a good eraser. A pocket calculator may also come in handy. You may use a programmable calculator if that is the kind you have, but take it into your exam "empty." Don't program equations ahead of time, because you may be asked to demonstrate that there is nothing in the calculator's memory. If you use a slide rule, that should also be allowed, although you will probably not be allowed to take math tables, such as trigonometry tables or logarithm tables into the exam with you.

The Volunteer Examining Team is required to check two forms of identification before you enter the test room. This includes your *original* Amateur Radio license, if you have one. A photo ID of some type is best for the second type, but is not required by the FCC. Other acceptable forms of identification include a driver's license, a piece of mail addressed to you, a birth certificate, or some other such document.

The following description of the testing procedure applies to exams coordinated by the ARRL/VEC, although many other VECs use a similar procedure.

Code Tests

The code tests are usually given before the written exams. The 20 wpm exam normally is given first, then the 13 wpm exam and finally the 13 wpm test. There is no harm in trying the 20 wpm exam even though you are testing for the General license.

Before you take the code test, you'll be handed a piece of paper to copy the code as it's sent. The test will begin with about a minute of practice copy. Then comes the actual test: five minutes of Morse code. You are responsible for knowing the 26 letters of the alphabet, the numerals 0 through 9, the period, comma, question mark, and procedural signals $\overline{AR}$, $\overline{SK}$, $\overline{BT}$ and $\overline{DN}$ (/ or fraction bar, sometimes called "slant bar"). You may copy the entire text word for word, or just take notes on the content. At the end of the transmission, the examiner will hand you 10 questions about the text. Simply fill in the blanks with your answers. (You must spell each answer exactly as it was sent.) If you get at least 7 correct, you pass! Alternatively, the exam team has the option to look at your copy sheet if you fail the 10-question exam. If you have one minute of solid copy (65 characters for the 13 wpm exam), they can certify that you passed the test on that basis. The format of the test transmission is generally similar to one side of a normal on-the-air amateur conversation.

A sending test probably won't be required. The Commission has decided that if applicants can demonstrate receiving ability, they most likely can also send at that speed. But be prepared, just in case! Subpart 97.503(a) of the FCC Rules says, "A telegraphy examination must be sufficient to prove that the examinee has the ability to send correctly by hand and to receive correctly by ear texts in the international Morse code at not less than the prescribed speed...."

Written Tests

After all the code tests have been administered, you'll then take the written examination. The examiner will give each applicant a test booklet, an answer sheet and scratch paper. After that, you're on your own. The first thing to do is read the instructions. Be sure to sign your name every place it's called for. Do all of this at the beginning to get it out of the way.

Next, check the examination to see that all pages and questions are there. If not, report this to the examiner immediately. When filling in your answer sheet, make sure your answers are marked next to the numbers that correspond to each question.

Go through the entire exam, and answer the easy questions first. Next, go back to the beginning and try the harder questions. Leave the tough questions for last. Guessing can only help, as there is no additional penalty for answering incorrectly.

If you have to guess, do it intelligently: At first glance, you may find that you can eliminate one or more "distracters." Of the remaining responses, more than one may seem correct; only one is the best answer, however. To the applicant who is fully prepared, incorrect distracters to each question are obvious. Nothing beats preparation!

After you've finished, check the examination thoroughly. You may have read a question wrong or goofed in your arithmetic. Don't be overconfident. There's no rush, so take your time. Think, and check your answer sheet. When you feel you've done your best and can do no more, return the test booklet, answer sheet and scratch pad to the examiner.

The Volunteer Examiner Team will grade the exam right away. The passing mark is 74%. (That means no more than 8 incorrect answers on the 30-question exam.) You will receive a Certificate of Successful Completion of Examination

(CSCE) showing all exam elements that you pass. If you are already licensed, and you pass the exam elements required to earn a higher license class, the CSCE authorizes you to operate with your new privileges. When you use your new privileges, you must sign your call sign, followed by the slant mark ("/"; on voice say "stroke" or "slant") and the letters "AG." You only have to follow this special identification procedure until your new license is issued by the FCC, however.

If you pass only some of the exam elements required for a higher class license you will still receive a CSCE. That certificate shows what exam elements you passed, and is valid for one year. Use it as proof that you passed those exam elements so you won't have to take them over again the next time you try for the upgrade.

AND NOW, LET'S BEGIN

The complete General question pool (Element 3B) is printed in Chapter 12. Chapters 1 through 10 explain the material covered in subelements G1 through G0 of the question pool. This book provides the background in FCC Rules, operating procedures, radio-wave propagation, Amateur Radio practices, electrical principles, circuit components, practical circuits, signals and emissions, antennas and feed lines, and RF safety you will need to know to pass the Element 3B General license exam.

Table 4 shows the study guide, or syllabus, for the Element 3B exam. This study guide was released by the Volunteer Examiner Coordinators' Question Pool Committee. The syllabus lists the topics to be covered by the General exam, and so forms the basic outline for the remainder of this book.

The question numbers used in the question pool refer to this syllabus. Each question number begins with a syllabus-point number (G1C, G2A, G3B). The question numbers end with a two-digit number. For example, question G1C03 is the third question in the series about syllabus point G1C (transmitter power standards; type acceptance of external RF-power amplifiers; standards for type acceptance of external RF-power amplifiers; HF data emission standards). G3B09 is the ninth question about the G3B syllabus point (maximum useable frequency; propagation "hops").

The Question Pool Committee designed the syllabus and question pool so there are the same number of points in each subelement as there are exam questions from that subelement. For example, the FCC specifies four questions on the General exam must come from the "Commission's Rules" subelement. There are four groups of questions for this subelement, G1A through G1D. Three exam questions must be from the "Radio-Wave Propagation" subelement, so there are three groups for that point. These are numbered G3A, G3B and G3C. The RF Safety subelement is new to this question pool, and the FCC specifies that there must be five questions on your exam from that subelement. So you will find five groups of questions (G0A through G0E) in the RF Safety section. While not a requirement of the FCC Rules, the Question Pool Committee recommends that one question be taken from each group to make the best possible General license exam.

Good luck with your studies!

Table 4

General (Element 3B) Syllabus

SUBELEMENT G1 — COMMISSION'S RULES

[4 Exam Questions — 4 Groups]

G1A General control operator frequency privileges; local control; repeater and harmful interference definitions; third party communications

G1B Antenna structure limitations; good engineering and good amateur practice; beacon operation; restricted operation; retransmitting radio signals

G1D Examination element preparation; examination administration; temporary station identification

SUBELEMENT G2 — OPERATING PROCEDURES

[3 Exam Questions — 3 Groups]

G2A Phone; RTTY; repeater; VOX and full break-in CW

G2B Operating courtesy; antenna orientation and HF operations; including logging practices; ITU Regions

G2C Emergencies; including drills; communications and amateur auxiliary to the FCC's Compliance and Information Bureau

SUBELEMENT G3 — RADIO-WAVE PROPAGATION

[3 Exam Questions — 3 Groups]

G3A Ionospheric disturbances; sunspots and solar radiation

G3B Maximum usable frequency; propagation "hops"

G3C Height of ionospheric regions; critical angle and frequency; HF scatter

SUBELEMENT G4 — AMATEUR RADIO PRACTICES

[5 Exam Questions — 5 Groups]

G4A Two-tone test; electronic TR switch; amplifier neutralization

G4B Test equipment: oscilloscope; signal tracer; antenna noise bridge; monitoring oscilloscope; field-strength meters

G4C Audio rectification in consumer electronics; RF ground

G4D Speech processors; PEP calculations; wire sizes and fuses

G4E Common connectors used in amateur stations: types; when to use; fastening methods; precautions when using; HF mobile radio installations; emergency power systems; generators; battery storage devices and charging sources including solar; wind generation

SUBELEMENT G5 — ELECTRICAL PRINCIPLES

[2 Exam Questions — 2 Groups]

G5A Impedance; including matching; resistance; including ohm; reactance; inductance; capacitance and metric divisions of these values

G5B Decibel; Ohm's Law; current and voltage dividers; electrical power calculations and series and parallel components; transformers (either voltage or impedance); sine wave root-mean-square (RMS) value

SUBELEMENT G6 — CIRCUIT COMPONENTS
[1 Exam Question — 1 Group]

G6A Resistors; capacitors; inductors; rectifiers and transistors; etc.

SUBELEMENT G7 — PRACTICAL CIRCUITS
[1 Exam Question — 1 Group]

G1C Transmitter power standards; type acceptance of external RF-power-amplifiers; standards for type acceptance of external RF-power amplifiers; HF data emission standards

SUBELEMENT G8 — SIGNALS AND EMISSIONS
[2 Exam Questions — 2 Groups]

G8A Signal information; AM; FM; single and double sideband and carrier; bandwidth; modulation envelope; deviation; overmodulation

G8B Frequency mixing; multiplication; bandwidths; HF data communications

SUBELEMENT G9 — ANTENNAS AND FEED LINES
[4 Exam Questions — 4 Groups]

G9A Yagi antennas — physical dimensions; impedance matching; radiation patterns; directivity and major lobes

G9B Loop antennas — physical dimensions; impedance matching; radiation patterns; directivity and major lobes

G9C Random wire antennas — physical dimensions; impedance matching; radiation patterns; directivity and major lobes; feed point impedance of $1/2$-wavelength dipole and $1/4$-wavelength vertical antennas

G9D Popular antenna feed lines — characteristic impedance and impedance matching; SWR calculations

SUBELEMENT G0 — RF SAFETY
[5 Exam Questions — 5 Groups]

G0A RF safety principles

G0B RF safety rules and guidelines

G0C Routine station evaluation and measurements (FCC Part 97 refers to RF radiation evaluation)

G0D Practical RF-safety applications

G0E RF-safety solutions

CHAPTER 1 KEYWORDS KEYWORDS KEYWORDS

Beacon station — An amateur station transmitting communications for the purposes of observation of propagation and reception or other related experimental activities. [§97.3(a)(9)]

Broadcasting — Transmissions intended to be received by the general public, either direct or relayed. [§97.3(a)(10)] Broadcasting is prohibited on Amateur Radio.

Emission types — Any signals from a transmitter. Phone, data and CW are emission types.

Frequency privileges — The specific band segments assigned to holders of each particular license . General operators have frequency privileges on the amateur high-frequency bands.

Harmful interference — Interference that seriously degrades, obstructs or repeatedly interrupts a radiocommunication service operating in accordance with the Radio Regulations. [§97.3(a)(22)]

International Telecommunication Union (ITU) — The international organization with responsibility for dividing the range of communications frequencies between the various services for the entire world.

One-way communications — Radio signals not directed to a specific amateur station, or for which no reply is expected. The FCC Rules provide for limited types of one-way communications on the amateur bands. [§97.111(b)]

Repeater — An amateur station that automatically retransmits the signals of other amateur stations. [§97.3(a)(37)]

Third-party communication — A message from the control operator (first party) of an amateur station to another amateur station (second party) on behalf of another person (third party). [§97.3(a)(44)]

COMMISSION'S RULES

Part 97 of the Federal Communications Commission's Rules govern the Amateur Radio Service in the United States. Each Amateur Radio license exam includes questions covering sections of these rules. The General license exam includes four rules questions. In this chapter of *The ARRL General Class License Manual*, you will learn about the specific rules covered on the General (Element 3B) license exam.

This book does not contain a complete listing of the Part 97 Rules. The FCC modifies Part 97 on an irregular basis, and it would be impossible to keep an up-to-date set of rules in a book designed to be revised every four years, to coincide with the release of a new General Question Pool. We do recommend, however, that every Amateur Radio operator have an up-to-date copy of the rules in their station for reference. *The FCC Rule Book*, published by the ARRL, contains the complete text of Part 97, along with detailed explanations of all the regulations. *The FCC Rule Book* is updated as necessary to keep it current with the latest rule changes.

The four rules questions on your General license exam will come from four exam-question groups. Each group forms a subelement section on the syllabus or study guide, and the question pool. The four groups are:

G1A General control operator frequency privileges; local control, repeater and harmful interference definitions, third-party communications

G1B Antenna structure limitations; good engineering and good amateur practice; beacon operation; restricted operation; retransmitting radio signals

G1C Transmitter power standards; type acceptance of external RF-power amplifiers; standards for type acceptance of external RF-power amplifiers; HF data emission standards

G1D Examination element preparation; examination administration; temporary station identification

GENERAL CONTROL OPERATOR FREQUENCY PRIVILEGES

As a General Amateur Radio licensee, you will have all Amateur Radio **frequency privileges** above 50 MHz, just like a Technician licensee. These frequency privileges are listed in Section 97.301(a) of the FCC Rules. (Section is often represented by the § character when referencing a specific portion of the FCC Rules.) You will also have extensive privileges on the high-frequency (HF) bands, as listed in §97.301(d). Table 1-1 shows this section of the Rules, along with the appropriate notes from §97.303.

The **International Telecommunication Union (ITU)** is the organization responsible for international regulation of the radio spectrum. The ITU regulations state that communications between amateurs in foreign countries must be limited to technical topics or "remarks of a personal nature of relative unimportance" — you can talk about your new rig or what you had for dinner, but don't get into a serious political discussion with a foreign ham.

Under the ITU, the world has been separated into three areas, or Regions. See Figure 1-1. Amateurs in different Regions may not be able to use all the same frequencies or operating modes as US operators. The United States, including Alaska and Hawaii, is in ITU Region 2. Region 3 comprises most of the islands in the Pacific Ocean, including American Samoa, the Northern Mariana Islands, Guam and Wake Island. (Many Pacific islands are under FCC regulation.) Also included

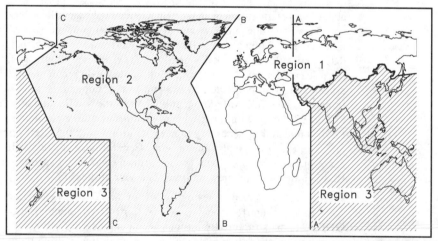

Figure 1-1 — This map shows the world as divided into three ITU Regions.

Table 1-1

Authorized Frequency Bands and Sharing Requirements

§97.301 Authorized frequency bands.

The following transmitting frequency bands are available to an amateur station located within 50 km of the Earth's surface, within the specified ITU Region, and outside any area where the amateur service is regulated by any authority other than the FCC.

(d) For a station having a control operator who has been granted an operator license of General:

Wavelength Band	ITU Region 1	ITU Region 2	ITU Region 3	Sharing requirements See §97.303, Paragraph:
MF	kHz	kHz	kHz	
160 m	1810-1850	1800-2000	1800-2000	(a), (b), (c)
HF	MHz	MHz	MHz	
80 m	3.525-3.750	3.525-3.750	3.525-3.750	(a)
75 m	—	3.85-4.00	3.85-3.90	(a)
40 m	7.025-7.100	7.025-7.150	7.025-7.100	(a)
40 m	—	7.225-7.300	—	(a)
30 m	10.10-10.15	10.10-10.15	10.10-10.15	(d)
20 m	14.025-14.150	14.025-14.150	14.025-14.150	
20 m	14.225-14.350	14.225-14.350	14.225-14.350	
17 m	18.068-18.168	18.068-18.168	18.068-18.168	
15 m	21.025-21.200	21.025-21.200	21.025-21.200	
15 m	21.30-21.45	21.30-21.45	21.30-21.45	
12 m	24.89-24.99	24.89-24.99	24.89-24.99	
10 m	28.0-29.7	28.0-29.7	28.0-29.7	

§97.303 Frequency sharing requirements.

The following is a summary of the frequency sharing requirements that apply to amateur station transmissions on the frequency bands specified in §97.301 of this Part. (For each ITU Region, each frequency band allocated to the amateur service is designated as either a secondary service or a primary service. A station in a secondary service must not cause harmful interference to, and must accept interference from, stations in a primary service. See §§2.105 and 2.106 of the FCC Rules, United States Table of Frequency Allocations for complete requirements.)

(a) Where, in adjacent ITU Regions or Subregions, a band of frequencies is allocated to different services of the same category, the basic principle is the equality of right to operate. The stations of each service in one region must operate so as not to cause harmful interference to services in the other Regions or Subregions. (See ITU Radio Regulations, No. 346 (Geneva, 1979).)

(b) No amateur station transmitting in the 1900-2000 kHz segment, the 70 cm band, the 33 cm band, the 13 cm band, the 9 cm band, the 5 cm band, the 3 cm band, the 24.05-24.25 GHz segment, the 76-81 GHz segment, the 144-149 GHz segment and the 241-248 GHz segment shall cause harmful interference to, nor is protected from interference due to the operation of, the Government radiolocation service.

(c) No amateur station transmitting in the 1900-2000 kHz segment, the 3 cm band, the 76-81 GHz segment, the 144-149 GHz segment and the 241-248 GHz segment shall cause harmful interference to, nor is protected from interference due to the operation of, stations in the non-Government radiolocation service.

(d) No amateur station transmitting in the 30 meter band shall cause harmful interference to stations authorized by other nations in the fixed service. The licensee of the amateur station must make all necessary adjustments, including termination of transmissions, if harmful interference is caused.

in Region 3 are China, India and parts of the Middle East. Region 1 comprises Europe, Africa, Russia and the remainder of the Middle East.

If you will be operating in an FCC-regulated area in ITU Regions 1 or 3, be sure to look in §97.301 (a) and (d) for your frequency privileges in those Regions. In addition to the land areas described, your operation is under FCC regulation if you are operating from onboard a US-registered ship sailing in international waters. In such cases, you must follow the frequency privileges authorized for use in the ITU region in which you are located.

[After you have learned the HF frequency privileges described in Table 1-1, turn to Chapter 12 and study questions G1A01 through G1A08. Also study question G2B11. Review this section of the chapter if you have difficulty with any of these questions. As you study the questions, turn the edge of the question-pool page under to hide the answer key.]

UNDER CONTROL

Every amateur station must have a control operator. When the station is being *locally controlled*, the control operator must be at the control point (§97.109(b)). Sometimes the control operator may have license privileges that exceed those of the station licensee. For example, an operator with a General Amateur Radio license may operate a station licensed to a Novice or Technician operator. If the General licensee is operating the station outside of the Novice or Technician licensee's privileges, such as on 7250 kHz, special identification procedures apply. According to §97.119(e), the General operator would use the station licensee's call sign followed by a slant mark (/) or by a word that denotes the slant mark, and the control operator's call sign.

A **repeater** is an amateur station that automatically retransmits the signals of other amateur stations (§97.3(a)(37)). Section 97.205 of the FCC Rules outlines some restrictions and standards for repeaters.

One common question about repeater operation is whether an operator may use a repeater if the repeater output is on a frequency the operator is not allowed to use. For example, may a Technician operator (who has *not* passed a Morse code exam) use a 2-meter repeater that has an output on the 10-meter band? There are two tests to determine if such operation is legal. First, the operator in question must be transmitting *to* the repeater on a frequency on which he or she is authorized to operate. In our example, the Technician operator is transmitting to the repeater on 2 meters, so this part is legal. The second test is that the repeater control operator must have privileges on the repeater output frequency §97.205(a). So in this example, the repeater control operator must have a General or higher license. As long as both conditions are met, the operation is completely legal.

Section 97.3(a)(22) defines **harmful interference** as "interference which endangers the functioning of a radionavigation service or of other safety services or seriously degrades, obstructs or repeatedly interrupts a radiocommunication service operating in accordance with the Radio Regulations." In other words, any type of signal that causes interference to any type of radio service produces harmful interference. Your amateur station may receive harmful interference from other amateurs or from other radio signals. This could happen, for example, if a nearby business-radio transmitter produces an unwanted signal on an amateur band. Your amateur station might also cause harmful interference to another radio signal. Any time you receive a report that your signal may be interfering with another radio service you should investigate the possible causes of this interference and take every means possible to ensure that your station does not cause continued interference.

Third-party communication is defined in §97.3(a)(44). This definition says, "A message from the control operator (first party) of an amateur station to another amateur station control operator (second party) on behalf of another person (third party)." There are further details about such communications in §97.115 and §97.117 of the FCC Rules. See Table 1-2.

While these rules can seem confusing at times, basically they mean you can allow an unlicensed person to talk over the air on your Amateur Radio station provided you remain at the radio controls. They also mean you can send a message on behalf of another person, or to an unlicensed person. This is the basic idea of the ARRL's National Traffic System, designed to relay messages around the US and to many parts of the world.

Table 1-3
Third-Party Traffic Agreements List

Countries that share third-party traffic agreements with the US:

Occasionally, DX stations may ask you to pass a third-party message to a friend or relative in the States. This is all right as long as the US has signed an official third-party traffic agreement with that particular country, or the third party is a licensed amateur. The traffic must be noncommercial and of a personal, unimportant nature. During an emergency, the US State Department will often work out a special temporary agreement with the country involved. But in normal times, never handle traffic without first making sure it is legally permitted.

US Amateurs May Handle Third-Party Traffic With:

C5	The Gambia	J6	St Lucia		VE	Canada
CE	Chile	J7	Dominica		VK	Australia
CO	Cuba	J8	St Vincent and the		VR6**	Pitcairn Island
CP	Bolivia		Grenadines		XE	Mexico
CX	Uruguay	JY	Jordan		YN	Nicaragua
D6	Federal Islamic	LU	Argentina		YS	El Salvador
	Rep. of the Comoros	OA	Peru		YV	Venezuela
DU	Philippines	PY	Brazil		ZP	Paraguay
EL	Liberia	TG	Guatemala		3DA0	Swaziland
GB*	United Kingdom	TI	Costa Rica		4U1ITU	ITU Geneva
HC	Ecuador	T9	Bosnia-Herzegovina		4U1VIC	VIC, Vienna
HH	Haiti	V2	Antigua and Barbuda		4X	Israel
HI	Dominican Republic	V3	Belize		6Y	Jamaica
HK	Colombia	V4	St Christopher and		8R	Guyana
HP	Panama		Nevis		9G	Ghana
HR	Honduras	V6	Federated States of		9L	Sierra Leone
J3	Grenada		Micronesia		9Y	Trinidad and Tobago
		V7	Marshall Islands			

Notes:

*Third-party traffic permitted between US amateurs and special-events stations in the United Kingdom having the prefix GB only, with the exception that GB3 stations are not included in this agreement.

**Since 1970, there has been an informal agreement between the United Kingdom and the US, permitting Pitcairn and US amateurs to exchange messages concerning medical emergencies, urgent need for equipment or supplies, and private or personal matters of island residents.

Please note that the Region 2 Division of the International Amateur Radio Union (IARU) has recommended that international traffic on the 20 and 15-meter bands be conducted on the following frequencies:

14.100-14.150 MHz

14.250-14.350 MHz

21.150-21.200 MHz

21.300-21.450 MHz

The IARU is the alliance of Amateur Radio societies from around the world; Region 2 comprises member-societies in North, South and Central America, and the Caribbean.

Note: At the end of an exchange of third-party traffic with a station located in a foreign country, an FCC-licensed amateur must also transmit the call sign of the foreign station as well as his own call sign.

Current as of February 1998

There are two important rule points to keep in mind when you are conducting any type of third-party communication with another country. First, the US and the other government must have made prior arrangements to allow such third-party communications. This agreement is called a "third-party agreement." Table 1-3 is a list of countries with which the US currently has such an agreement. This list changes from time to time because of additions or deletions. Occasionally there are temporary agreements, such as during some special event such as the Olympic Games, or during certain times of the year, such as the Christmas/New Year Holiday season.

Many governments operate the public telephone and other telecommunications services in their country. They do not look kindly on losing the fees that would be paid for such services because Amateur Radio operators bypassed the system. For this reason, all international communications are limited to comments of a technical nature related to Amateur Radio experiments and personal remarks. Such communications are considered relatively unimportant because you wouldn't normally use the public telecommunications system for those messages.

[Now turn to Chapter 12 and study questions G1A09 through G1A13. You should also study question G2C09. If you have any difficulty with these questions, review the Under Control section of the text.]

GOOD ENGINEERING AND GOOD AMATEUR PRACTICE

The Amateur Service is a radiocommunication service intended to encourage Amateur Radio operators to train themselves in the technical and operating phases of electronics and communications technology by experimenting and communicating with other amateurs. Amateur Radio operators should strive always to maintain and operate their stations in a manner that will meet the highest standards.

Part 97 of the FCC Rules spells out many technical and operating standards that all US Amateur Radio stations must meet. The Rules describe various operating modes and set minimum standards for transmitted signal quality. The Rules must also be sufficiently vague, however, so as to encourage experimentation and the development of new communications techniques.

The FCC can't anticipate every question amateurs may have about how to set up or operate their stations, nor should we expect them to. After all, that's what experimentation is all about. So what should we do when faced with those unanswered questions about our stations? One place to look is in §97.101(a), under General standards, where it says, "In all respects not specifically covered by FCC Rules each amateur station must be operated in accordance with good engineering and good amateur practice." This means you should comply with the conventions that have evolved within the amateur community to promote efficient use of our limited radio spectrum. It means cooperating with other amateurs who have interests in diverse operating modes and activities. Band plans and "gentlemen's agreements" *may not* be specifically addressed in the Rules, but following them is part of operating your station "in accordance with good engineering and good amateur practice."

[Turn to the question pool in Chapter 12 and study question G1B02 before going on. Review this section if you do not understand this question.]

PROHIBITED TRANSMISSIONS

The FCC Rules are generally intended to allow flexibility and room to try new types of communication. Still, there are some things the Rules clearly prohibit. Some of these prohibitions provide for your safety, or the safety of others. Some restrictions are required to preserve the very nature of Amateur Radio. Several questions in the General question pool are about these restrictions. Section 97.113 lists specific types of prohibited transmissions. See Table 1-4.

No amateur station may transmit music. The FCC doesn't want the general public tuning in to your Amateur Radio transmissions to listen to music. This would be a form of **broadcasting**, also forbidden on the amateur bands. The rules specifically state that transmitting music using a phone emission is prohibited. If you wanted to exchange digital files containing music scores with another ham, that would be okay. Likewise, if you wanted to experiment with sending MIDI control codes as part of a digital transmission, you could do that. Just don't play the actual composition over the air.

The prohibition against transmitting music also includes background music. If you have a radio or recorded music playing in the background while you are talking into the microphone of your transmitter, you could be in violation of this rule. Turn down the background audio before transmitting, to keep your station from transmitting music.

There is one exception to the "no music" rule. Amateur stations are permitted to retransmit signals that originate on US Government frequencies between a space shuttle and its associated Earth stations, with prior approval from NASA. Under these conditions, if there is incidental music transmitted between the shuttle and the Earth station, the amateur station is allowed to continue the retransmission.

In general, an amateur station may not retransmit signals from any other radio service. The exception to this rule is the retransmission of propagation and weather forecast information transmitted from US Government stations, and the space shuttle communications just discussed.

No amateur station may transmit communications intended to facilitate a criminal act. Amateur stations may not transmit obscene or indecent words, nor may they transmit false or deceptive messages, signals or identification.

No amateur station in two-way communication may transmit messages using codes or ciphers that are intended to obscure the meaning of the communications. It doesn't matter if the communication is domestic (between US amateurs) or international (between a US amateur and an amateur in another country). Procedural signals and common abbreviations are not considered to be codes or ciphers under this rule. So it is okay to use Q signals, procedural signals (prosigns) and other abbreviations that you commonly hear over the air. You and your friend may not make up your own "secret code," however, in order to keep your communications "private."

A station designated as a telecommand station of an amateur space station (such as a satellite) may transmit special telecommand messages to the space station, however. Those telecommand messages may use special codes intended to obscure the meaning of the message. This rule allows the use of special codes so only properly authorized stations can transmit control codes to the space station. Telecommand signals transmitted to control a model craft are also not considered

Table 1-4

§97.113 Prohibited transmissions.

(a) No amateur station shall transmit:

(1) Communications specifically prohibited elsewhere in this Part;

(2) Communications for hire or for material compensation, direct or indirect, paid or promised, except as otherwise provided in these rules;

(3) Communications in which the station licensee or control operator has a pecuniary interest, including communications on behalf of an employer. Amateur operators may, however, notify other amateur operators of the availability for sale or trade of apparatus normally used in an amateur station, provided that such activity is not conducted on a regular basis;

(4) Music using a phone emission except as specifically provided elsewhere in this Section; communications intended to facilitate a criminal act; messages in codes or ciphers intended to obscure the meaning thereof, except as otherwise provided herein; obscene or indecent words or language; or false or deceptive messages, signals or identification;

(5) Communications, on a regular basis, which could reasonably be furnished alternatively through other radio services.

(b) An amateur station shall not engage in any form of broadcasting, nor may an amateur station transmit one-way communications except as specifically provided in these rules; nor shall an amateur station engage in any activity related to program production or news gathering for broadcasting purposes, except that communications directly related to the immediate safety of human life or the protection of property may be provided by amateur stations to broadcasters for dissemination to the public where no other means of communication is reasonably available before or at the time of the event.

(c) A control operator may accept compensation as an incident of a teaching position during periods of time when an amateur station is used by that teacher as a part of classroom instruction at an educational institution.

(d) The control operator of a club station may accept compensation for the periods of time when the station is transmitting telegraphy practice or information bulletins, provided that the station transmits such telegraphy practice and bulletins for at least 40 hours per week; schedules operations on at least six amateur service MF and HF bands using reasonable measures to maximize coverage; where the schedule of normal operating times and frequencies is published at least 30 days in advance of the actual transmissions; and where the control operator does not accept any direct or indirect compensation for any other service as a control operator.

(e) No station shall retransmit programs or signals emanating from any type of radio station other than an amateur station, except propagation and weather forecast information intended for use by the general public and originated from United States Government stations and communications, including incidental music, originating on United States Government frequencies between a space shuttle and its associated Earth stations. Prior approval for shuttle retransmissions must be obtained from the National Aeronautics and Space Administration. Such retransmissions must be for the exclusive use of amateur operators. Propagation, weather forecasts, and shuttle retransmissions may not be conducted on a regular basis, but only occasionally, as an incident of normal amateur radio communications.

(f) No amateur station, except an auxiliary, repeater or space station, may automatically retransmit the radio signals of other amateur stations.

to be codes or ciphers intended to obscure the meaning of the communication.

One important restriction designed to protect others is an antenna-height limitation. You may not build an antenna structure (including the radiating elements, tower, supports or any other attachments) that is over 200 feet high, unless you obtain prior FCC approval. In addition, if you live within 4 miles of an airport the height of your antenna may be further limited by the Rules. Section 97.15 contains the details of these antenna-height limitations. Check *The FCC Rule Book*, published by ARRL, for the complete text if you think you may be affected by the airport limitation.

[Now turn to Chapter 12 and study questions G1B01 and G1B05 through G1B11. Review this section if any of these questions give you difficulty.]

BROADCASTING

No amateur station may engage in any type of **broadcasting**. Broadcasting generally refers to any type of communication intended to be received by the general public. Broadcasts would often be transmitted as a form of **one-way communication**, because they are not transmitted specifically to another amateur.

According to the Rules, "...an amateur station may transmit the following types of one-way communications: (1) Brief transmissions necessary to make adjustments to the station; (2) Brief transmissions necessary to establishing two-way communications with other stations; (3) Telecommand; (4) Transmissions necessary to providing emergency communications; (5) Transmissions necessary to assisting persons learning, or improving proficiency in, the international Morse code; (6) Transmissions necessary to disseminate information bulletins; (7) Transmissions of telemetry." [§97.111(b)] The information bulletins mentioned in (6) refer to information bulletins of interest to amateurs, not information intended for the general public.

In addition to this section, §97.203(g) says, "A beacon may transmit one-way communications." A **beacon station** is "an amateur station transmitting communications for the purposes of observation of propagation and reception or other related experimental activities." [§97.3(a)(9)]

When a natural disaster such as an earthquake, flood or severe storm hits an area, normal means of communication are often wiped out. Amateur Radio plays a significant role in providing communications with the disaster area because many hams maintain complete emergency stations that can be put on the air without commercial power or other services. Amateur Radio operators practice their communications skills under these difficult conditions during the annual ARRL Field Day and other emergency drills.

During such disasters, the broadcast news media may be cut off from their normal news-gathering methods. They often turn to Amateur Radio operators for news and information. Amateurs must be careful not to become part of the news media in such cases. In their eagerness for information, the media may take advantage of a well-meaning amateur's eagerness to help. They may request the amateur to ask specific questions of stations in the disaster area, and even attempt to conduct "interviews" over Amateur Radio. The FCC Rules state some limited conditions under which an amateur station may assist in such "news-gathering" activities. These are spelled out in §97.113(b). (See Table 1-4 for the complete text.) The communications must be directly related to the immediate safety of human life or the protection of property and there must be no other means of communication reasonably available before or at the time of the event. Of course the news information must be directly related to the event. The news media is interested in obtaining the information by the fastest method possible, but that isn't reason enough to use Amateur Radio.

The real test here is that you, as the amateur operator, must feel confident that what you are doing falls within the Rules. Don't be swayed into asking questions for (or turning the mike over to) an eager reporter. If the FCC decides the news-gathering was inappropriate, you are the one left to face the consequences!

[Now turn to Chapter 12 and study questions G1B03 and G1B04. If you are uncertain about the answers, review this section.]

TRANSMITTER POWER STANDARDS

As a General Amateur Radio licensee, you will be authorized to use up to 1500 watts peak envelope power (PEP) output on many amateur frequencies. It is especially important to understand that there are band segments where you may not use that much power, however. (Of course you must always follow the rule that requires you to use the minimum power necessary to carry out the desired communications — §97.313(a).) The remainder of §97.313 describes maximum power standards for various amateur bands.

No amateur station may use more than 200 W PEP on the 30-meter band, 10.10 to 10.15 MHz. This is a shared band, and US amateurs must not cause harmful interference to stations authorized by other nations in the fixed service — §97.303(d).

In addition, no amateur station may use more than 200 W PEP on the Novice segments of the 80, 40 and 15-meter bands. (The Novice 80-meter band is from 3675 to 3725 kHz. The Novice 40-meter band is from 7100 to 7150 kHz. The Novice 15-meter band is from 21.100 to 21.200 MHz.)

When you transmit on other frequencies, you may use a maximum of 1500 W PEP. So if you are operating on a frequency of 7080 kHz on the 40-meter band, for example, you may use the maximum power of 1500 W PEP output. Likewise, if you were operating on a frequency of 24.950 MHz, in the 12-meter band, you may use the maximum 1500 W PEP output.

[Turn to Chapter 12 and study questions G1C01 through G1C05. Review this section as needed.]

RF POWER AMPLIFIERS

RF power amplifiers capable of operating on frequencies below 144 MHz may require FCC type acceptance. Sections 97.315 and 97.317 describe the conditions under which type acceptance is required, and set out the standards to be met for type acceptance. See Table 1-5.

Many of these rules apply to manufacturers of amplifiers or kits, but several points are important for individual amateurs. Amateurs may build their own ampli-

Table 1-5

§97.315 Type acceptance of external RF power amplifiers.

(a) No more than 1 unit of 1 model of an external RF power amplifier capable of operation below 144 MHz may be constructed or modified during any calendar year by an amateur operator for use at a station without a grant of type acceptance. No amplifier capable of operation below 144 MHz may be constructed or modified by a non-amateur operator without a grant of type acceptance from the FCC.

(b) Any external RF power amplifier or external RF power amplifier kit (see §2.815 of the FCC Rules), manufactured, imported or modified for use in a station or attached at any station must be type accepted for use in the amateur service in accordance with Subpart J of Part 2 of the FCC Rules. This requirement does not apply if one or more of the following conditions are met:

  (1) The amplifier is not capable of operation on frequencies below 144 MHz. For the purpose of this part, an amplifier will be deemed to be incapable of operation below 144 MHz if it is not capable of being easily modified to increase its amplification characteristics below 120 MHz and either:

  (i) The mean output power of the amplifier decreases, as frequency decreases from 144 MHz, to a point where 0 dB or less gain is exhibited at 120 MHz; or

  (ii) The amplifier is not capable of amplifying signals below 120 MHz even for brief periods without sustaining permanent damage to its amplification circuitry.

  (2) The amplifier was manufactured before April 28, 1978, and has been issued a marketing waiver by the FCC, or the amplifier was purchased before April 28, 1978, by an amateur operator for use at that amateur operator's station.

  (3) The amplifier was:

  (i) Constructed by the licensee, not from an external RF power amplifier kit, for use at the licensee's station; or

  (ii) Modified by the licensee for use at the licensee's station.

  (4) The amplifier is sold by an amateur operator to another amateur operator or to a dealer.

  (5) The amplifier is purchased in used condition by an equipment dealer from an amateur operator and the amplifier is further sold to another amateur operator for use at that operator's station.

(c) A list of type accepted equipment may be inspected at FCC headquarters in Washington, DC or at any FCC field location. Any external RF power amplifier appearing on this list as type accepted for use in the amateur service may be marketed for use in the amateur service.

§97.317 Standards for type acceptance of external RF power amplifiers.

(a) To receive a grant of type acceptance, the amplifier must satisfy the spurious emission standards of §97.307(d) or (e) of this Part, as applicable, when the amplifier is:

  (1) Operated at its full output power;

fiers or modify amplifiers for use in their own station without concern for the type acceptance rules. If you build or modify an amplifier for use by another amateur operator, then §97.315(a) applies. This rule says you cannot build or modify more than one amplifier of any particular model during any calendar year without obtaining a grant of type acceptance from the FCC.

To receive a grant of type acceptance, an amplifier must satisfy the spurious emission standards specified in §97.307(d) or (e) when operated at full power output. The amplifier must not be capable of reaching its designed output power when driven with less than 50 watts. The amplifier must also not be capable of operation on any frequency between 24 and 35 MHz. (This is to prevent the amplifier from

(2) Placed in the "standby" or "off" positions, but still connected to the transmitter; and

(3) Driven with at least 50 W mean RF input power (unless higher drive level is specified).

(b) To receive a grant of type acceptance, the amplifier must not be capable of operation on any frequency or frequencies between 24 MHz and 35 MHz. The amplifier will be deemed incapable of such operation if it:

(1) Exhibits no more than 6 dB gain between 24 MHz and 26 MHz and between 28 MHz and 35 MHz. (This gain will be determined by the ratio of the input RF driving signal (mean power measurement) to the mean RF output power of the amplifier); and

(2) Exhibits no amplification (0 dB gain) between 26 MHz and 28 MHz.

(c) Type acceptance may be denied when denial would prevent the use of these amplifiers in services other than the amateur service. The following features will result in dismissal or denial of an application for the type acceptance:

(1) Any accessible wiring which, when altered, would permit operation of the amplifier in a manner contrary to the FCC Rules;

(2) Circuit boards or similar circuitry to facilitate the addition of components to change the amplifier's operating characteristics in a manner contrary to the FCC Rules;

(3) Instructions for operation or modification of the amplifier in a manner contrary to the FCC Rules;

(4) Any internal or external controls or adjustments to facilitate operation of the amplifier in a manner contrary to the FCC Rules;

(5) Any internal RF sensing circuitry or any external switch, the purpose of which is to place the amplifier in the transmit mode;

(6) The incorporation of more gain in the amplifier than is necessary to operate in the amateur service; for purposes of this paragraph, the amplifier must:

(i) Not be capable of achieving designed output power when driven with less than 40 W mean RF input power;

(ii) Not be capable of amplifying the input RF driving signal by more than 15 dB, unless the amplifier has a designed transmitter power of less than 1.5 kW (in such a case, gain must be reduced by the same number of dB as the transmitter power relationship to 1.5 kW; This gain limitation is determined by the ratio of the input RF driving signal to the RF output power of the amplifier where both signals are expressed in peak envelope power or mean power);

(iii) Not exhibit more gain than permitted by paragraph (c)(6)(ii) of this Section when driven by an RF input signal of less than 50 W mean power; and

(iv) Be capable of sustained operation at its designed power level.

(7) Any attenuation in the input of the amplifier which, when removed or modified, would permit the amplifier to function at its designed transmitter power when driven by an RF frequency input signal of less than 50 W mean power; or

(8) Any other features designed to facilitate operation in a telecommunication service other than the Amateur Radio Services, such as the Citizens Band (CB) Radio Service.

being used illegally on the Citizen's Band frequencies.) The amplifier may be capable of operation on all amateur bands with frequencies below 24 MHz, however.

If there is any wiring that can be simply altered to allow the amplifier to operate outside of the amateur bands, or if there are instructions describing how to modify or operate the amplifier in a way that violates FCC Rules, the amplifier would not be granted FCC type acceptance. The main reason for these rules is to prevent amateur equipment from being used illegally on the Citizen's Band.

[Now turn to Chapter 12 and study questions G1C06 through G1C09. If any of these questions give you difficulty, review this section.]

EXAM ELEMENT PREPARATION AND ADMINISTRATION

As a General Amateur Radio operator, you will earn some important new privileges that have nothing to do with on-the-air operation. A General licensee is eligible to be certified as a Volunteer Examiner (VE) by a Volunteer-Examiner Coordinator (VEC). This privilege is very important, and one you should take very seriously. You will be responsible for maintaining the high standards set for the Amateur Radio examination process.

Part 97, Subpart F of the FCC Rules describes the Qualifying Examination Systems of the amateur service. This section of the Rules describes the VEC system and outlines the procedures used to make Amateur Radio exams and administer them. The FCC's basic principle for preparing or administering exams is that a Volunteer Examiner can only prepare or administer those exam elements one license grade below the VE's own license. An Amateur Extra licensee may prepare or administer all exam elements, but an Advanced licensee may only work with the exam elements for Novice, Technician, Technician Plus and General. A General licensee, then, may prepare or administer those exam elements needed for the Novice, Technician and Technician Plus licenses.

A General licensee may prepare or administer the Element 1A telegraphy examination, which is the 5 words-per-minute Morse code exam. This is the code exam for the Novice license, and for a Technician licensee wishing to gain the Novice HF privileges with a Technician Plus license.

A General licensee may prepare or administer the Element 2 and Element 3A written exam. Element 2 is the 35-question Novice written exam and Element 3A is the 30-question Technician written exam. If you are preparing one of these exam elements you must select questions from the appropriate current question pool, as maintained by the Question Pool Committee of the Volunteer-Examiner Coordinators. These question pools are released into the public domain and are published by the ARRL and other exam-preparation publishers in the applicable license study guides.

Section 97.501 of the Rules specifies the minimum examination elements an applicant must pass to qualify for any particular Amateur Radio license. Section 97.503 specifies the standards for the various Amateur Radio exam elements. Table 1-6 lists those points of these Rules that pertain to Novice through General licenses.

The rules for administering all license exams are the same. Sections 97.509 and 97.511 describe how to conduct an exam session. Section 97.509 lists some requirements for being a Volunteer Examiner. A VE must be at least 18 years of age, and be accredited by the coordinating VEC. No VE may administer an examination to any member of their family, including in-laws. If your amateur station license or operator license has ever been revoked or suspended by the FCC, you are not eligible to be a VE.

If you meet all these qualifications, you can apply for accreditation with a Volunteer-Examiner Coordinator. When you are accredited by a VEC, you will receive an ID badge or other form of accreditation. If you would like more information about becoming a Volunteer Examiner, contact the ARRL/VEC Office, 225 Main Street, Newington, CT 06111-1494.

Every exam session must be coordinated by a VEC and conducted by three VEs accredited by that VEC. All three VEs must hold the proper license for the

Table 1-6
Novice through General License Element Standards

§97.501 Qualifying for an amateur operator license.

Each applicant for the grant of a new amateur operator license or for the grant of a modified license to show a higher operator class, must pass or otherwise receive credit for the examination elements specified for the class of operator license sought:

(c) General Class operator: Elements 1(B) or 1(C), 2, 3(A) and 3(B);

(d) Technician Plus Class operator: Elements 1(A) or 1(B) or 1(C), 2, and 3(A).

(e) Technician Class operator: Elements 2 and 3(A).

(f) Novice Class operator: Elements 1(A) or 1(B) or 1(C), and 2.

§97.503 Element standards.

(a) A telegraphy examination must be sufficient to prove that the examinee has the ability to send correctly by hand and to receive correctly by ear texts in the international Morse code at not less than the prescribed speed, using all the letters of the alphabet, numerals 0-9, period, comma, question mark, slant mark and prosigns AR, BT and SK.

(1) Element 1(A): 5 words per minute;

(2) Element 1(B): 13 words per minute;

(3) Element 1(C): 20 words per minute.

(b) A written examination must be such as to prove that the examinee possesses the operational and technical qualifications required to perform properly the duties of an amateur service licensee. Each written examination must be comprised of a question set as follows:

(1) Element 2: 35 questions concerning the privileges of a Novice Class operator license. The minimum passing score is 26 questions answered correctly.

(2) Element 3(A): 30 questions concerning the additional privileges of a Technician Class operator license. The minimum passing score is 22 questions answered correctly.

(3) Element 3(B): 30 questions concerning the additional privileges of a General Class operator license. The minimum passing score is 22 questions answered correctly.

(c) The topics and number of questions required in each question set are listed below for the appropriate examination element:

Topics	Element:		
	2	3(A)	3(B)
(1) FCC Rules for the amateur radio services	10	5	4
(2) Amateur station operating procedures	2	3	3
(3) Radio wave propagation characteristics of amateur service frequency bands	1	3	3
(4) Amateur radio practices	4	4	5
(5) Electrical principles as applied to amateur station equipment	4	2	2
(6) Amateur station equipment circuit components	2	2	1
(7) Practical circuits employed in amateur station equipment	2	1	1
(8) Signals and emissions transmitted by amateur stations	2	2	2
(9) Amateur station antennas and feed lines	3	3	4
(10) Radiofrequency environmental safety practices at an amateur station	5	5	5

exam elements being administered at that session. So to conduct a Novice or Technician exam you will need three VEs who hold at least General licenses.

[Now it is time to review a few more questions from the question pool printed in Chapter 12. Study questions G1D01 through G1D08. Review this section if any of these questions give you difficulty.]

STATION IDENTIFICATION

At the end of your General license exam you will receive a Certificate of Successful Completion of Examination (CSCE) showing those exam elements you passed. This certificate is valid as proof that you passed those elements, and is valid for 365 days. So if you don't pass all the exam elements to earn your new license, you can retake only the ones you didn't pass to earn the license. You can also use this certificate to show that you passed certain elements if you want to go back to another exam session before your license actually arrives from the FCC. If you want to upgrade as fast as possible, you might go to another exam session the following month (or sooner) and take the Advanced exam, for example.

If you pass all the exam elements for the General license, and have a Novice or Technician license, you may begin using your new General license privileges on the air immediately. Your CSCE serves as a temporary "endorsement" to your license, until the FCC grants your new license. You must follow a special identification procedure when you use these new privileges with the CSCE, however. In §97.119(f) we read that "When the control operator who is exercising the rights and privileges authorized by §97.9(b) of this Part, an indicator must be included after the call sign as follows: ... (2) For a control operator who has requested a license modification from Novice or Technician Class to General Class: AG." Section 97.9(b) is the Rule point that allows you to use your new privileges after an upgrade, as long as you have a CSCE to prove your new privileges, until the upgraded license is granted by the FCC.

There is a bit more detail about how to use this special identifier in §97.119(c): "An indicator may be included with the call sign. It must be separated from the call sign by the slant mark or by any suitable word that denotes the slant mark..." So if you are operating on the 20-meter band, transmitting phone emissions on 14.325 MHz, for example, you would give your station identification with your call sign, some word to denote the slant mark, and the letters AG. This would sound like "This is WB3IOS slant AG." You may also hear stations use words like "stroke," "interim," or "temporary" instead of "slant."

Remember that you only have to give this temporary identifier when you operate using your new privileges. If you previously had a Novice license, and are operating in the Novice segment of the 10-meter band, you need not use the "slant AG." Or if you had a Technician license and are operating on the 2-meter band, you don't have to say "temporary AG."

[Congratulations! You have completed your study of the Commission's Rules section of the question pool. Before you go on to the next chapter, though, you should turn to Chapter 12 and study questions G1D09 through G1D11. Review this last section of Chapter 1 if you have any difficulty with these questions.]

CHAPTER 2
KEYWORDS
KEYWORDS
KEYWORDS

Amateur Auxiliary — A voluntary organization, administered by the ARRL. The primary objectives are to foster amateur self-regulation and compliance with the rules.

Amateur Teleprinting Over Radio (AMTOR) — AMTOR provides error-correcting capabilities. See **Automatic Repeat Request** and **Forward Error Correction**.

American National Standard Code for Information Interchange (ASCII) — A seven-bit digital code used in computer and radioteleprinter applications.

Automatic Repeat Request (ARQ) — One of two AMTOR communications modes. In ARQ, also called Mode A, the two stations are constantly confirming each other's transmissions. If information is lost, it is repeated until the receiving station confirms reception.

Azimuthal-equidistant projection map — A map made with its center at one geographic location and the rest of the continents projected from that point. Also called a great-circle map, this map is the most useful type for determining where to point a directional antenna to communicate with a specific location.

Band plan—An agreement for operating within a certain portion of the radio spectrum. Band plans set aside certain frequencies for each different mode of amateur operation, such as CW, SSB, RTTY, SSTV, FM, repeaters and simplex.

Baudot — A five-bit digital code used in teleprinter application.

Directional antenna — An antenna that concentrates more of the transmitted energy in a particular direction. A directional antenna must be turned to provide the best signal coverage in various directions. Such antennas also receive signals better from the direction they are pointed. Also called a beam antenna.

Emergency communications — Communications involving the immediate safety of human life and immediate protection of property when normal communication systems are not available.

Forward Error Correction (FEC) — One of two AMTOR communications modes. In the FEC mode, each character is sent twice. The receiving station checks for errors in the mark/space ratio. If an error is detected, a space is printed to show that an incorrect character was received. Also called Mode B.

Frequency separation — The difference between a repeater input frequency (the frequency the repeater receives on) and the output frequency (the frequency it transmits on). Repeaters on the 10-meter band normally use a frequency separation of 100 kHz. (Also called **offset**.)

Full break-in (QSK) — With QSK, an amateur can hear signals between code characters. This allows another amateur to break into the communication without waiting for the transmitting station to finish.

Great-circle path — Either one of two direct paths between two points on the surface of the Earth. One of the great-circle paths is the shortest distance between those two points. Great-circle paths can be visualized if you think of a globe with a rubber band stretched around it, connecting the two points.

Long-path communication — Communication made by pointing beam antennas in the directions indicated by the longer **great-circle path** between the stations. To work each other by long-path, an amateur in Hawaii would point his antenna west and an amateur in Florida would aim east.

Net — A group of amateurs who meet at regular times on a specific frequency to share common interests.

Offset — The difference between a repeater's input and output frequencies. On 10 meters, for example, the repeater transmit offset is usually 100 kHz higher than the receive frequency. (Also called **frequency separation**.)

Radio Amateur Civil Emergency Service (RACES) — Part of the amateur service that provides radio communications only for civil defense purposes.

Repeater — An amateur station that receives a signal and retransmits it for greater range.

Short-path communication — Communication made by pointing beam antennas in the direction indicated by the shorter **great-circle path**.

Single sideband (SSB) — The type of voice (phone) operation used most often on the amateur high-frequency (HF) bands. One sideband and the carrier are removed from a double-sideband amplitude modulated (AM) signal, leaving only a single sideband to convey the voice information.

Voice-Operated Transmit (VOX) — Circuitry that activates the transmitter when the operator speaks into the microphone.

OPERATING PROCEDURES

On-the-air operation is the thrill of Amateur Radio. There are many different operating modes available, and true enjoyment of the hobby comes from taking advantage of this diversity. This chapter covers rules and procedures normally followed on the air when using some of the modes that you, as a General licensee, are authorized. Your General exam will have three questions from the material covered in this chapter. Those questions come from the following three syllabus groups:

G2A Phone, RTTY, repeater, VOX and full break-in CW.

G2B Operating courtesy, antenna orientation and HF operations, including logging practices; ITU Regions.

G2C Emergencies, including drills, communications and amateur auxiliary to FCC's Compliance and Information Bureau.

TELEPHONY

Radiotelephony is probably the most natural communication mode of all. Although "phone" operation appears to be as simple as grabbing a microphone and talking, there is a little more to it. There are a few rules and guidelines to keep in mind for courteous and legal on-the-air operation.

Most phone operation on the high frequency (HF) bands uses **single sideband (SSB)**. A double-sideband, full-carrier, amplitude-modulated (DSB AM) signal takes twice the spectrum bandwidth necessary to convey the information, since both sidebands contain the same information, as mirror images of each other. (Chapter 8 gives more information about this signal type and how it relates to SSB signals.) An SSB signal transmits only one of the sidebands. But which one? The lower sideband is normally used on the 160-meter band (1800 to 2000 kHz), the 75-meter band (3850 to 4000 kHz) and the 40-meter band (7225 to 7300 kHz). The lower sideband is given this name because it is *lower* in frequency than the carrier. The upper sideband is *higher* in frequency than the carrier. The upper sideband is normally used on the 20-meter band (14,225 to 14,350 kHz), the 17-meter band (18,110 to 18,168 kHz), the 15-meter band (21,300 to 21,450 kHz), the 12-meter band (24,930 to 24,990 kHz) and the 10-meter band 28,300 to 29,700 kHz). While neither of these sideband choices is specified in the FCC Rules, they are common practice on the amateur bands. You might decide to use the opposite sideband for some reason, but you would not be able to understand the other stations on the band, and no one would be able to understand what you were saying unless they also switched to the opposite sideband.

[Now turn to the question pool in Chapter 12 and study questions G2A01 and G2A02. Review this section if you have difficulty with either of these questions.]

Voice-Operated Transmit (VOX)

The purpose of a **voice-operated transmit (VOX)** circuit is to provide automatic TR (transmit/receive) switching within an amateur station. When using VOX, the transmitter switches on, the antenna is connected to the transmitter, and the receiver is muted as soon as you begin to speak; when you stop talking, the transmitter is turned off and the antenna is connected to the receiver. VOX circuits can be used with separate transmitter/receiver combinations, and most modern transceivers have a VOX circuit built in.

Three controls must be adjusted before using VOX: VOX sensitivity, anti-VOX and VOX delay. These adjustments will vary with different pieces of equipment, and even with different operators using the same gear. Since VOX activates the transmitter, any VOX-circuit control adjustments should be made with the transmitter connected to a dummy load.

Normally, VOX sensitivity is adjusted first. The setting of this control determines the level of audio input necessary to activate the transmitter. With the VOX delay and anti-VOX controls set to the middle of their adjustment ranges, turn the receiver volume to minimum. Speak into the microphone and slowly increase the setting of the VOX sensitivity control until the transmitter activates. Stop talking and allow the transmit relay to switch back to receive. Speak again, and "fine-tune" the sensitivity adjustment: your voice should activate the transmitter instantly, but background noise in the shack shouldn't.

Next, adjust the VOX delay. This part of the VOX circuit controls the amount of time the transmitter remains activated after you stop talking. Set it so the transmitter deactivates ("drops") when you stop to take a breath between thoughts. That way, a radiotelephone contact can approach a face-to-face conversation.

The anti-VOX control is adjusted last. Anti-VOX prevents receiver audio from tripping the transmitter. It accomplishes this by applying a portion of the receiver audio to the microphone amplifier circuit 180° out of phase with the actual receiver audio. The anti-VOX control varies the feedback level. If the anti-VOX control is set too high, you'll have trouble activating the VOX circuit when you speak into the microphone. Insufficient anti-VOX will allow receiver audio to trip the transmitter. The VOX sensitivity and anti-VOX control settings may interact slightly, so you may need to readjust the VOX sensitivity after setting the anti-VOX level.

For CW (Morse code) operation, many transceivers use the VOX circuitry to key the transmitter when you begin sending, and to shut it off when you stop. With proper adjustment, you can hear other signals between words in your transmission. This is called semi-break-in operation. With this type of circuit, the VOX delay is set to hold the transmitter on during the transmission of entire words. Nevertheless, the receiver can come back on between words, so at speeds above about 15 wpm the effect is almost the same as **full-break-in (QSK)** operation. Full-break-in operation on CW allows you to listen to your transmit frequency between character elements (dots and dashes) and between words.

QSK operation is especially useful when you are sending message traffic — the receiving station can send a few dots and "break" (stop) the transmitting station for repeats (fills) of missed words. The transmitting station can also hear if another station comes on frequency and interferes with the QSO.

[Now turn to Chapter 12 and study questions G2A10 and G2A11. Review this section as needed.]

Repeater Operation

A **repeater** is an amateur station that receives a signal and retransmits (repeats) that signal. Often located on top of a tall building or a high mountain, repeaters greatly extend the operating coverage of amateurs using mobile and hand-held VHF and UHF transceivers. Most repeaters used for voice communication receive on one frequency and simultaneously retransmit the signal on another frequency. Some repeaters (particularly those designed for digital communications) hold the message for transmission later. These repeaters may receive and transmit on the same frequency.

While most repeater operation occurs on the VHF and UHF bands, there is a repeater segment on the 10-meter band, between 29.5 and 29.7 MHz. As a General licensee, you will be able to use these repeaters, and may even become a control operator of one.

Repeaters have an input frequency (the frequency the repeater receives on), and an output frequency (the frequency the repeater transmits on). This **frequency separation** is usually 100 kHz for repeaters operating on the 10-meter band. Frequency separation is often called **offset**. Repeater frequencies are sometimes specified as a pair of frequencies, with the input frequency given first. One 10-meter repeater "pair" is 29.520/29.620 MHz, for example. Sometimes the repeater frequencies are specified by giving the repeater transmit frequency (output), and then giving the offset as either a + or a − to indicate the offset direction. A + offset means the repeater receive frequency is higher than the transmit frequency, while a − offset means it is lower. If a repeater frequency is listed as 29.620 MHz with a − offset, you must know the normal frequency separation for repeaters on that band. Otherwise, you won't know the frequency on which to set your transmitter for the listed repeater.

Be careful with the terms discussed here. Your radio must *transmit* on the repeater input or *receive* frequency, and must *receive* on the repeater *transmit* frequency.

Many 10-meter repeaters are also linked to VHF or UHF repeaters. This means an operator may be transmitting to the repeater on 2 meters, 1¼ meters or another band, and their signal is linked to the 10-meter repeater. This permits an operator with a Technician or Novice license to transmit on a frequency they are allowed to use, and have their signals transmitted over the 10-meter frequency. Such a "cross-band repeater" makes it possible to contact stations hundreds or thousands of miles away, using VHF or UHF equipment.

The *Repeater Directory*

The ARRL publishes a *Repeater Directory*, a listing of over 20,000 repeaters in the US and Canada as well as Central and South America. If you own a rig that operates above 29.5 MHz, and is capable of FM operation, you'll find the *Repeater Directory* useful for locating repeaters in your area and indispensable when you're traveling away from home.

[Now turn to Chapter 12 and study question G2A09. Review this section if you don't remember the 10-meter repeater frequency separation.]

DIGITAL COMMUNICATIONS

Amateur Radio digital communications normally involve the use of the **ASCII**, **Baudot** or **AMTOR** codes, as well as the original digital code, Morse. The Baudot code, also known as the International Telegraph Alphabet Number 2 (or ITA2) was the only digital code (other than Morse) allowed on the amateur bands until 1980. The Baudot code uses five information bits, with additional bits (called "start" and "stop" bits) to indicate the beginning and end of the character.

ASCII stands for American National Standard Code for Information Interchange; ASCII is the code commonly used for computer systems. The ASCII code uses seven information bits, so more characters can be defined than with the five-bit Baudot code.

AMTOR, which stands for *Amateur Teleprinting Over Radio*, combines a modified Baudot code with error correcting capabilities. As with radiotelephone operation, there are a few standard operating practices for the digital modes. We'll cover a few of the main points here. For more details, consult *The ARRL Operating Manual*.

Radioteletype

Radioteleprinter operation uses *frequency-shift keying (FSK)* to convey information. This shift is between two frequencies, called "mark" and "space." On HF, the mark and space are normally 170 Hz apart. On VHF, there is a variety of mark and space frequency shifts. (Some common shifts on VHF are 170 Hz, 850 Hz and 1 kHz. Presently, the most common shift is 170 Hz.) Common speeds for HF radioteletype (RTTY) operation are 60, 75 and 100 WPM (45.45, 56 and 75 bauds).

On the HF bands, most of the RTTY operation is found at the top of the CW portion of each band. Traditionally, the 20-meter RTTY subband has received the heaviest use during daylight hours; the 80-meter RTTY subband is active at night. Recently, the increased popularity of RTTY has brought about greater use of the 40-meter RTTY subband.

Besides SSB voice operation, you can find AM voice, CW, slow-scan TV (SSTV) and satellite operation, as well as RTTY and other digital communications modes on the HF bands. On the amateur bands between 3.5 and 148 MHz FCC-mandated subband restrictions apply, but different operating modes must still share spectrum space (RTTY and CW operators, and slow-scan television and phone operators, for example). Voluntary **Band Plans** help minimize conflicts. More information on band plans can be found in *The ARRL Operating Manual*. VHF and UHF band plans are covered in *The ARRL Repeater Directory*. A **Band Plan** refers to an agreement between concerned radio amateurs for operating within a certain portion of the radio spectrum. The goal is to minimize interference between the various modes sharing each band, by setting aside certain sections of a band for each different operating mode.

The recommended frequencies for RTTY operation on the 80-meter band are between 3580 kHz and 3620 kHz. On the 20-meter band, the Band Plan calls for RTTY operation to be between 14.070 MHz and 14.095 MHz. Most operators try to keep their RTTY operations inside these limits. Suggested operating frequencies for RTTY on the HF bands are shown in Table 2-1.

To call CQ on RTTY, you might use this standard calling sequence:

CQ CQ CQ DE W1AW W1AW W1AW
CQ CQ CQ DE W1AW W1AW W1AW
CQ CQ CQ DE W1AW W1AW W1AW
THIS IS JOE IN NEWINGTON CT
K

If you copied this CQ and you want to answer the station, here's the accepted method:

W1AW W1AW W1AW DE WB8IMY WB8IMY WB8IMY K

RTTY operators will occasionally send a string of the letters "R" and "Y": RYRYRYRYRY. The letter "R" in the Baudot code has a space for bits 1, 3 and 5 and a mark for the other two bits; "Y" is just the opposite, with a space in bits 2 and 4 and mark in bits 1, 3 and 5. A string of "RYs" alternates between the mark and space bits, and is useful for testing equipment, and was quite common in the days of mechanical teleprinter machines. It can help other amateurs tune their equipment, but is generally not needed in these days of computerized RTTY stations and modern transceivers.

Table 2-1

Suggested US RTTY Operating Frequencies (kHz)

3590 RTTY DX
3580-3620
7040 RTTY DX
7080-7100
10,130-10,140
14,070-14,095
18,100-18,105
21,070-21,095
24,920-24,925
28,070-28,120

There are only 32 possible character combinations with the Baudot code, so all letters are sent as upper case. One character is called the FIGS shift and one is the LTRS shift, allowing each character to serve two purposes. When you send the FIGS character, everything you type after that will be received as numbers, punctuation or other control codes until you send a LTRS character. The FIGS and LTRS characters select between two different character sets on the printer.

The reason for this limitation is that each character consists of five information bits, and each bit can have one of two possible conditions: mark or space (often represented by 1 and 0). The total number of possible characters is defined by the calculation $2^5 = 32$.

AMTOR

The benefit of using AMTOR is its error detection and correction properties. There are two AMTOR modes: Mode A, called **Automatic Repeat Request (ARQ)**, and Mode B, called **Forward Error Correction (FEC)**. Since the AMTOR code is a variation of the Baudot code, there are 32 possible character combinations, with FIGS and LTRS shift characters to change between two characters sets on the printer.

When two stations are in AMTOR Mode A communication, they are constantly confirming each other's transmissions: If a piece of information is missed or lost (because of interference or any other reason), it is repeated until the receiving station confirms reception. The transmitting station sends three characters, then pauses for the receiving station to confirm or deny correct reception. The same block of three characters is repeated or the next three are sent, depending on the reply. This interactive "handshaking" takes 450 milliseconds for every cycle between the two stations.

Mode B AMTOR is a "broadcast" mode, in which the transmitting station sends each character twice. The receiving station examines each character as it is received, looking for any errors in the mark/space ratio (each character contains four mark elements and three space elements). The first character of the pair is stored in memory as it is received. When the second character is received, the character pair is checked for errors. If one or both characters contain the proper mark/space ratio, the character is printed on the screen. If neither character has the correct ratio, the receiving station records an error signal, signified by a space.

To establish an AMTOR contact, get on a calling frequency and make a general CQ call in Mode B. (The Band Plans put all of these digital modes in the same band segments as the Baudot RTTY operation.) Once contact is established, switch to Mode A.

ASCII

ASCII is a coded character set used for computer systems and related equipment. ASCII differs from the Baudot code in that it has a larger character set. The 7 information bits in each character make it possible for the ASCII character set to provide upper- and lower-case letters, numbers, punctuation and special characters. (With 7 information bits, each with two possible values — 1 and 0 — the ASCII character set has $2^7 = 128$ character combinations.) In addition to the 7 information bits, ASCII characters include start, stop and parity bits. To establish a contact using ASCII, use the same procedure described for Baudot RTTY.

HF ASCII transmissions are normally sent at 110 or 300 bauds, using 170-Hz shift. The maximum data symbol rate for RTTY and other digital modes such as packet radio on HF (below 28 MHz) is 300 bauds. Higher data rates are used on higher-frequency bands. On 28 MHz and above, for instance, the FCC permits use of symbol rates of up to 1200 bauds. As the speed of an RTTY transmission is increased, the bandwidth required for that transmission also increases. More spectrum space is available on the VHF and UHF bands, so the FCC permits the use of speeds up to 19.6 kilobauds on frequencies above 50 MHz and up to 56 kilobauds above 220 MHz. More about the technical requirements and restrictions on RTTY will be covered in Chapter 8.

ASCII is also used for packet-radio communication. Packet radio is a communication mode that allows transmission of short bursts (packets) of information at high speed. The format (protocol) of information packets allows several stations to hold conversations on the same frequency at the same time without interfering with each other. For more information on packet radio, see *The ARRL Handbook for Radio Amateurs*, *The ARRL Operating Manual* or any of several other books about packet radio and digital communications published by the ARRL.

PACTOR and other Hybrid Modes

Amateur Radio operators are always experimenting and trying to develop more efficient means of communication. Continued amateur innovation has produced advanced HF digital modes such as G-TOR, CLOVER and PACTOR II. The operating procedures used with these modes are generally the same as for the digital modes already discussed. To learn more about the use of these modes, consult one of the ARRL publications mentioned earlier.

[You should now turn to Chapter 12 and study questions G2A03 through G2A08 and G2B10. Also study questions G1C10 and G1C11 at this time. Review this section as needed.]

GENERAL OPERATING PRACTICES

Operating Courtesy

On today's crowded ham bands, operating courtesy becomes extremely important. Operating courtesy is really nothing more than common sense; a good operator sets an example for others to follow. A courteous amateur operator always listens before transmitting so as not to interfere with stations already using the frequency. If the frequency is occupied, move to another frequency far enough away to prevent interference (QRM). Know how much bandwidth each mode occupies and act accordingly. A good rule of thumb is to leave 150 to 500 Hz between CW signals, approximately 3 kHz between the suppressed carriers of single-sideband signals and 250 to 500 Hz center-to-center for RTTY signals.

A good amateur operator transmits only what is necessary to accomplish his or her purpose and keeps the contents of the transmission within the bounds of propriety and good taste. Also, a good operator always reduces power to the minimum necessary to carry out the desired communications. This is not only operating courtesy; it's an FCC Rule! §97.313(a) states "An amateur station must use the minimum transmitter power necessary to carry out the desired communications." (A complete copy of Part 97 appears in *The FCC Rule Book*, published by the ARRL.)

It shows inexcusably bad manners to interfere with a station thousands of miles away because you are talking to a buddy across town on a DX band. Judicious selection of a band is important to reduce unintentional QRM. Use VHF and UHF bands for local communications. Sometimes propagation conditions may change while you are talking with another station. If you become aware of increasing interference from other activity on the frequency you are using, you are probably also causing interference to the other conversation. The most courteous thing to do in such a case is to move your contact to another (clear) frequency.

Nets are groups of amateurs who meet at regular times on a specific frequency to share common interests. Nets have many purposes. Some nets are part of the ARRL National Traffic System, designed to relay messages across the United States. Other nets provide Morse code practice, a chance to discuss shared interests with other hams or just a gathering place for Amateur Radio friends to chat.

Nets help reduce congestion on the ham bands because many operators gather on a single frequency. A little courtesy goes a long way to reduce frequency conflicts that sometimes arise.

Suppose you are in contact with another station and become aware that a net is about to start, and they normally use the frequency on which you are operating. What should you do? The most courteous action you can take is to move your contact to another (unused) frequency. It is true that you have just as much right to a frequency as the net participants, but think about the difficulty of moving a large group of operators to another frequency. It is much easier for two or three operators to change frequency, and you will do the net participants a great favor by allowing them to use their predetermined frequency. Of course, you might also want to stand by and simply join the net. You will be most welcome to participate with the group, and you may even become one of the "regulars."

From the other side, consider what you should do as the net control station when the normal net frequency is occupied at net time. The net doesn't own the frequency either, and you have no right to demand the other stations to give up the frequency. Most net participants understand that the announced frequency is just a starting point, so you may be able to find a clear frequency 3 to 5 kHz away. Sometimes you may even have to move a little farther than that. You might also join the ongoing conversation and make a polite announcement that it is time for a net that normally meets on the frequency. This will often lead the other stations to move their conversation to another frequency, or perhaps join your net.

Testing and "loading up" a transmitter should be done into a dummy antenna (or dummy load) without putting a signal on the air. On-the-air tests should be made only when necessary and kept as brief as possible while conducting the test. If your amateur station is within a mile of an FCC monitoring station or you are planning portable operation near a monitoring station, you should consult with the staff at the monitoring station to ensure that your amateur operations do not cause them any harmful interference. Always be more courteous than the other person — you contribute to the image of the Amateur Radio Service as being a self-disciplined, self-policing service with high standards.

[Before going to the next section, turn to Chapter 12 and study questions G2B01 through G2B06. Review this section if you have difficulty with any of these questions.]

Aiming Directional Antennas

Many Amateur Radio operators use a **directional antenna** or beam antenna on the HF bands, especially for the 20-meter band through the 10-meter band. You can take greatest advantage of the changing radio-wave-propagation conditions if you have a directional antenna, and can rotate it to point at various parts of the world.

The best propagation path between any two points on the Earth's surface is usually by the shortest direct route — the **great-circle path** that can be found by stretching a string tightly between the two points on a globe. If we replace the string with a rubber band going around the globe, we can see another, longer great-circle path. With the proper conditions, **long-path communication** is possible. To attempt communication by long-path propagation, you must rotate your antenna 180° from the "normal" (**short-path**) direction. For instance, using long-path propagation, an amateur in eastern Pennsylvania could work a station in Hawaii by pointing her beam a few degrees north of east — the Hawaiian amateur would point his beam a few degrees south of west. It is interesting to note that because Antarctica is at the South Pole, the short-path heading from anywhere to Antarctica is south, or 180° and the long-path heading is north, or 0°.

The long path seems to work best for communication between two places when the path is mostly over water. Since sunlight is an important ingredient for good ionospheric propagation on frequencies above 7.5 MHz, long-path communication also seems to work best when the signals will travel mostly through sunlight. From the East Coast of the United States, for example, you might try the long path to reach Hawaii just before your sunrise. If you are in Hawaii, you might try pointing your antenna to the west around sunset and shortly after that to contact stations on the East Coast. It is important that stations on both ends of a long-path circuit point their antennas in the long-path direction.

You can understand several aspects of long-path propagation if you become accustomed to thinking of the Earth as a ball. This is easy if you use a globe frequently. If you must use a flat map to find great-circle paths, an **azimuthal-equidistant projection map** (also called a great-circle map) is a useful substitute. See Figure 2-1. The azimuthal map centered on or near your location will show you beam headings for both long and short paths to other locations on the surface of the Earth.

[Turn to Chapter 12 and study questions G2B07 through G2B09. Review this section as needed.]

EMERGENCY COMMUNICATIONS

While no one *wants* to be involved with an emergency situation, it is something with which every amateur should be prepared to deal. If you are in need of some emergency help, your Amateur Radio station may be the best (or only) means to obtain that help. You may also find yourself on the receiving end of such a

Figure 2-1 — N5KR's computer-generated azimuthal-equidistant projection map centered on Newington, Connecticut. Information showing long paths to Perth and Tokyo have been added. Notice that the paths in both cases lie almost entirely over water, rather than over land masses.

communication. In §97.101 of the Rules, we find "(c) At all times and on all frequencies, each control operator must give priority to stations providing emergency communications..." **Emergency communications** is a serious obligation every amateur should be aware of, then.

Suppose you hear an emergency call for help while you are tuning around one of the ham bands, or a station breaks into your conversation with another amateur to make an emergency call. What should you do? Immediately acknowledge that you heard the call for help and stand by to receive the location of the emergency station and what assistance may be needed. Then you should relay the information to the proper authorities, and stay on frequency with the emergency station for further information, or until help arrives. Your responsibility in this case is to react to the call for help, and to do your best to obtain help for the station in distress.

Before you can think about how *you* should react in an emergency, let's define what a real emergency is. You may *think* you have an emergency situation, when all you really have is a minor inconvenience.

In discussing emergency communications in §97.403, the FCC Rules define an emergency as "the immediate safety of human life and immediate protection of property when normal communication systems are not available." So it seems that the best test of a real emergency is a life-threatening situation. A car accident with injuries could be life threatening, but a flat tire or other breakdown with the car safely off the side of the road probably is not. An earthquake or flood would be an emergency situation, but an inch of water in your basement again after a heavy rain probably is not.

You can use Amateur Radio to call for help even if the situation is not life threatening. You should not go outside your normal amateur privileges to call for help, however.

If you do have a *real* emergency, you can take any means at your disposal to attract attention, make known your condition and location, and obtain assistance — §97.405. This means you can use any frequency, with any amount of power necessary to conduct the communications. Table 2-2 is a copy of Subpart E — Providing Emergency Communications from the FCC Rules. This includes §97.401 through §97.407.

Section 97.111(2) even says you can make "Transmissions necessary to exchange messages with a station in another FCC-regulated service while providing emergency communications." You had better be certain you really do have a life-threatening emergency and no other communications means at your disposal before making such a call, though!

When normal communications systems are overloaded, damaged or disrupted because of a disaster in the US, an amateur station may make transmissions necessary to meet essential communications needs and assist relief operations — §97.401(a).

When a disaster disrupts normal communication systems in a particular area, the FCC may declare a temporary state of communication emergency. The declaration will set forth any special conditions and special rules to be observed by stations during the communication emergency — §97.401(c). The FCC Engineer in Charge of the particular area will issue such a declaration if he or she feels it is appropriate.

RACES

The **Radio Amateur Civil Emergency Service (RACES)** is part of the amateur service that provides radio communications only for civil defense purposes. It is active *only* during periods of local, regional or national civil emergencies.

You must register with the responsible civil defense organization in your area to operate as a RACES station. RACES stations may not communicate with amateurs not operating in a RACES capacity. Restrictions do not apply when stations are operating in a non-RACES amateur capacity, such as ARES, the Amateur Radio Emergency Service. (ARES is part of the ARRL Field Organization.)

Proper operating procedures are important for efficient handling of any emergency. This is especially true of a civil emergency that would result in RACES

Table 2-2

Part 97 Subpart E — Providing Emergency Communications

§97.401 Operation during a disaster.

(a) When normal communication systems are overloaded, damaged or disrupted because a disaster has occurred, or is likely to occur, in an area where the amateur service is regulated by the FCC, an amateur station may make transmissions necessary to meet essential communication needs and facilitate relief actions.

(b) When normal communication systems are overloaded, damaged or disrupted because a natural disaster has occurred, or is likely to occur, in an area where the amateur service is not regulated by the FCC, a station assisting in meeting essential communication needs and facilitating relief actions may do so only in accord with ITU Resolution No. 640 (Geneva, 1979). The 80 m, 75 m, 40 m, 30 m, 20 m, 17 m, 15 m, 12 m, and 2 m bands may be used for these purposes.

(c) When a disaster disrupts normal communication systems in a particular area, the FCC may declare a temporary state of communication emergency. The declaration will set forth any special conditions and special rules to be observed by stations during the communication emergency. A request for a declaration of a temporary state of emergency should be directed to the EIC in the area concerned.

(d) A station in, or within 92.6 km of, Alaska may transmit emissions J3E and R3E on the channel at 5.1675 MHz for emergency communications. The channel must be shared with stations licensed in the Alaska-private fixed service. The transmitter power must not exceed 150 W.

§97.403 Safety of life and protection of property.

No provision of these rules prevents the use by an amateur station of any means of radiocommunication at its disposal to provide essential communication needs in connection with the immediate safety of human life and immediate protection of property when normal communication systems are not available.

§97.405 Station in distress.

(a) No provision of these rules prevents the use by an amateur station in distress of any means at its disposal to attract attention, make known its condition and location, and obtain assistance.

(b) No provision of these rules prevents the use by a station, in the exceptional circumstances described in paragraph (a), of any means of radiocommunications at its disposal to assist a station in distress.

§97.407 Radio amateur civil emergency service.

(a) No station may transmit in RACES unless it is an FCC-licensed primary, club, or military recreation station and it is certified by a civil defense organization as registered with that organization, or it is an FCC-licensed RACES station. No person may be the control operator of a RACES station, or may be the control operator of an amateur station transmitting in RACES unless that person holds a FCC-issued amateur operator license and is certified by a civil defense organization as enrolled in that organization.

(b) The frequency bands and segments and emissions authorized to the control operator are available to stations transmitting communications in RACES on a shared basis with the amateur service. In the event of an emergency which necessitates the invoking of the President's War Emergency Powers under the provisions of §706 of the Communications Act of 1934, as amended, 47 U.S.C. §606, RACES stations and amateur stations participating in RACES may only transmit on the following frequencies:

(1) The 1800-1825 kHz, 1975-2000 kHz, 3.50-3.55 MHz, 3.93-3.98 MHz, 3.984-4.000 MHz, 7.079-7.125 MHz, 7.245-7.255 MHz, 10.10-10.15 MHz, 14.047-14.053 MHz, 14.22-14.23 MHz, 14.331-14.350 MHz, 21.047-21.053 MHz, 21.228-21.267 MHz, 28.55-28.75 MHz, 29.237-29.273 MHz, 29.45-29.65 MHz, 50.35-50.75 MHz, 52-54 MHz, 144.50-145.71 MHz, 146-148 MHz, 2390-2450 MHz segments;

(2) The 1.25 m, 70 cm and 23 cm bands; and

(3) The channels at 3.997 MHz and 53.30 MHz may be used in emergency areas when required to make initial contact with a military unit and for communications with military stations on matters requiring coordination.

(c) A RACES station may only communicate with:

(1) Another RACES station;

(2) An amateur station registered with a civil defense organization;

(3) A United States Government station authorized by the responsible agency to communicate with RACES stations;

(4) A station in a service regulated by the FCC whenever such communication is authorized by the FCC.

(d) An amateur station registered with a civil defense organization may only communicate with:

(1) A RACES station licensed to the civil defense organization with which the amateur station is registered;

(2) The following stations upon authorization of the responsible civil defense official for the organization with which the amateur station is registered:

(i) A RACES station licensed to another civil defense organization;

(ii) An amateur station registered with the same or another civil defense organization;

(iii) A United States Government station authorized by the responsible agency to communicate with RACES stations; and

(iv) A station in a service regulated by the FCC whenever such communication is authorized by the FCC.

(e) All communications transmitted in RACES must be specifically authorized by the civil defense organization for the area served. Only civil defense communications of the following types may be transmitted:

(1) Messages concerning impending or actual conditions jeopardizing the public safety, or affecting the national defense or security during periods of local, regional, or national civil emergencies;

(2) Messages directly concerning the immediate safety of life of individuals, the immediate protection of property, maintenance of law and order, alleviation of human suffering and need, and the combating of armed attack or sabotage;

(3) Messages directly concerning the accumulation and dissemination of public information or instructions to the civilian population essential to the activities of the civil defense organization or other authorized governmental or relief agencies; and

(4) Communications for RACES training drills and tests necessary to ensure the establishment and maintenance of orderly and efficient operation of the RACES as ordered by the responsible civil defense organizations served. Such drills and tests may not exceed a total time of 1 hour per week. With the approval of the chief officer for emergency planning the applicable State, Commonwealth, District or territory, however, such tests and drills may be conducted for a period not to exceed 72 hours no more than twice in any calendar year.

operation. Unless there is some way to practice, RACES operators may not know the proper procedures, however. The FCC Rules provide for RACES drills to assist RACES operators in practicing orderly and efficient operations for the civil defense organization they serve.

Only civil-preparedness communications can be transmitted during RACES operation. These are defined in §97.407 of the FCC regulations. (See Table 2-2.) The Rules permit tests and drills for a maximum of one hour per week. All test and drill messages must be clearly identified as such.

[Now turn to Chapter 12 and study questions G2C01 through G2C08. If you are uncertain about the answers to any of these questions, review this section.]

The Amateur Auxiliary

An important aspect of the Communications Amendments Act of 1982, commonly known as Public Law 97-259, is one that authorized the FCC to formally enlist the use of amateur volunteers for monitoring the airwaves for rules violations. The ARRL has taken a leadership role in the volunteer monitoring function, through the **Amateur Auxiliary** to the FCC's Compliance and Information Bureau. The primary objectives of the Amateur Auxiliary are to foster amateur self regulation and compliance with the Rules.

The Amateur Auxiliary is concerned with both maintenance monitoring and amateur-to-amateur interference. Maintenance monitoring is a term that refers to a program of formally enlisted amateurs monitoring the transmissions from other amateur stations for compliance with the FCC Rules and technical standards. Maintenance monitoring is conducted through the ARRL Official Observer program, while amateur-to-amateur interference is handled by specifically authorized interference committees.

[Turn to Chapter 12 and study questions G2C10 and G2C11. Review any material you are not sure of before proceeding.]

CHAPTER 3
KEYWORDS
KEYWORDS
KEYWORDS

Beacon — An amateur station transmitting communications for the purposes of observing propagation and reception or other related experimental activities.

Critical angle — If radio waves leave an antenna at an angle greater than the critical angle for that frequency they will pass through the ionosphere instead of returning to Earth.

Critical frequency — The highest frequency at which a vertically incident radio wave will return from the ionosphere. Above the critical frequency radio signals pass through the ionosphere instead of returning to the Earth.

D region — The lowest region of the ionosphere. The D region contributes very little to short-wave radio propagation, acting mainly to absorb energy from radio waves below about 7.5 MHz during daylight.

E region — The second lowest ionospheric region, the E region exists only during the day, and under certain conditions may refract radio waves enough to return them to Earth.

F region — The highest ionospheric region, the F region refracts radio waves and returns them to Earth. The height of the F region varies greatly depending on the time of day, season of the year and amount of sunspot activity. During the day this region often splits into two regions, called the F1 and F2 regions.

Geomagnetic disturbance — A dramatic change in the Earth's magnetic field that occurs over a short time.

Gray line — A band around the Earth that separates daylight from darkness. It is a transition region between day and night.

Ionosphere — A region in the atmosphere about 30 to 260 miles above the Earth. The ionosphere is made up of charged particles, or ions.

Maximum usable frequency (MUF) — The highest frequency that allows a radio wave to reach a desired destination.

Propagation — The means by which radio waves travel from one place to another.

Refract — To bend. Electromagnetic energy is refracted when it passes through a boundary between different types of material. Light is refracted as it travels from air into water or from water into air.

Scatter — Several factors may cause some energy from a radio signal to follow a path other than the idealized "straight line" shown on diagrams like Figure 3-1. Scattering can take place from Earth's ionospheric and atmospheric layers as well as objects in the wave path.

Sky waves — Radio waves that travel from an antenna upward to the ionosphere, where they either pass through the ionosphere into space or are refracted back to Earth.

Solar flare — A large eruption of energy and solar material from the surface of the sun.

Solar flux — Radio energy coming from the sun.

Solar flux index — A measure of solar activity. The solar flux is a measure of the radio noise on 2800 MHz.

Sudden Ionospheric Disturbance (SID) — A blackout of HF sky-wave communications that occurs after a solar flare.

Sunspots — Dark blotches that appear on the surface of the sun.

RADIO-WAVE PROPAGATION

Radio amateurs have been interested in the study of radio **propagation** since the early days of radio. Amateurs have sought to understand how different factors affect radio waves as they travel from one place to another. The height of your antenna above ground, the type of antenna used, the frequency of operation, the terrain, the weather and the height and density of the **ionosphere** (a region of charged particles high above the surface of the Earth) all affect how radio waves travel. It is important to understand the nature of radio waves and how their behavior is affected by the medium in which they travel.

There will be three questions from this Radio-Wave Propagation chapter on your General license exam. These questions will come from the three groups in Subelement G3 of the General Class Question Pool:

G3A Ionospheric disturbances; sunspots and solar radiation.
G3B Maximum usable frequency; propagation "hops."
G3C Height of ionospheric regions; critical angle and frequency; HF scatter.

IONOSPHERIC PROPAGATION

Nearly all amateur communication on frequencies below 30 MHz is by means of **sky waves**. After leaving the transmitting antenna, this type of wave travels from the Earth's surface at an angle that would send it out into space if its path were not bent enough to bring it back to Earth. As the radio wave travels outward from the

Earth, it encounters a region of ionized particles in the atmosphere. This region, called the **ionosphere**, begins about 30 miles from the surface of the Earth, and extends to about 260 miles. See Figure 3-1. The ionosphere **refracts** (or bends) radio waves, and at some frequencies the radio waves are refracted enough so they return to Earth at a point far from the originating station.

The Earth's upper atmosphere is composed mainly of oxygen and nitrogen with traces of hydrogen, helium and several other gases. The atoms that make up these gases are electrically neutral — they have no charge and exhibit no electrical force outside their own structure. When the gas atoms absorb ultraviolet radiation from the sun, however, electrons are knocked free and the atoms become positively charged. These positively charged atoms are called ions, and the process by which they are formed is called ionization. Several ionized regions are created at different heights in the atmosphere. Each region has a central region where the ionization is greatest. The intensity of the ionization decreases above and below this central region in each region. These regions have been given letter designations, as shown in Figure 3-2.

The Ionosphere: A Closer Look

D Region: The lowest region of the ionosphere is called the D region. This region is in a relatively dense part of the atmosphere about 30 to 60 miles above the Earth. The ions formed when sunlight is absorbed by the atmosphere are very short-lived in this region. The positive and negative ions quickly revert to their neutral atomic form. The amount of ionization in this region varies widely depending on how much sunlight hits the region. Around noon local standard time, D-region ionization overhead is maximum or very close to it. By sunset, this ionization disappears.

The D region is actually ineffective in bending high-frequency signals back to Earth. The major effect the D region has on long-distance communication is to

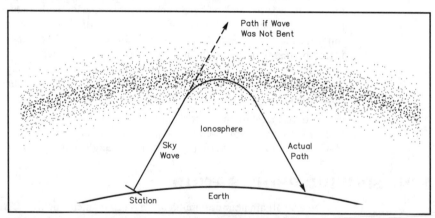

Figure 3-1 — Radio waves are bent in the ionosphere, so they return to Earth far from their origin. Without refraction (bending) in the ionosphere, radio waves would pass into space.

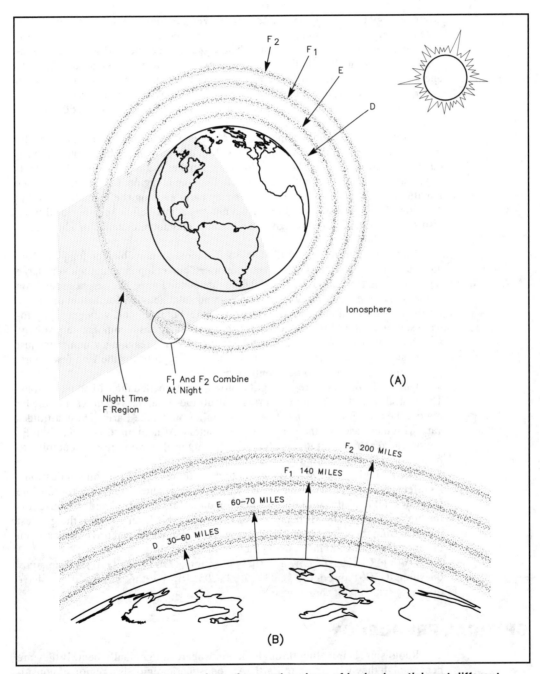

Figure 3-2 — The ionosphere consists of several regions of ionized particles at different heights above the Earth. At night, the D and E regions disappear and the F1 and F2 regions combine to form a single F region.

absorb energy from radio waves. As radio waves pass through the ionosphere, they give up energy and set some of the ionized particles into motion. Lower frequencies are affected more by absorption than higher frequencies. Absorption also increases proportionally with the amount of ionization: the more ionization, the more energy the radio waves will lose as they pass through the ionosphere. D-region absorption is most pronounced at midday, and it is responsible for the short daytime communication ranges on the lower amateur frequencies (160, 80 and 40 meters).

E region: The E region appears at an altitude of about 60 to 70 miles above the Earth. At this height, the atmosphere is still dense enough so that ionization produced by sunlight does not last very long. This makes the E region useful for bending radio waves only when it is in sunlight. Like the D region, the E region reaches maximum ionization around midday, and by early evening the ionization level is very low. The ionization level reaches a minimum just before sunrise, local time. Using the E region, a radio signal can travel a maximum distance of about 1200 miles in one hop.

F region: The region of the ionosphere most responsible for long-distance amateur communication is called the F region. This region is actually a very large region ranging from about 100 to 260 miles above the Earth. The height depends on the season of the year, latitude, time of day and solar activity. Ionization reaches a maximum shortly after noon local standard time, but tapers off very gradually toward sunset. At this altitude, the positive ions and electrons recombine very slowly, so the F region remains ionized throughout the night, reaching a minimum just before sunrise. After sunrise, ionization increases rapidly for the first few hours. Then it increases slowly to its noontime maximum.

During the day, the F region splits into two parts, called the F1 and F2 regions. The central area of the F1 region forms at an altitude of about 140 miles. For the F2 region, the central area forms at about 200 miles above the Earth. These altitudes vary with the season of the year and other factors. At noon in the summer, the F2 region can reach an altitude of 300 miles. At night, the two regions recombine to form a single F region slightly below the higher altitude.

The F1 region does not have much to do with long-distance communications. Its effects are similar to those caused by the E region. The F2 region is responsible for almost all long-distance communication on the amateur HF bands because it is the highest region. Signals bent back to Earth from this layer return at the greatest distance from the transmitter. A one-hop radio transmission can travel a maximum distance of about 2500 miles using the F2 region.

[Turn to Chapter 12 now and study questions G3B10 and G3B11. Also study questions G3C01 through G3C03 and G3C05. Review this section if you have difficulty with any of these questions.]

CRITICAL FREQUENCY

Radio signals traveling through the ionosphere are gradually bent. If they are bent enough they will return to Earth. An ionospheric region is a region of considerable depth, but for practical purposes it is sometimes convenient to think of each region as having a definite height. If we think of the ionosphere as a reflecting surface at a certain height, then we can picture the radio waves bouncing off that surface and returning to Earth. The height of this imagined reflecting surface is called the *virtual height* of the region. See Figure 3-3.

The virtual height of an ionospheric region for various frequencies is determined with a variable-frequency sounding device (called an ionosonde) that directs energy vertically and measures the time required for the round-trip path. As the frequency is increased, a point is reached where no energy will be returned from the ionosphere. The highest frequency at which a vertically incident radio wave will return from the ionosphere is called the **critical frequency**. Signals at higher frequencies pass through the ionosphere into space.

Radiation Angle and Skip Distance

A radio wave at a low angle above the horizon requires less refraction (bending) to bring the wave back to Earth. This is why we want antennas with low radiation angles to work DX.

Figure 3-4 illustrates some of the effects of radiation angle. The high-angle waves are bent only slightly in the ionosphere, and so pass through it. The wave at the somewhat lower angle is just able to be returned from the ionosphere. In daylight, it might be returned from the E region. The point of return for high-angle waves is relatively close to the transmitting station. (See point A on Figure 3-4.) The lowest-angle wave returns farther away, at point B of Figure 3-4.

The highest radiation angle that will return a radio wave of a certain frequency to Earth under specific ionospheric conditions is called the **critical angle**. Waves meeting the ionosphere at greater than the critical angle will pass through the ionosphere into space. Note that the critical angle will be different for different frequencies.

MAXIMUM USABLE FREQUENCY

There is little doubt that the critical frequency is important to amateur communication. Radio amateurs, however, are more interested in the frequency range over which communication can be carried via the ionosphere. Most amateurs want to

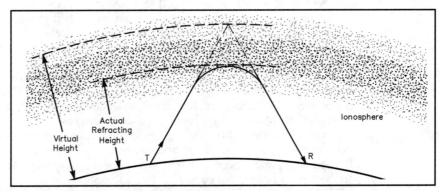

Figure 3-3 — The virtual height of a region in the ionosphere is the height at which a simple reflection would return the wave to the same point as the gradual bending that actually takes place.

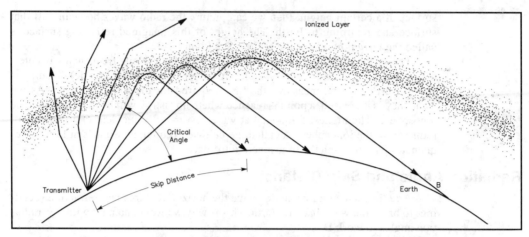

Figure 3-4 – This drawing illustrates ionospheric propagation. Waves that leave the transmitter above the critical angle are refracted in the ionosphere, but not enough to return to Earth. The wave at the critical angle will return to Earth. The lowest-angle wave will return to Earth farther away than the wave at the critical angle. This explains the emphasis on low radiation angles for DX work.

know the **maximum usable frequency** (abbreviated **MUF**) for a particular propagation path at the time of day when communication is desired. The MUF is the highest frequency that allows a radio wave to reach the desired destination, using E- or F-region propagation. The MUF is subject to seasonal variations as well as changes throughout the day, based on the amount of ultraviolet solar radiation. Radio waves with frequencies below the maximum usable frequency are usually bent back to Earth, and return some distance away.

The vertical incidence critical frequency measurement can help determine the MUF for long-distance communication at the time of the measurement. Most amateurs would use computer software or read published charts to help them determine the MUF for a certain propagation path, however.

Why is the MUF so important? If we know the MUF, we can make an accurate prediction as to which amateur band will give us the best chance for communication via a particular path. For example, suppose an amateur in Minnesota wants to contact a station in France. Using a propagation-prediction computer program or propagation charts, the ham estimates the MUF to be 24 MHz at the time of the desired contact. The closest amateur band below that frequency (the 15-meter, or 21-MHz, band in this case) offers the best chance for contact. If the MUF is predicted to be 17 MHz on a path between Ohio and Germany, the 20-meter (14-MHz) band probably offers the best chance of a successful contact.

There is no single MUF for a given location at any one time — the MUF will vary depending on the direction and distance to the station we wish to contact. Understanding and using the MUF is just one of the many ways we can change the study of propagation from guesswork into a science.

[Before going on, turn to Chapter 12 and study questions G3B01, G3B02 and G3B05. Also study questions G3C04 and G3C11. Review this section if you have difficulty with any of these questions.]

SOLAR ACTIVITY AND RADIO-WAVE PROPAGATION

From the discussion in the previous sections, it should be clear that the sun plays a major role in the ionization of the ionosphere. In fact, the sun is the dominant factor in sky-wave communication. If we want to communicate over long distances, we must understand how solar conditions will eventually affect our radio signals.

You know about the day-to-day sun-related cycle on Earth, related to the time of day. You also know about the annual cycle, related to the seasons of the year. Conditions affecting radio communication vary with these same cycles. Long- and short-term solar cycles also influence propagation in ways that are not so obvious. The condition of the sun at any given moment has a very large effect on long-distance radio communication, and the sun is what makes propagation prediction an inexact science.

Man's interest in the sun is older than recorded history. **Sunspots** are dark regions that appear on the surface of the sun. They were observed and described thousands of years ago. Observers noted that the number of sunspots increased and decreased in cycles. The solar observatory in Zurich, Switzerland, has been recording solar data on a regular basis since 1749. Accordingly, the solar cycle that began in 1755 was designated Cycle 1. The low sunspot numbers marking the end of Cycle 22 and the beginning of Cycle 23 occurred in October 1996. Sunspot cycles average roughly 11 years in length, but some cycles have been as short as 9 years, and some as long as 13 years. The highs and lows of individual sunspot cycles also vary a great deal. For example, Cycle 19 peaked with a record-high smoothed mean (average) sunspot number of over 200, yet Cycle 14 peaked at only 60 and Cycle 20 peaked at just over 100. Cycles 21 and 22 both peaked at a smoothed mean sunspot number of just over 150.

Solar activity seems to influence all radio communication beyond ground-wave or line-of-sight ranges. Maximum ionization occurs during a sunspot cycle peak. High sunspot numbers usually indicate good worldwide radio communications on the higher-frequency amateur HF bands, such as the 15, 12 and 10-meter bands. Long-distance communication can even be enhanced on the lower VHF bands, especially the 6-meter band and sometimes the 2-meter band. During a peak in the sunspot cycle, the 20-meter amateur band is open to distant parts of the world almost continuously. Even during periods of low solar activity, however, the 20-meter band will usually provide worldwide propagation during daylight hours. When sunspot numbers are high, frequencies up to 60 MHz or higher are often usable for long-distance communication. During times of low solar activity, frequencies above 20 MHz (such as the 15-meter band and shorter wavelengths) are not as likely to provide reliable worldwide propagation.

The Cycle 19 peak in 1957 and 1958 was responsible for the best propagation conditions in the history of radio. Sunspot cycles do not follow consistent patterns — there can be highs that seem to come from nowhere during periods of relatively low sunspot activity.

An important clue for anticipating variations in solar radiation levels, and radio propagation changes resulting from them, is the time it takes the sun to rotate on its axis, approximately 28 days. Active areas on the sun capable of influencing propagation may recur at four-week intervals for four or five solar rotations. If the MUF is high and propagation conditions are good for several days, you can expect similar conditions to develop approximately 28 days later.

Another useful indication of solar activity is **solar flux**, or radio energy coming from the sun. Increased solar activity produces higher levels of solar energy, which produces greater ionization in the ionosphere. Sophisticated receiving equipment and large antennas that can be pointed at the sun are required to measure solar flux. When this measurement is made, a number called the **solar-flux index** is given to represent the amount of solar flux. The solar-flux index is gradually replacing the sunspot number as a means of predicting radio-wave propagation.

The solar-flux measurement is taken daily on 2800 MHz (10.7 centimeters). The information is transmitted by the US National Institute of Science and Technology station WWV in Fort Collins, Colorado, and WWVH in Hawaii. Both the sunspot number and the solar-flux measurements tell us similar things about solar activity, but to get the sunspot number the sun must be visible. The solar-flux measurement may be taken under any weather conditions. In addition, sunspot numbers are usually given as a smoothed average value, based on the previous six months of data.

Using the Solar Flux

We can use the solar flux numbers to make general predictions about band conditions from day to day. The solar flux varies directly with the activity on the sun. Values range from around 60 to 250 or so. Flux values in the 60s and 70s generally indicate fair to poor propagation conditions on the 14-MHz (20-meter) band and higher frequencies. Values from 90 to 110 or so indicate good conditions up to about 24 MHz (12 meters), and values over 120 indicate very good conditions on 28 MHz (10 meters), and even up to 50 MHz (6 meters) or higher at times. The higher the frequency, the higher the flux value that will be required for good propagation. On the 6-meter band, for example, the flux values must be in the 200s for reliable long-range communication.

Propagation Beacons

Section 97.3(a)(9) of the FCC Rules defines a **beacon** as "an amateur station transmitting communications for the purposes of observation of propagation and reception or other related experimental activities." In the US, automatic beacon stations are permitted on 28.2 to 28.3 MHz as well as the 6, 2 and 1¼-meter bands, and the 70-cm band. (There are several US beacons on 14.10 MHz on the 20-meter band, but these are not operated under automatic control.) Several beacons are also operated at 14.1 MHz on the 20-meter band from other countries around the world.

There are numerous beacons operating on the 10-meter band between 28.2 and 28.3 MHz. You can determine 10-meter propagation conditions to various parts of the world by tuning this segment of the band listening for beacon stations. You can find the latest information about active beacons on ARRL's Hiram computer bulletin board (860-594-0306) as well as the Northern California DX Foundation World Wide Web page. (**http://www.ncdxf.org/beacon.htm/**) The NCDXF page includes a listing of the known beacons with call signs, locations and transmitter frequency. Other interesting information is also included. By listening on the beacon frequencies, you can estimate propagation conditions on the band of interest.

[Turn to Chapter 12 and study questions G3A04, G3A05, G3A09, G3A11, G3B03, G3B04, G3B06, G3B07 and G3B08. Review this section of the text if any of these questions give you difficulty.]

SUDDEN IONOSPHERIC DISTURBANCES

One solar phenomenon that can severely disrupt HF sky-wave radio communication is a solar flare. A **solar flare** is a large eruption of energy and solar material from the surface of the sun. A large amount of ultraviolet and X-ray radiation travels from the sun at the speed of light, reaching the Earth approximately 8 minutes after the flare begins. When the ultraviolet radiation reaches the Earth, the level of ionization in the ionosphere increases rapidly and D-region absorption is greatly enhanced. This is called a **sudden ionospheric disturbance (SID)**. See Figure 3-5.

If the Earth and the solar flare producing the radiation are directly in line, the SID will be most severe. The D region may be so heavily ionized that HF sky-wave

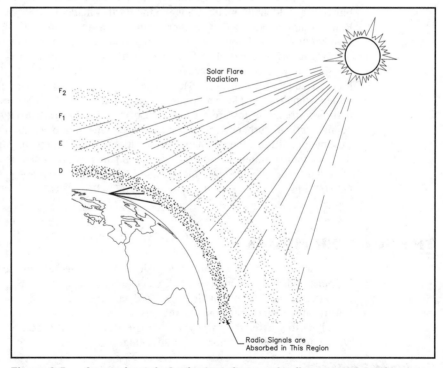

Figure 3-5 — Approximately 8 minutes after a solar flare occurs on the sun, the ultraviolet and X-ray radiation released by the flare reaches the Earth. This radiation causes increased ionization and radio-wave absorption in the D region.

Radio-Wave Propagation   3-9

communications are completely blacked out. If the area of the solar flare is off to the side of the sun, the SID will be less severe. Since D-region ionization is responsible for the disruption of HF communications during an SID, the lower frequency bands will be affected first. Communications may still be possible on a higher frequency band. Because an SID only affects the side of the Earth facing the sun, dark-path communications will be relatively unaffected. An SID may last from a few minutes to a few hours, with conditions gradually returning to normal.

GEOMAGNETIC DISTURBANCES

Another result of a solar flare is a large increase in emission of charged particles from the sun. These charged particles, along with the electromagnetic radiation from the sun, influence radio-wave propagation conditions. The particles travel more slowly than the ultraviolet radiation, and reach the Earth from 20 to 40 hours after the solar flare. When the charged particles come close to the Earth, they are trapped by the Earth's magnetic field in the north and south polar regions. The particles cause increased ionization of the gases in the E region and higher parts of the atmosphere. This produces auroral displays.

The particles also disrupt the Earth's magnetic field. A **geomagnetic disturbance** is a sudden, dramatic change in the Earth's magnetic field over a short time. Radio communications along higher-latitude paths (North or South latitudes greater than about 45°) will be more affected than those closer to the equator.

These charged particles affect the upper regions of the ionosphere first — the F region may seem to disappear or even split into many regions. This means the higher-frequency bands are most affected. The highest frequency that will be returned from the ionosphere may be only half what it would be normally. The charged particles streaming toward the poles also increase auroral activity. In general, a geomagnetic disturbance will degrade long-distance radio communications. Under extreme conditions, the geomagnetic disturbance may completely black out long-distance radio communication, especially on paths that pass near the Earth's poles.

[Now it is time to study some questions in Chapter 12. Study questions G3A01, G3A02 and G3A03. Also study questions G3A06, G3A07, G3A08 and G3A10. Review this section as needed.]

THE SCATTER MODES

When we consider radio propagation, it is convenient to look first at what happens under ideal conditions. All electromagnetic-wave propagation is subject to scattering influences that alter idealized patterns to a great degree, however. The Earth's atmosphere, ionospheric regions and any objects in the path of the radio signal act to **scatter** the energy. If we understand how this scattering takes place, we can use the phenomenon to our advantage.

Forward Scatter

There is an area between the outer limit of ground-wave propagation and the point where the first signals are returned from the ionosphere, as shown in

Figure 3-6. We call this area the *skip zone*. This zone is often described as if communications between stations in each other's skip zone were impossible. Actually, because some of the transmitted signal is scattered in the atmosphere, the transmitted signal can be heard over much of the skip zone, if sufficiently sensitive receiving devices and techniques are used.

Ionospheric scatter, mostly from the height of the E region, is most marked at frequencies up to about 60 or 70 MHz, and this type of forward scatter may be discernible in the skip zone out to about 1200 miles. Ionospheric scatter propagation is most noticeable on frequencies above the MUF.

Another means of ionospheric scatter is provided by meteors entering Earth's atmosphere. As the meteor passes through the ionosphere, a column of ionized particles is formed. These particles can act to scatter radio energy. See Figure 3-7. This ionization is a short-lived phenomenon that can show up as short bursts of little communication value or as sustained periods of usable signal level, lasting up to a minute or more. Most common between midnight and dawn, and peaking between 5 and 7 AM local time, meteor scatter can be an interesting adjunct to amateur communication at 21 MHz or higher, especially during periods of low solar activity.

Scatter signals are generally rather weak because only a small portion of the radio-signal energy is scattered into the area where it is being received. Scatter signals often sound distorted because the signal may arrive at the receiver from many different directions. When a signal arrives from several directions, the signal fading is called multipath interference. This may result in a signal with a fluttering, or wavering sound. With optimum equipment, scatter is usable at distances from just beyond the reliable local range out to several hundred miles.

A complex form of scatter is readily observed when you are working very near the maximum usable frequency. The transmitted wave is refracted back to Earth at

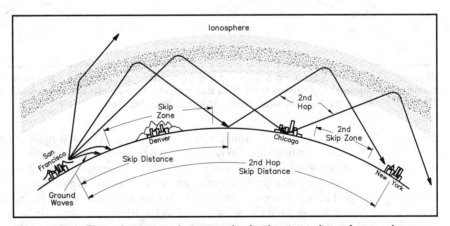

Figure 3-6 — There is an area between the farthest reaches of ground-wave propagation and the closest return of sky waves from the ionosphere. This region is known as the skip zone. Signals scattered in the ionosphere can help "fill in" the skip zone with weak signals.

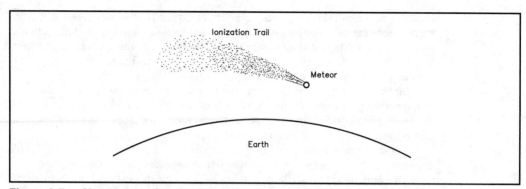

Figure 3-7 — Meteors passing through the atmosphere create trails of ionized gas. These ionized trails can be used for short-duration communications.

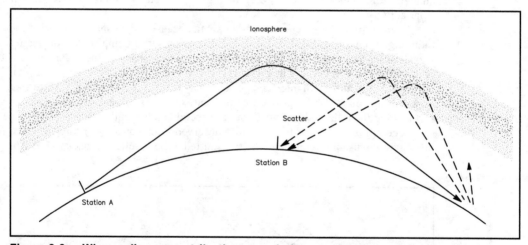

Figure 3-8 — When radio waves strike the ground after passing through the ionosphere, some of the signal may reflect back into the ionosphere toward the transmitting station. Some of this energy may be scattered back into the skip zone.

some distant point, which may be an ocean area or land mass. A small portion of the transmitted signal may be reflected back into the ionosphere toward the transmitter when it reaches the Earth. This is sometimes called *backscatter*. The reflected wave helps fill in the skip zone, as shown in Figure 3-8. The received signal will be at a distance that is too far for ground-wave reception, but may seem to be at a distance too close for normal sky-wave propagation. Under ideal conditions, backscatter is possible over 3000 miles or more, though the term "sidescatter" is probably more descriptive of what most likely happens on such long paths.

[Before going on, turn to Chapter 12 and study questions G3C06 through G3C10. Review this section as needed.]

GRAY-LINE PROPAGATION

The **gray line** (sometimes called the "twilight zone") is a band around the Earth that separates daylight from darkness. It is a somewhat "fuzzy" region, because the atmosphere tends to diffuse the light into the darkness. Figure 3-9 illustrates the gray line around the Earth. Notice that on one side of the Earth, the gray line is coming into daylight (sunrise), and on the other side it is coming into darkness (sunset).

Propagation along the gray line is very efficient. One major reason for this is that the D region, which absorbs HF signals, disappears rapidly on the sunset side of the gray line, and it has not yet built up on the sunrise side.

The gray line runs generally north and south. It varies as much as 23° because of the Earth's tilt on its axis. Local sunrise and sunset are good times to look for enhanced propagation along paths following the gray line.

[Turn to Chapter 12 and study question G3B09 before you go on to the next chapter. Review this section if you are not sure of the characteristics of gray-line propagation.]

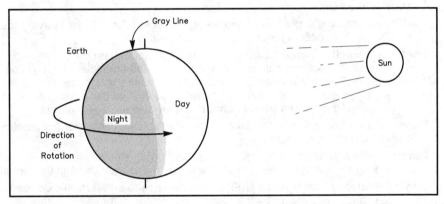

Figure 3-9 — The gray line is a transition region between daylight and darkness. One side of the Earth is coming into sunrise, and the other side is just past sunset.

CHAPTER 4
KEYWORDS
KEYWORDS
KEYWORDS

Audio rectification — Interference to electronic devices caused by a strong RF field that is rectified and amplified in the device.

Cathode-ray tube (CRT) — A vacuum tube with a phosphor coating on the inside of the face. CRTs are used in oscilloscopes and as the "picture tube" in television receivers.

Field-strength meter — A simple test instrument used to show the presence of RF energy and the relative strength of the RF field.

Monitor oscilloscope — A test instrument connected to an amateur transmitter and used to observe the shape of the transmitted-signal waveform.

Negative feedback — The process in which a portion of the amplifier output is returned to the input, 180° out of phase with the input signal.

Neutralization — Feeding part of the output signal from an amplifier back to the input so it arrives out of phase with the input. This negative feedback neutralizes the effect of positive feedback caused by coupling between the input and output circuits in the amplifier.

Noise bridge — A test instrument used to determine the impedance of an antenna system.

Oscilloscope — An electronic test instrument used to observe waveforms and voltages on a cathode-ray tube.

Peak envelope power (PEP) — The average power of the RF cycle having the greatest amplitude. (This occurs during a modulation peak.)

Photovoltaic cell – A wafer of semiconductor material that produces electricity when light shines on it. Sometimes called a *solar cell*, each cell produces about $1/2$ volt when fully illuminated. Cells are connected in series to increase the voltage. The size or surface area of the cell determines the maximum current that the cell can supply. An array of cells forms a *solar panel* that can be used to charge a lead-acid storage battery.

Photovoltaic conversion – The process by which a semiconductor PN junction changes sunlight directly into electricity.

Power — The rate at which energy is consumed. In an electric circuit, power is found by multiplying the voltage applied to the circuit by the current through the circuit.

Radio-Frequency Interference (RFI) — Interference to an electronic device (radio, TV, stereo) caused by RF energy from an amateur transmitter or other source.

S meter — A meter in a receiver that shows the relative strength of a received signal.

Signal tracer — A test instrument that shows the presence of RF or AF energy in a circuit. The signal tracer is used to trace the flow of a signal through a multistage circuit.

Speech processor — A device used to increase the average power contained in a speech waveform. Proper use of a speech processor can greatly improve the readability of a voice signal.

Transmit-receive (TR) switch — A mechanical switch relay or electronic circuit used to switch an antenna between a receiver and transmitter in an amateur station.

Two-tone test — Problems in a sideband transmitter can be detected by feeding two audio tones into the microphone input of the transmitter and observing the output on an oscilloscope.

AMATEUR RADIO PRACTICE

It's easy to form good operating habits in Amateur Radio. By understanding the fundamentals of radio, you should be able to maintain your station so that its operation is in accordance with FCC Rules and Regulations. In addition, you'll want to put out the best possible signal. If you know the principles behind the operation of your station, correctly adjust and measure its performance, and take advantage of available test equipment, you should have no problem keeping your station "up to par."

There are five questions on the General license exam from the Amateur Radio Practice subelement. These questions will come from the five syllabus groups for this subelement:

G4A Two-tone test; electronic TR switch; amplifier neutralization.

G4B Test equipment: oscilloscope; signal tracer; antenna noise bridge; monitoring oscilloscope; field-strength meters.

G4C Audio rectification in consumer electronics, RF ground.

G4D Speech processors; PEP calculations; wire sizes and fuses.

G4E Common connectors used in amateur stations: types; when to use; fastening methods; precautions when using; HF mobile radio installations; emergency power systems; generators; battery storage devices and charging sources including solar; wind generation.

TEST EQUIPMENT

You will find various types of test equipment helpful in maintaining your Amateur Radio station and ensuring your equipment operates properly. In this section you will learn about the use of several types of test equipment for your General exam.

The Oscilloscope

The **oscilloscope** (sometimes called a *scope*), is probably the most versatile of all test instruments. Oscilloscopes measure instantaneous voltage by the vertical deflection of an electron beam as it sweeps horizontally across the face of a **cathode-ray tube (CRT)**. One signal is applied to the oscilloscope vertical channel, and a second input is applied to the horizontal channel.

An oscilloscope has amplifiers in line with its horizontal- and vertical-channel inputs and responds to a wide range of frequencies. Expensive oscilloscopes can handle frequencies over 30 MHz while the scopes most amateurs use only respond well up to 5 MHz or so. This lets you display audio- or low radio-frequency signals.

Oscilloscopes contain *sweep circuits*, which are oscillators used to draw the trace horizontally across the screen. The internal sweep circuits supply a signal to the horizontal channel. The sweep-oscillator frequency must be adjusted to the proper range to display various signal frequencies. For Amateur Radio use, a properly adjusted scope can display the output waveform of your transmitted signal as shown in Figure 4-1. This can be especially useful if you wish to check the modulation level of your signal. It can also show if there is carrier present on your single-

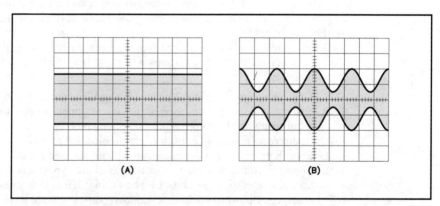

Figure 4-1 — Oscilloscope displays of RF signals. At A is an unmodulated carrier. The signal at B is from a full-carrier AM transmitter modulated with a single-frequency sine wave.

sideband (SSB) signal. Another use for the oscilloscope is to display circuit frequency response.

A useful comparison between signals can be made using a dual-trace oscilloscope. This type of scope has two separate vertical-input channels. The two channels can be swept in the horizontal direction at the same rate and if two different signals are applied to the separate vertical inputs, both signals can be viewed on the screen at the same time. This function is especially useful for comparing the characteristics of a signal before and after passing through a stage in a circuit. Figure 4-2 shows how a dual-trace oscilloscope can display the Morse code keying characteristics of a transmitter. The top trace shows the key closure or keyed line from an electronic keyer. The lower trace shows the actual transmitter CW output that results from the keying signal. This display also gives a graphic demonstration of the rise and fall times of the transmitted waveform from a properly adjusted CW transmitter.

There is a variety of controls on any oscilloscope and you should follow the instructions in the manual that comes with the scope when adjusting them. The focus control should be carefully adjusted for a sharp fine line on the CRT. The intensity control sets the brightness of the trace. Setting the brightness too high can damage the phosphor on the face of the oscilloscope CRT.

A **monitor oscilloscope** is used to show the signal quality of a transmitter. It lets you know if your SSB signal is flattopping, what your CW dot-dash ratio is and the shape of your CW signal waveform. The vertical input of the monitor scope is connected to the transmitter RF output. *The ARRL Handbook* provides details about how to connect an oscilloscope to monitor your signal.

Oscilloscopes have been built using analog technology for many years. (Analog means the circuits measure and display continuously variable physical quanti-

Figure 4-2 – A dual-trace oscilloscope is useful to display two waveforms for comparison. The top trace here is the key closure on the line used to key a CW transmitter. The lower trace shows the resulting CW waveform. Note the rounded corners and the smooth rise and decay times on the keyed output. Five milliseconds is generally agreed to be the ideal rise and fall time of a CW envelope. The horizontal divisions for this display each represent 5 milliseconds. If the CW signal rises too sharply, or drops off too quickly, key clicks or other keying problems can result.

ties.) Modern electronics is making more use of digital circuits, however. (Digital circuits represent the measured physical quantities with a series of numbers, or digits. Values are rounded off to the nearest allowable whole digit, so values between those digits are not allowed.) Using inexpensive digital integrated circuits, a **digital oscilloscope** can store, change and compare waveforms.

Some inexpensive digital scopes do not include a CRT display. They are designed for use with a personal computer. Measurement parameters are adjusted through the computer rather than by front-panel knobs and switches. The computer displays the measured waveform.

Analog-to-digital converter circuits measure the analog signal and change the measured amplitude values into digital data for processing, storage and display. The sampling rate of the converter limits the highest frequency signals that a digital scope can accurately display. Unfortunately, the digital circuits may process and display a waveform that does not represent the actual waveform if you try to measure a signal with a frequency that is too high for the converter. The signal must be sampled more than twice during each cycle of the highest frequency signal. So a digital-to-analog circuit that samples the input signal at a rate of 10 MHz will only be able to accurately display signal frequencies up to a little less than 5 MHz.

[Now turn to Chapter 12 and study questions G4B01, G4B02, G4B06 and G4B07. Review this section if you have difficulty with any of these questions.]

The Signal Tracer

With today's multistage rigs, most problems that come about are a result of a defective component in one stage. Isolating the problem stage is the first step in the repair process. Armed with a block diagram of your radio and a **signal tracer**, you can proceed to locate the trouble spot in a straightforward manner.

A signal tracer, as the name implies, is a device that allows you to trace the path of a signal through the various stages in your rig until it disappears or begins to show unusual characteristics. This helps you identify the stage that isn't operating properly, so you can concentrate your repair efforts in that section. Any device that reacts to RF or AF energy can be used as a signal tracer. A typical signal tracer consists of a diode detector and a high-gain audio amplifier, which detects amplitude variations in RF signals. An oscilloscope or a VTVM can also be used to isolate trouble in your ham equipment.

The Antenna Noise Bridge

A properly operating antenna system is essential for a top-quality amateur station. If you build your own antennas, you must be able to tune them for maximum operating efficiency. Even if you buy commercial antennas, there are tuning adjustments that must be made because of differences in mounting location. Height above ground and proximity to buildings and trees will have some effect on antenna operating characteristics.

You must be able to measure your antenna's performance. After installation, you should be able to periodically monitor your antenna system for signs of problems, and troubleshoot failures as necessary.

An antenna **noise bridge** is a device that allows you to measure the impedance of antennas and other electrical circuits. The bridge produces a wide-band noise signal that is applied to the circuit under test. The noise bridge is connected between a receiver and an antenna of unknown impedance. (You can also connect other circuits with an unknown impedance to a noise bridge and receiver, but antenna measurements are the most common.) The receiver is tuned to the desired operating frequency and then you adjust the bridge controls until the noise heard in the receiver is nulled (decreased to a minimum). By noting the settings of the controls on the noise bridge, and then calculating the reactance of the indicated capacitance or inductance, you can determine the impedance of the unknown circuit.

The Field-Strength Meter

A **field-strength meter** is a simple instrument that measures the relative strength of an RF field. This makes it useful for monitoring the radiated signal strength during antenna and transmitter adjustments. A field-strength meter usually contains a diode detector and a milliameter (to indicate signal strength). An antenna is attached to the detector input. By placing a field-strength meter a fixed distance from a rotatable antenna, you can get a relative indication of the antenna's horizontal radiation pattern by observing variations in signal strength as the antenna is rotated.

It is important to note that the simple field-strength meter described here is used to make *relative* measurements. You can observe changes in strength, but this instrument is not designed to measure actual electric or magnetic field strengths. This simple instrument won't measure the RF radiated field strengths from your station for the purposes of meeting the FCC RF radiation exposure limits.

[Before going on to the next section turn to Chapter 12 and study questions G4B03, G4B04, G4B05, G4B08, G4B09 and G4B10. Review this section as needed.]

TESTING TRANSMITTER PERFORMANCE

Some of the most important tests and measurements you make as an amateur are those that tell you about the quality of your transmitted signal. Other hams form their first opinions of you on the air from the quality of your signal. Improperly adjusted amateur transmitters wreak havoc all over the bands and make operating unpleasant for everyone. An improperly adjusted transmitter can radiate energy all over the spectrum — not just in the amateur bands! Unless you know how to monitor your transmitted signal, you are asking for problems with radio-frequency interference and television interference (TVI).

Two-Tone Tests

The **two-tone test** is used to check the amplitude linearity of an SSB transmitter. Instead of the continuously varying pattern produced by a voice signal, a two-tone test produces a stationary pattern that can be examined on an oscilloscope. Figure 4-3A shows a pattern that is representative of a properly operating SSB transmitter. Figure 4-3B represents a signal that exhibits flattopping and crossover distortion. In Figure 4-4, a single cycle of a sine-wave signal is compared with a

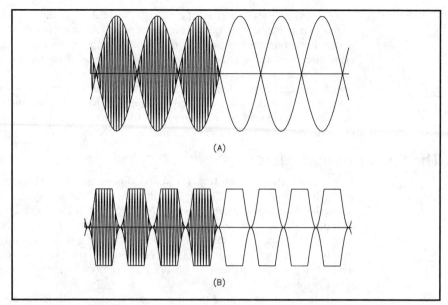

(A)

(B)

Figure 4-3 — The two-tone test waveform at A is from a properly operating SSB transmitter. Note the smooth sinusoidal shape of the curves, especially as they cross the zero axis. At B is the waveform of a two-tone test showing severe flattopping and crossover (zero-axis) distortion.

cycle of a signal that exhibits flattopping and crossover distortion.

To perform a two-tone test, you inject two audio signals of equal level into the transmitter microphone jack. The signals used should be about 1 kHz apart for a good display on the monitor oscilloscope and must be within the audio passband of the transmitter. The frequencies must not be harmonically related, so don't use frequencies like 1000 and 2000 Hz. Tones at 700 Hz and 1900 Hz are used in the ARRL lab for equipment testing.

In a "clean" transmitter, this two-tone input will produce an RF signal at the output of the transmitter that contains only the two input signals. No amplifier is

Figure 4-4 — A comparison of a sine-wave signal with a signal that exhibits flattopping and crossover distortion.

perfectly linear, so some mixing of the two input signals will take place. The sum and difference products produced by this mixing should be very weak in comparison with the main output. They should be weak enough that they cannot be detected on an oscilloscope pattern. What you will see on an oscilloscope is the pattern of two sine-wave signals as they add and subtract, forming peaks and valleys, as shown in Figure 4-3A.

A spectrum analyzer will tell you much more about your transmitter output, but such instruments are expensive, and few amateurs have access to one for transmitter testing. Oscilloscopes are relatively inexpensive and readily available. A two-tone test pattern observed on a scope will show only major defects in the output of an SSB transmitter, but it is still a very useful indication of how the transmitter is operating. If you keep a monitor oscilloscope connected to your transmitter output at all times you will be able to quickly notice any changes in operation. The speech pattern from a correctly adjusted SSB transmitter is shown in Figure 4-5A. The top and bottom halves of the oscilloscope display produce mirror images of the input waveform. Notice that the peaks are smoothly rounded. Overdriving the transmitter will cause the waveform to look more like the one shown in Figure 4-5B, with the peaks flattened, or clipped.

[Turn to Chapter 12 and study questions G4A01 through G4A04 now. Review this section if you have any difficulty with these questions.]

Neutralization of Power Amplifiers

Most RF amplifiers operate with their input and output circuits tuned to the same frequency. Unless the circuit is carefully designed, some of the amplified output signal may be fed back to the input. If the signal is fed back "in phase" (so it adds to the input signal), the amplifier will oscillate. This is sometimes called *self oscillation* because there is no feedback path designed into the circuit to produce these oscillations. Care should be used in arranging components and wiring of the input and output circuits so that coupling is kept to a minimum. Keep all RF leads as short as possible, and pay particular attention to the RF return paths from input and output tank circuits to the emitter, drain or cathode.

Figure 4-5 — The speech pattern from a correctly adjusted sideband transmitter is shown at A. Part B shows the same transmitter with excessive drive, causing distortion in the final amplifier.

Even with proper shielding and careful design, interelectrode capacitance in vacuum-tube amplifiers can cause oscillation. The internal elements are so close in modern vacuum tubes that signals can couple from the plate back to the grid, causing the amplifier to oscillate. This interelectrode capacitance is represented by C_{GP} in Figure 4-6. With tetrode and pentode tubes, interelectrode capacitance is greatly reduced by the addition of a screen grid between the control grid and the plate. Nevertheless, the power sensitivity of these tubes is so great that only a small amount of feedback is necessary to start oscillation.

In many cases, a technique called **neutralization** is used to provide stable amplifier operation. Neutralization is the process of deliberately feeding a portion of the amplifier output back to the input, 180° out of phase with the input. (This is called **negative feedback** because the feedback signal subtracts from the input.) The feedback is usually accomplished by connecting a neutralizing capacitor to the tank circuit (C_N in Figure 4-6). If done correctly, neutralization will cancel any positive feedback in the plate-to-grid capacitance. This will render the amplifier much more stable and make it less likely to have self oscillations.

Neutralizing a Screen-Grid Amplifier Stage

One way to accomplish neutralization is to reduce to a minimum the RF-driver

Figure 4-6 — In most vacuum tube amplifiers, some form of neutralization must be used to cancel positive feedback from the plate to the grid. In this circuit, a neutralizing capacitor (C_N) is added to counteract the effects of the grid-to-plate capacitance (represented by C_{GP}). The signal at the bottom of the tank circuit is 180º out of phase with the signal at the top of the tank, and careful adjustment of C_N will effectively cancel the positive feedback.

voltage fed from the input of the amplifier to its output circuit through the grid-to-plate capacitance of the tube.

If the tube is operated with grid current, the grid-current meter can be used to indicate neutralization. With this technique the plate voltage may remain on, but the screen voltage must be zero during the neutralization process. The dc circuit must be completed between the screen and cathode. There will be a change in grid current as the unloaded plate tank circuit is tuned through resonance. The neutralizing capacitor (or inductor) should be adjusted until this deflection is brought to a minimum. A minimum change in the grid-current reading as the output-circuit tuning is changed will indicate that you have almost achieved proper neutralization.

As a final adjustment, screen voltage should be reapplied and the neutralizing adjustment continued to the point where minimum plate current, maximum grid current and maximum screen current occur simultaneously. An increase in grid current when the plate tank circuit is tuned slightly to the high-frequency side of resonance indicates that the neutralizing capacitance is too small. If the increase is on the low frequency side, the neutralizing capacitance is too large. When neutralization is complete, there should be a slight decrease in grid current on either side of resonance.

If the screen-grid tube is operated without grid current, a sensitive output indicator can be used to indicate neutralization. With this technique, both screen and plate voltages must be removed from the tube(s). The dc circuits from the plate and screen to the cathode are left intact. The neutralizing capacitor or link coils are then carefully adjusted until the output indicator reads minimum.

[Now turn to Chapter 12 and study questions G4A07 through G4A11. Review this section if you have difficulty with any of these questions.]

SSB POWER MEASUREMENT

In a single-sideband, suppressed carrier transmission, there is no signal when there is no modulation applied to the transmitter. When the transmitter is modulated, a constantly varying RF envelope is produced, like the one shown in Figure 4-7. Two amplitude values associated with the wave are of particular interest. One is the peak envelope voltage, the greatest amplitude reached by the enve-

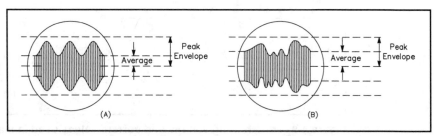

Figure 4-7 — Two RF-envelope patterns that show the difference between average amplitude and peak amplitude. In B, the average amplitude has been increased, but the peak amplitude remains constant.

lope at any time. The other is the RMS voltage of the envelope, as read on an RMS-reading voltmeter with an RF probe. See Figure 4-8. Chapter 5 includes additional information about RMS and peak voltage readings. There is also more information about power calculations in Chapter 5.

The **power** measurement used to rate transmitter output is **peak envelope power (PEP)**. This is the *average* power of the wave at a *modulation peak*. One way to calculate PEP is to measure the peak envelope voltage, using an oscilloscope. Then multiply this value by 0.707 to calculate the RMS value of the peak envelope voltage. Remember that power equals current times voltage:

$$P = I \times E \qquad \text{(Equation 4-1)}$$

We don't have to calculate current if we know the load impedance, however. For most amateur antenna systems we want a load impedance of about 50 ohms. From Ohm's Law, current equals voltage divided by resistance:

$$I = \frac{E}{R} \qquad \text{(Equation 4-2)}$$

So we can substitute for I in the power equation:

$$\qquad \text{(Equation 4-3)}$$

Another way to write this equation is given as Equation 4-4. Here we show the peak envelope voltage times 0.707, and multiply this quantity by itself. This is the same as squaring the term. Divide by the load resistance, often written as R_L, to obtain the peak envelope power.

$$PEP = \frac{(0.707 \text{ PEV})(0.707 \text{ PEV})}{R_L} \qquad \text{(Equation 4-4)}$$

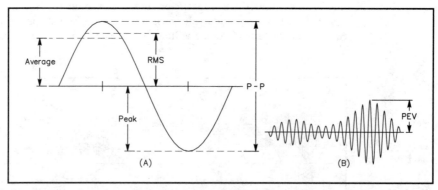

Figure 4-8 — Alternating voltage and current values used in making power measurements. The sine-wave parameters are illustrated at A, while B shows the peak envelope voltage (PEV) for a composite waveform.

Suppose we measured the output of a transmitter using an oscilloscope and found 200-V peak-to-peak across a 50-Ω dummy load. This represents a peak value of 100 V, and an RMS value of 70.7 V:

$$\text{Peak Envelope Voltage} = \frac{\text{Peak - to - Peak Voltage}}{2}$$

$$\text{PEV} = \frac{200 - \text{V Peak} - \text{to} - \text{Peak}}{2} = 100 \text{ V} \qquad \text{(Equation 4-5)}$$

$$V_{RMS} = \text{PEV} \times 0.707$$

$$V_{RMS} = 100 \text{ V} \times 0.707 = 70.7 \text{ V}$$

Using this value for E in Equation 4-3, we can calculate the PEP of our transmitter.

$$P = \frac{E^2}{R} = \frac{(70.7 \text{ V})^2}{50 \text{ }\Omega}$$

$$P = \frac{5000 \text{ V}^2}{50 \text{ }\Omega} = 100 \text{ W}$$

Notice here that the units of volts squared divided by ohms give watts for the answer.

As another example, suppose we measure 500 V peak-to-peak across a 50-Ω load resistor at the output of a transmitter. What is the PEP output?

First we will find the peak envelope voltage, which is 250 V. Then we will find the RMS value by multiplying by 0.707:

$$V_{RMS} = 250 \text{ V} \times 0.707 = 176.75 \text{ V}$$

Next we use Equation 4-3 to calculate the peak envelope power:

$$P = \frac{E^2}{R} = \frac{(176.75 \text{ V})^2}{50 \text{ }\Omega}$$

$$P = \frac{31240 \text{ V}^2}{50 \text{ }\Omega} = 625 \text{ W}$$

Average power is found by using the value for RMS voltage as read on a voltmeter with an RF probe attached. (This reading will not be the same as the RMS value of the peak envelope voltage, since the meter reads an average over many RF cycles rather than just the voltage of a single RF cycle.) Substitute that value for E in Equation 4-3.

For a constant-amplitude sine wave, such as for a CW signal, PEP and average power are the same. If an average-reading wattmeter measures 1060 W for an *unmodulated* carrier from a transmitter, the PEP output of that signal is also 1060 W. This is not true for a modulated wave.

Another way to measure the power of an amateur transmitter is with a peak reading wattmeter. This type of power meter has capacitors in the metering circuit that charge to the peak voltage of the input wave. This voltage is then measured with a voltmeter and displayed on a scale calibrated in watts. To measure the actual transmitter power output, the wattmeter should be connected as close to the transmitter output terminal as possible. There are more details about alternating current and its measurement in Chapter 5.

[Study the following questions in Chapter 12 before you go on to the next section: G4D03 through G4D06. Review this section as needed.]

STATION ACCESSORIES

There are a number of station accessories that make the difference between simply operating a radio and having a full awareness of the communications medium called Amateur Radio. In this section we will look at some of the accessories you may find useful when operating your station. Most amateur transceivers include these accessories.

The S Meter

Because reception is (or should be) the first aspect of station operation, we'll examine the **S meter** first. S meters are used to indicate the strength of a received signal. Signal-strength meters are useful when there is a need to make comparative readings.

S meters are calibrated in S units from S1 to S9; above S9 they are calibrated in decibels (dB). (You will learn more about decibels in Chapter 5.) An attempt was made by at least one manufacturer in the 1940s to establish some significant numbers for S meters. S9 was to be equal to a signal level of 50 microvolts, with each S unit equal to 6 dB. This means that for an increase of one S unit, the received signal power would have to increase by a factor of four. Such a scale is useful for a theoretical discussion, although real S-meter circuits fall far short of this ideal for a variety of reasons.

Suppose you were working someone who was using a 25-watt transmitter, and your S meter was reading S8. If the other operator increased power to 100 watts (an increase of four times), your S meter would read S9. If the signal was S9, the operator would have to multiply his power 10-fold to make your S meter read 10 dB over S9.

S meters on modern receivers may or may not respond in this manner. S-meter operation is based on the output of the automatic gain-control (AGC) circuitry; the S meter measures the AGC voltage. As a result, every receiver S meter responds differently; no two S meters will give the exact same reading. The S meter is useful for giving relative signal-strength indications, however. You can see changes in signal levels on an S meter that you may not be able to detect just by listening to the audio output level.

[Now turn to Chapter 12 and study question G4B11. Review the material in this section if you have difficulty with this question.]

TR Switching

The **transmit-receive (TR) switch** connects the antenna to the transmitter during periods of sending, and to the receiver during periods of reception. With a separate receiver and transmitter, the TR switch may be a manually operated switch, an antenna relay that is switched by the transmitter or receiver, or an electronic circuit. When an electronic TR switch is used, the transmitter is continuously connected to the antenna. The receiver antenna connection is made through the TR switch. During transmit periods, the TR switch prevents large amounts of RF from reaching the receiver by electronically disconnecting the receiver from the antenna.

Since no mechanical device is involved in the antenna switching, an electronic TR switch can follow CW keying. An electronic TR switch operates faster than a mechanical switch. The receiver is left operative continuously, and if it can recover from a strong signal quickly enough, it will be sensitive to received signals between the transmitted character elements. The higher operating speed of an electronic TR switch can provide what is called "full-break-in (QSK) operation," in which the operator is able to hear signals between the dots and dashes of his code transmission.

The tube or transistor that performs the switching function in a TR switch may be driven into nonlinearity by the strong transmitter signal. This is why some electronic TR switches can generate harmonics, which may cause television interference (TVI). A low-pass filter placed between the TR switch and the antenna, as shown in Figure 4-9, may eliminate the TVI, but the low-order harmonics (say, the second harmonic of 40 meters) may cause interference to other communications (on 20-meter SSB, for instance).

This discussion also describes the TR switching between the receiver and transmitter stages in a transceiver. Figure 4-9 can represent a transceiver block diagram as well as a separate transmitter and receiver. The TR switch is still followed by a low-pass filter to block any harmonics generated in the switch.

[Now turn to Chapter 12 and study questions G4A05 and G4A06. Review the material in this section if you have difficulty with either of these questions.]

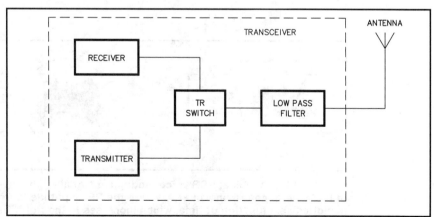

Figure 4-9 — A low-pass filter connected between the TR switch and the antenna will help filter out harmonics generated in the TR switch.

Speech Processors

The human voice does not have a constant amplitude. When you speak, the speech amplitude is constantly changing, and only occasionally reaches a maximum, or peak, value. As can be seen in Figure 4-10A, there are large "valleys" between the voice peaks — periods where there is very little voice energy, hence little transmitter output. Because of the valleys in the speech waveform, the average power contained in a voice signal is small, as compared to the peak power. Peak-to-average ratios of 2 or 3 are quite common. Using a **speech processor**, the amplitude of the valleys can be increased while leaving the voice peaks unchanged. See Figure 4-10B. This serves to increase the *average* power contained in the waveform and improve the signal-to-noise ratio, but can lead to excessive background noise pickup. Properly used, speech processing can improve speech intelligibility at the receiver when propagation conditions are poor or the interference level is high.

The increased average power contained in a processed signal places a higher power demand on the transmitter. This can result in overheating of final amplifier and power supply components. If overheating becomes evident, you may need to reduce the processing level or transmitter power.

Speech processing, by its very nature, is a distortion of the audio signal, so processed signals sound less natural at the receiving end than unprocessed ones. For these reasons, processing should be employed only when necessary. If the frequency is clear and propagation is good, keep your speech processor turned off. If you do need the processor, use the minimum amount of processing necessary to increase intelligibility for the receiving station. Over processed, distorted signals are more difficult to copy than unprocessed ones. Distortion products generated during speech processing can increase the bandwidth of your signal and cause "splatter" (interference to stations on nearby frequencies). Keep in mind that speech processing cannot increase the peak power of the signal, even if the transmitter is 100% modulated. A speech processor adds nothing to the transmitter output PEP.

Figure 4-10 — A typical SSB voice-modulated signal might have an envelope of the general nature shown at A, where the RF amplitude (current or voltage) is plotted as a function of time, which increases to the right. The envelope pattern after speech processing to increase the average level of power output is shown at B.

[Turn to Chapter 12 and study questions G4D01 and G4D02 at this time. If you have difficulty with any of these questions, review the material in this section.]

RADIO-FREQUENCY INTERFERENCE (RFI)

At one time or another, many amateurs have suffered the wrath of neighbors or family as their transmission was intercepted by a radio or television set. If you've never suffered problems like these, consider yourself lucky. An important means of survival in this age of electric and electronic devices is the ability to recognize and cure **radio-frequency interference**. Even if your transmitter puts out no harmonics or other spurious signals, interference is still an unfortunate possibility. Your RF signal can result in audio interference to another electronic device, such as a radio, television, stereo, electronic organ or intercom. For the purpose of this discussion, we'll call these audio devices.

RFI to audio devices is usually caused by **audio rectification**. Audio rectification happens when the RF signal gets into the audio device and is rectified (detected). The resulting audio signal is then amplified by the audio device, resulting in interference.

When the amateur operator is using double-sideband AM voice, the interference to the electronic device will be heard like any normal signal applied to the amplifier. The amateur's voice will be heard through the electronic equipment, and may be only slightly distorted. Audio rectification from an amateur SSB transmitter will sound like an unintelligible, garbled noise. If the amateur is using an FM transmitter, no sound will usually be heard: Instead, a decrease in volume will occur when the transmitter is on. A humming or clicking sound may be heard when the transmitter is keyed on and off. Similar humming or clicking will be heard if the interference is from a CW transmitter.

The first step in curing audio rectification involves finding out how the RF energy is entering the device, and "closing the door" with bypassing and filtering to keep it out. Several entry points are possible: the ac line cord, the antenna connection (if any), speaker wires or interconnecting cables (in a component stereo system). Another possibility is direct radiation into the circuitry of the audio device itself (usually through a wooden or plastic case).

Speaker wires and the ac power cord on an audio device form good entry points for RF, especially for signals on the higher amateur bands. On the higher bands, these lines can become a sizable fraction of a wavelength, and act as an antenna. A simple ac line filter, shown in Figure 4-11, can be built from readily available parts and installed at the audio device. The preferred location for the filter is inside the audio device, where the ac line enters. Notice that this filter uses inductors (often called RF chokes) in series with the lines, along with capacitors to *bypass* the unwanted signals to ground.

If RF is entering through external speaker wires, a simple filter using an RF choke and bypass capacitors at the speaker terminals can be effective. You should not install bypass capacitors directly across the output of a transistor amplifier. This can produce unwanted oscillations on the amplifier, even leading to destruction of the transistors. For transistor amplifiers you should place an RF choke in

Figure 4-11 — A method of ac line filtering.
C1, C2 — 0.01-μF disc ceramic, 1.2-kV capacitors
RFC1, RFC2 — 24 turns number 18 AWG enameled wire, close spaced and wound on a ¼-inch-diameter form (such as a pencil).

series with the amplified output, and then connect the bypass capacitors after the chokes, as shown in Figure 4-12.

Another common victim of audio rectification is the telephone. If you or your neighbor are experiencing telephone interference, first determine who owns the phone and who maintains the phone lines inside the home. If the phones are rented from the phone company and the phone company maintains the lines inside the home, contact your local telephone company. They have inductors and other filter components to help eliminate the problem. With so many consumer-owned electronic telephones, and customers maintaining the phone wires inside their own homes, you may have to install filters (or have the owner install them) yourself. Figure 4-13 shows a K-Com filter, available at many consumer-electronics stores. Simply plug this filter into the phone, and then plug the phone line into the filter.

Installation of any of the devices mentioned in this section should be performed only by a qualified repair technician. If you install a filter in your neighbor's equipment, you may be blamed for any problems that occur with the equipment later, whether they relate to the work you did or not!

Figure 4-12 — A speaker filter for installation at the output of a transistor audio amplifier. The capacitors bypass the undesired signals to ground.
C1, C2 — 0.001 to 0.05-μF disc ceramic, 1.4-kV capacitors.
RFC1, RFC2 — 24 turns number 18 AWG enameled wire, close spaced and wound on a ¼-inch diameter form (such as a pencil).

Figure 4-13—A typical telephone interference filter. This model, manufactured by K-Com, has modular phone connectors to simplify the installation right at the telephone.

Station Grounding

Make sure your station equipment is operating properly, and that it does not cause interference to audio equipment in your own home. Your transmitter should be effectively connected to a rod that is at least 8 feet long, driven entirely into the ground. The ground lead must be at least number 10 wire or heavier conductor such as copper ribbon. The greater the surface area of the ground lead, the more effective it will be. The outer shield braid from a piece of RG-213 or other large-diameter coaxial cable can be used as a conductor to connect your station equipment to a station ground.

The National Electrical Code forms the basis for electrical safety regulations in most building codes. You should be familiar with the requirements of the National Electrical Code or have a licensed electrician install the station ground for you. The Code specifies that there be only one grounding *system* for a building. That means your RF station ground must be connected to the electrical safety ground.

Keep the ground lead as short as possible. Proper equipment grounding is one of the most effective steps you can take to minimize the possibility of audio rectification of your transmitter's signals in a stereo or other electronics equipment.

An effective station ground connection should be short; not more than a few feet in length. If your ground wire is a resonant length at your operating frequency, it will act more like an antenna than an RF ground connection. A resonant "ground lead" won't act like a ground at all, and may lead to stray RF energy in your amateur station equipment. It may also lead to stray RF energy getting into home entertainment equipment, causing audio rectification or other types of RFI.

Suppose your amateur station is located in a third-floor apartment, or on the third floor of your house. The shortest ground lead you can have is 33 feet to the ground. This length will be resonant on several HF bands, and will bring stray RF into your "shack." In fact, you may even get an *RF burn* if you touch the front panel of your transceiver while you are transmitting. Such *RF hot spots* are quite common in a station located above the ground floor when the equipment ground includes a long ground wire.

An effective RF ground will reduce electrical noise, and reduce the possibility of interference. Even more important, however, a good ground connection will reduce the possibility of electric shock.

Remember that amateurs may use only the amount of power necessary to establish the desired communication. Operating with excessive power is more likely to cause audio-rectification problems than with low power.

[Before going to the next chapter, turn to Chapter 12 and study questions G4C01 through G4C10. Review the material in this section if you have difficulty with any of these questions.]

AMATEUR RADIO SAFETY

Your station equipment not only makes use of ac line voltage, which can be dangerous in itself — it also generates additional potentially lethal voltages of its own. For your own safety, and that of others who may come in contact with your equipment, you should be familiar with some basic precautions.

Power-Line Connections

In most residential electrical power systems, three wires are brought in from the outside to the distribution board. Older systems may use only two wires. In the three-wire system, the voltage between the two "hot" wires is normally 240. The third wire is neutral and is grounded. Half of the total voltage appears between each of the hot wires and neutral, as indicated in Figure 4-14. In systems of this type, the 120-V outlets, lights and appliances are divided as evenly as possible between the two sides of the circuit. Half of the load is connected between one hot wire and the neutral, and the other half of the load is connected between the other hot wire and neutral.

Heavy appliances, such as electric stoves and most high-power amateur amplifiers, are designed for 240-V operation and are connected across the two hot wires. While *both* ungrounded wires should be fused, a fuse or switch should *never*

Figure 4-14 — In home electrical systems, two wires carrying 240 V are split between the house circuits carrying 120 V each. Some heavy appliances use the full 240 V. As shown, a fuse should be placed in each hot wire, but no fuse or switch should be placed in the neutral wire.

be used in the neutral wire. If the appliance is connected to the supply voltage with a four-conductor power cord, the black and red wires should be connected to the fused hot wires. The white and green (or bare) wires should not have a fuse or switch in the line. The reason for this is that opening the neutral wire does not disconnect the equipment from the household voltage. It simply leaves the equipment on one side of the 240-V line in series with whatever load may be across the other side of the circuit. Furthermore, with the neutral wire open, the voltage will then be divided between the two sides in inverse proportion to the load resistance. The voltage will drop below normal on one side and soar on the other, unless both loads happen to be equal.

High-power amateur amplifiers are designed to use the full 240 V because only half as much current is required to supply the same power as would be needed with a 120-V supply. The power-supply circuit efficiency improves with the higher voltage and lower current from a 240-V supply. Having a separate 240-V line for the amplifier also ensures that the capacity of the house circuit supplying 120 V to the shack is not exceeded. If your amplifier draws more current than the house wiring was designed to handle, it could cause the house lights to dim when the amplifier is operating. This is because the heavy current causes the power-line voltage to drop in value.

Three-Wire 120-V Power Cords

To meet the requirements of state and national electrical-safety codes, electrical tools, appliances and many items of electronic equipment now being manufactured to operate from the 120-V line must be equipped with a three-conductor power cord. The National Electrical Code, published by the National Fire Protection Association, is concerned with all aspects of electrical safety. The Code specifies the size and composition of electrical conductors, including grounding conductors. It also specifies proper wiring practices for all electrical wiring, and this helps ensure electrical safety inside your ham shack. The Code even specifies minimum conductor sizes for different lengths of amateur antennas. The code does not mention RF exposure limits to the human body, however. The FCC Rules establish safe RF exposure limits from all types of RF transmitters. These Rules are based on guidelines from the Institute of Electrical and Electronics Engineers (IEEE) and the American National Standards Institute (ANSI). See Chapter 10 of this book for further information about RF radiation exposure and the FCC Rules regarding this exposure.

In a three-wire power cord, two of the conductors (the "hot" and "neutral" wires) carry power to the device, while the third conductor (the ground wire) is connected to the metal frame of the device. See Figure 4-15. The "hot" wire is usually covered with black or red insulation, the "neutral" wire has white insulation, and the frame/ground wire has green insulation, or is bare.

When plugged into a properly wired mating receptacle, a three-contact plug connects the third conductor to an earth ground, thereby grounding the chassis or frame of the appliance and preventing the possibility of electric shock to the user. A defective power cord that shorts to the case of the appliance will simply blow a fuse. Without the ground connection, the case could carry the full line voltage, presenting a severe shock hazard. All commercially manufactured electronic test equipment and most ac-operated amateur equipment is supplied with these three-

Figure 4-15 — Correct wiring technique for 120-V and 240-V power cords and receptacles. The white wire is neutral, the green wire is ground and the black or red wire is the hot lead.

wire cords. Adapters are available for use where older electrical installations do not have mating receptacles. For proper grounding, the lug protruding from the adapter must be attached underneath the screw securing the cover plate of the outlet box. The outlet itself must be grounded for this to be effective. If the power wires coming into the electric box are inside a flexible metal covering, the outlet should be grounded through the metal covering. This type of wire is commonly referred to as armored cable.

A "polarized" two-wire plug and mating receptacle ensures that the hot wire and the neutral wire in the appliance are connected to the appropriate wires in the house electrical system. A polarized plug has one blade that is wider than the other. Without this polarized plug and receptacle, the power switch in the equipment may be in the hot wire when the plug is inserted one way, and in the neutral wire when inserted the other way. This can present a dangerous situation. It is possible for the equipment to be "hot" even with the switch off. With the switch in the neutral line, the hot line may be connected to the equipment chassis. An unsuspecting operator could form a path to ground by touching the case, and might receive a nasty shock!

Sometimes you may find it necessary to install a new plug on the end of an electrical power cord. This could occur because the cord is worn or the insulation broken, for example. Be sure to follow accepted wiring practices when you install the new plug. If the wires in the power cord are stranded, be sure to twist the wires tightly and wrap them around the proper screw terminals of the new plug. Loose strands that aren't secured neatly under the screw head may come in contact with the other terminals, causing a short circuit.

Be sure to follow the proper color coding. The hot (black or red) lead should connect to the brass-colored screw terminal. The neutral (white) lead should connect to the silver-colored terminal. Also be sure to follow proper grounding techniques for the wiring. The safety ground (green or bare) lead should connect to the green-colored terminal, or the terminal that connects to the longer, round pin of the plug. See Figure 4-16 for an illustration of this wiring.

Current Capacity

Another factor that must be taken into account when you are wiring an electrical circuit is the current-handling capability of the wire. Table 4-1 shows the current-handling capability of some common wire sizes. From the table we can see that number 14 wire could be used for a circuit carrying 15 A, while number 12 (or larger) would have to be used for a circuit carrying 20 A.

To remain safe, don't overload the ac circuits in your home. The circuit breaker or fuse rating indicates the maximum load that may be placed on the line at any one time. Simple mathematics can be used to calculate the current your ham radio equipment will draw. Most equipment has the power requirements printed on the back. If not, the owner's manual should contain such information. When calculating current requirements, make sure to include any other household appliances that may be on the same line — including lights! If you were to put a larger fuse in the circuit, too much current could be drawn, the wires would become hot and a fire could result. If the household

Figure 4-16 — This drawing shows the correct wiring of a 120-V ac line cord to a new plug. Be sure to observe correct color coding and grounding practices.

Table 4-1

Current-Carrying Capability of Some Common Wire Sizes

Wire Size (AWG)	Continuous-Duty Current*
8	46 A
10	33 A
12	23 A
14	17 A
16	13 A
18	10 A
20	7.5 A
22	5 A

* Wires or cables in conduits or bundles

wiring to the outlet is American Wire Gauge (AWG) number 12, the maximum fuse or circuit-breaker size is 20 amperes. If the household wiring uses AWG number 14 wire, the maximum fuse or circuit-breaker size is 15 amperes.

[Turn to Chapter 12 now and study question G4C11 and questions G4D07 through G4D11. Also study question G4E02. Review this section if you have difficulty with any of these questions.]

OTHER SOURCES OF ELECTRICAL POWER

Amateurs should always be concerned about alternate sources of electrical power for times when the commercial power may go off. Having a source of emergency power could be important for your communications ability during various types of natural or man-made disasters.

If you live in an area where the commercial power goes out frequently, you might want to consider an emergency generator. This could also be a good source of power for Field Day and other Amateur Radio portable situations.

Whether you plan a temporary or permanent installation for your generator, you should be sure to install it in a well-ventilated area. You don't want carbon monoxide and other exhaust fumes to accumulate in your garage, basement or other living area. You should also ensure proper grounding for your generator. This can be through a connection to your electrical system ground, for example. Of course you will need a supply of fuel, oil and other maintenance products for your generator. Don't store fuel in the generator fuel tank. Keep a fresh supply of fuel in a properly labeled, approved container. (Use stored gasoline in your car and get a fresh container once a month.) Don't store the fuel in an inhabited area. A detached garage or shed are safer storage locations.

Many modern rigs require a source of 12 V dc at 20 amps or so. A deep-discharge lead-acid storage battery is a good emergency power source for such radios. Of course the battery is only useful if it is kept charged and ready to go at all times. A lead-acid battery gives off hydrogen gas as it is being charged. Since hydrogen gas can explode if ignited by a spark, it is important to provide proper ventilation for the battery as you charge it.

Natural sources of energy are becoming more economical and more practical as a way to power your amateur station equipment. **Photovoltaic conversion** is the process by which a semiconductor PN junction converts sunlight into electricity. Each **photovoltaic cell** produces about 0.5 volt in full sunlight, if there is no load connected to the cell. This is called the *open-circuit voltage*. The size or surface area of the cell determines the maximum current that the cell can supply. A solar panel is an array of photovoltaic cells that convert light into electricity. Twenty eight such cells connected in series provide a 14-volt supply that can be regulated to 13.8 volts and used to charge a lead-acid storage battery. Solar panels are rated according to output voltage and maximum output current. When setting up a solar electric system you must select a solar panel that is designed to supply the proper voltage and maximum output current for your system. After the initial expense of building such a solar electric system, the sun will provide a ready supply of free energy. The storage batteries maintain the power supply for nighttime needs or for cloudy periods when the solar panel may not produce enough electricity to power your station.

Some amateurs have also built wind-powered generating systems. The design and construction of a suitable windmill is not trivial. These systems provide a source of free energy after the expense of the initial construction, however. Again, the greatest disadvantage is the need for a battery storage system to supply power when the wind is not blowing.

[Turn to Chapter 12 now and study questions G4E06 through G4E11. Review this section if you have difficulty with any of those questions.]

MOBILE OPERATING

Many amateurs enjoy operating their HF Amateur Radio stations from their cars. While you must be very careful not to allow your ham activity to interfere with your concentration while driving, you can have many enjoyable contacts while someone else is driving or while stopped. When you install a 100-watt HF radio in your car, you will have to pay attention to a few details that you may have overlooked for a low-power VHF FM radio installation. For example, you might be able to use the cigarette lighter as a power connection for a low-power hand-held radio, but not for a full-power HF rig. The cigarette lighter socket wiring probably is not adequate for the 20 amps or so your HF radio will draw when transmitting. Use heavy gauge wire and make a direct fused connection to the battery. (Both leads should have fuses, placed as close to the battery as possible.) See Figure 4-17.

HF mobile antenna systems are the most limiting factor for effective operation of your station. The best place to locate your mobile antenna is in the center of your metal car roof. Placing even an 8-foot vertical antenna on top of a small car makes

Figure 4-17 — A wiring diagram for a typical mobile transceiver installation.

(A)   **(B)**   **(C)**

Figure 4-18 — Some common coaxial-cable connectors. Part A shows a BNC connector pair. Many hand-held radios use BNC connectors. They are popular when a weatherproof connector is needed for RG-58 sized cables. Part B shows a pair of N connectors. These are often used for UHF equipment because of their low loss. Type N connectors provide a weatherproof connector for use with RG-8 sized cables. Part C shows a PL-259 coaxial connector and its mating SO-239 chassis connector. Most HF equipment uses these connectors. They are designed for use with RG-8 sized cables although reducer bushings are available for the smaller-diameter cables.

a dangerously tall system, however. If you have a mid-sized or larger vehicle such an antenna system is almost out of the question. For the lower-frequency bands, like 75 meters, the antenna will always use some type of inductive loading to shorten the length that would be required.

There are several types of connectors commonly used for coaxial cable RF transmission lines. Many hand-held radios use BNC connectors because this connector requires only about a quarter turn to install or remove the connector. BNC connectors are designed for use with RG-58-type coaxial cables. Type N connectors are common on UHF and higher-frequency equipment. Type N connectors are designed for use with RG-8 type coax. Most HF radios use the PL-259 connector, which is sometimes called a UHF connector (although it is generally considered to have too much loss for use at UHF). These connectors are designed for use with RG-8 type coaxial cable, although adapters are used with the smaller-diameter RG-58 cables. See Figure 4-18.

[This completes your study in Chapter 4. Before going on to Chapter 5, turn to Chapter 12 and study questions G4E01, G4E03, G4E04 and G4E05. Review this section if you are uncertain of the answers to any of these questions.]

CHAPTER 5
KEYWORDS
KEYWORDS
KEYWORDS

Alternating current (ac) — Electric current that flows first in one direction in a wire and then in the other direction. The applied voltage is changing polarity as the current direction changes. This direction reversal continues at a rate that depends on the frequency of the ac.

Capacitor — An electrical component composed of two or more conductive plates separated by an insulating material. A capacitor stores energy in an electric field.

Coil — A conductor wound into a series of loops. (Also see **inductor**.)

Current — A flow of electrons in an electric circuit.

Decibel (dB) — The smallest change in sound level that can be detected by the human ear. Power gains and losses are also expressed in decibels.

Direct current (dc) — Electric current that flows in one direction only.

Effective voltage — The value of a dc voltage that will heat a resistive component to the same temperature as the ac voltage that is being measured.

Electromotive force (EMF) — The force or pressure that pushes a current through a circuit.

Impedance — A term used to describe a combination of reactance and resistance in a circuit.

Inductor — An electrical component usually composed of a coil of wire wound on a central core. An inductor stores energy in a magnetic field.

Ohm — The basic unit of resistance, reactance and impedance.

Ohm's Law — A basic law of electronics, it gives a relationship between voltage, resistance and current (E = IR).

Power — The rate at which energy is consumed. In an electric circuit, power is found by multiplying the voltage applied to the circuit by the current through the circuit.

Reactance — The opposition to current that a capacitor or inductor creates in an ac circuit.

Resistance — The ability to oppose an electric current.

Root-mean-square (RMS) voltage — Another name for effective voltage. The term refers to the method of calculating the value.

Transformer — Two coils with mutual inductance used to change the voltage level of an ac power source to one more suited for a particular circuit.

Voltage — The EMF or pressure that causes electrons to move through an electrical circuit.

ELECTRICAL PRINCIPLES

To pass your FCC Element 2 and 3A written tests and receive a Novice or Technician license, you had to learn some basic radio theory. For your Element 3B test, you will need to understand a few more electrical principles. Your General exam will include two questions about the electrical principles covered in this chapter. Those questions come from the following two syllabus groups:

G5A Impedance, including matching; resistance, including ohm; reactance; inductance; capacitance and metric divisions of these values.

G5B Decibel; Ohm's Law; current and voltage dividers; electrical power calculations and series and parallel components; transformers (either voltage or impedance); sine wave root-mean-square (RMS) value.

Be sure to turn to Chapter 12 and study the appropriate FCC questions when the text tells you to study certain questions. This will help you check your progress, and decide if you need a little extra studying. We cannot tell you everything about a particular topic in one chapter — you may want to refer to some other reference books for additional information. *Understanding Basic Electronics*, published by the ARRL is a good place to start. *The ARRL Handbook for Radio Amateurs* and other ARRL publications also contain lots of additional information about electrical principles.

E = VOLTAGE

Electrons need a push to get them moving; we call the force that pushes electrons through a circuit **electromotive force (EMF)**. EMF is similar to water pressure in a pipe. The more pressure, the more water that flows through the pipe. The greater the EMF, the greater the flow of electrons in a circuit.

EMF is measured in volts, so it is usually called **voltage**. A voltage-measuring instrument is called a voltmeter. The more voltage applied to a circuit, the more electrons will flow through the circuit.

I = CURRENT

The word **current** comes to us from a Latin word meaning "to run" and it always implies movement. When someone speaks of the current in a river, we think of a flow of water; a current of air can be a light breeze or a hurricane; and a current of electricity is a flow of electrons.

Current is indicated in equations and diagrams by the letter I (from the French word *intensité*). We measure current in *amperes,* and the measuring device is called an ammeter. An ampere is often too large a unit for convenient use, so we can measure current in milliamperes (one thousandth of an ampere) or microamperes (one millionth of an ampere). Amperes are abbreviated amp or A; milliamperes as mA and microamperes as μA.

In considering current, it is natural to think of a single, constant force causing the electrons to move. (Think of this as similar to the pressure of water down a river or through a pipe.) When this is so, the electrons always move in the same direction through a circuit made up of conductors connected together in a continuous loop. Such a current is called a **direct current**, abbreviated **dc**. This is the type of current furnished by batteries and by certain types of generators.

R = RESISTANCE

Resistance is something that opposes motion. All materials have electrical resistance; there is always some opposition to the flow of electrons through the material, although the resistance of different materials varies widely. Some materials have very high resistance; we call these materials good insulators, or poor conductors. Other materials have very low resistance; we call these materials poor insulators, or good conductors. The basic unit of resistance is the **ohm**, and a resistance-measuring instrument is called an ohmmeter. The symbol for an ohm is Ω, the Greek capital letter omega.

Between the extremes of a very good insulator and a very good conductor, we can make devices with a range of opposition to the flow of electrons in a circuit. We call such devices resistors. If we use the analogy of water flowing in a pipe to help us understand electron flow, these materials act like a pipe with a sponge in it. Some water will still flow in the pipe, but the flow will be reduced. Figure 5-1 illustrates the concept of the water pressure in a pipe representing voltage, the water flowing through the pipe representing current and a valve that you can use to restrict the flow of water representing resistance.

Figure 5-1 — Water pressure can represent the voltage in an electric circuit. The amount of water can represent electric current and a blockage in the water line (such as the spigot shown here) can represent the resistance in a circuit. Part A shows a water faucet with the valve open. There is little resistance and a lot of water flowing out of the faucet. Part B shows a faucet with the valve almost closed. In this case there is a lot of resistance, and only a small amount of water flows out of the faucet.

The primary function of a resistor is to limit electron flow (current). The greater the resistance, the greater the reduction in current. If we want to control the current reduction over a certain range, we can use a variable resistor. A variable resistor, as its name implies, can be made to change resistance over a range. This allows us to control the electron flow between a maximum and a minimum value over the variable resistor's range.

This current reduction has a price, however; the energy lost by the electrons as they flow through a resistor must be dissipated in some way. The energy is converted into heat, and the resistor gets warm. If the current is higher than the resistor can handle, the resistor will get very hot and may even be destroyed.

OHM'S LAW

Resistance, voltage and current are related in a very important way by what is known as **Ohm's Law**. Georg Simon Ohm, a German scientist, discovered that the voltage drop across a resistor is equal to the resistance multiplied by the current through the resistor. In symbolic terms, Ohm's Law can be written:

$E = I \times R$ (Equation 5-1)

By simply rearranging the terms, we can show that the current is equal to the voltage drop divided by the resistance:

$$I = \frac{E}{R}$$ (Equation 5-2)

and that the resistance equals the voltage drop divided by the current:

$$R = \frac{E}{I} \qquad \text{(Equation 5-3)}$$

Ohm's Law is an important mathematical relationship; you should understand and memorize it. A simple way to remember the Ohm's Law equations is shown in Figure 5-2. If we draw the "Ohm's Law Circle" shown, we can find the equation for any of the three quantities in the relationship.

To use the circle, just cover the letter for which you want to solve the equation. If the two remaining letters are across from each other, you must multiply them. If the two letters are arranged one on top of the other, you must divide the top letter by the bottom. For example, if you cover I, you have "E over R" (Equation 5-2). Cover E, and you have "I times R" (Equation 5-1).

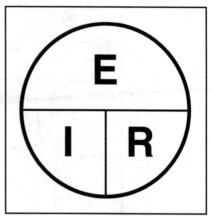

Figure 5-2 — The "Ohm's Law Circle." Cover the letter representing the unknown quality to find an equation to calculate the quantity. For example, if you cover the I, you are left with E / R.

When you know any of the two quantities in Ohm's Law, you can always find the third. See Figure 5-3. The three examples in this figure show how to calculate voltage, current and resistance given the other two quantities in each case. You won't go wrong if you write the equation you want to use first, and then substitute the values you are given and solve for the unknown, as shown in these examples.

KIRCHHOFF'S LAWS

When we analyze a circuit, it is sometimes useful to calculate the current through, and the voltage drop across a circuit or portion of a circuit. We have two electrical principles, called Kirchhoff's Laws, that make it easy for us to find the current and voltage drop.

Kirchhoff's First Law (Kirchhoff's Current Law) states that when a circuit branches into two or more directions, the current entering the branch point, or node, is the same as the current leaving the node. Another way to say this is that the total current equals the sum of the branch currents through each resistor. We can use this law to find an unknown quantity in a parallel circuit.

For example, look at Figure 5-4. We know that the total current I_T entering point A is 1 A. The diagram also shows that the current through R_1 is 0.25 A and that the current through R_2 is 0.5 A. What is the current through R_3? We can use Kirchhoff's Current Law to answer that question.

$$I_1 + I_2 + I_3 = I_T = 1 \text{ A} \qquad \text{(Equation 5-4)}$$

Figure 5-3 — Ohm's Law relates current, voltage and resistance.

Substituting our known values into this equation and solving for I_3, we have:

$$0.25 \text{ A} + 0.5 \text{ A} + I_3 = 1 \text{ A}$$

$$I_3 = 1 \text{ A} - 0.25 \text{ A} - 0.5 \text{ A} = 0.25 \text{ A}$$

Once we know the current through R_3 we can also find its resistance. This is a simple application of Ohm's Law. Since we know that 100 V is applied across points A and B, we can use Equation 5-3 to find the resistance:

$$R = \frac{E}{I}$$

$$R = \frac{100\ V}{0.25\ A} = 400\ \Omega$$

We can draw some general conclusions from this discussion. First, the example shows that for a parallel circuit, the total circuit current is always equal to the sum of the currents in each branch of the circuit. We can also say each branch current is less than the total circuit current.

If the branch resistors have equal values, the current divides equally between the branches. For example, if two equal-value resistors are connected in parallel, each resistor carries half the total current. We don't even need to know the resistor values or the applied voltage in such a case.

Figure 5-4 — Kirchhoff's First (Current) Law: The sum of the current flowing into a junction point (node) in a circuit must equal the sum of the current leaving the node.

If the total circuit current is 1 A with two equal-value resistors connected in parallel, each resistor will carry 0.5 A.

Kirchhoff's Second Law (Kirchhoff's Voltage Law) tells us that the sum of the voltage drops must equal the sum of the voltage rises around any closed loop in a circuit (such as in a series circuit). So in the series circuit in Figure 5-5, the sum of the voltage drops across the resistors must equal the applied voltage. The voltage drop across each resistor can be found by multiplying the current through the resistor by the resistance. (This is a simple Ohm's Law relationship, $E = I \times R$.) Since

Figure 5-5 — Kirchhoff's Second (Voltage) Law: The sum of the individual voltage drops in a closed loop (such as a series circuit) equals the sum of the voltage rises.

all the circuit current flows through each resistor, we can find the current value by dividing the applied voltage (120 V in this example) by the total resistance of the circuit, 60 Ω. (Did you remember that you simply add the values of resistors in series to find the total resistance?) From this, we find that 2 A flows through each resistor. We can then calculate the voltage drops.

$E_{R1} = 2\ A \times 20\ \Omega = 40\ V$
$E_{R2} = 2\ A \times 15\ \Omega = 30\ V$
$E_{R3} = 2\ A \times 25\ \Omega = 50\ V$

Total voltage drop = 40 V + 30 V + 50 V = 120 V

Notice that the larger the resistance, the larger the voltage drop across that resistor.

[Now turn to Chapter 12 and study question G5B02. Review any material in this section that you have difficulty with.]

P = POWER

Suppose we want to know how fast energy is being consumed in a circuit. If you want to compare how bright two different light bulbs will be, or how much it will cost to run a new freezer for a month, you will have to know how fast they use electric energy. **Power** is defined as the time rate of energy consumption. The basic unit for measuring power is the watt, named for James Watt, the inventor of the steam engine. The watt is usually abbreviated W.

Current is a measure of how many electrons are moving past a particular point in an electric circuit in a given time. Voltage is a measure of the force needed to move the electrons. There is a very simple way to calculate power using current and voltage. We use the equation:

$P = I \times E$ (Equation 5-5)

where:

   P = power, measured in watts
   E = EMF in volts
   I = current in amperes

To calculate the power in a circuit, multiply volts times amperes. For example, in Figure 5-6, a 12-V battery provides 0.2 A of current to a light bulb that is operating normally. Using Equation 5-5, we can find the power rating for the bulb by multiplying the voltage by the current:

$P = I \times E = 0.2\ A \times 12\ V = 2.4\ W$

If you know any two of the three quantities in Equation 5-5, you can find the unknown third quantity, just as you can find the unknown in an Ohm's Law problem. We can draw a "power circle" like the Ohm's Law Circle, as shown in Figure 5-7. Cover the unknown quantity to find the equation to use.

$$I = \frac{P}{E}$$ (Equation 5-6)

$$E = \frac{P}{I}$$ (Equation 5-7)

If 10 V is applied to a circuit consuming 20 W, how much current is flowing in the circuit? Use Equation 5-6 to find the current:

$$I = \frac{P}{E} = \frac{20\,W}{10\,V} = 2\,A$$

If a 5-A current flows in a 60-W circuit, how much voltage is applied to the circuit? Equation 5-8 will help us solve this problem:

$$E = \frac{P}{I} = \frac{60\,W}{5\,A} = 12\,V$$

Sometimes you may need to make a calculation involving power, but you will only know one of the quantities in these equations. In that case, you will probably know another quantity, such as a circuit resistance. Ohm's Law can help you find the additional information you need to solve the problem. For example, suppose we apply 400 V to an 800-Ω resistor, and want to know how much power the resistor will have to dissipate? First, we use Ohm's Law (Equation 5-2) to find the circuit current:

$$I = \frac{E}{R} = \frac{400\,V}{800\,\Omega} = 0.5\,A$$

Then, we can use Equation 5-5 to find the power:

$$P = I \times E = 0.5\,A \times 400\,V = 200\,W$$

This will have to be a pretty large resistor, or it will burn up! In a practical example, this might be an electric heater element.

What if we want to know the power dissipated in a 1.25-kΩ resistor that has 7.0 milliamps (mA) of current flowing through it? To use Equation 5-5 we must know the applied voltage — but we can find that with Ohm's Law (Equation

Figure 5-6 — Applied voltage multiplied by current equals power.

12 V

0.2 A

12 V x 0.2 A = 2.4 W

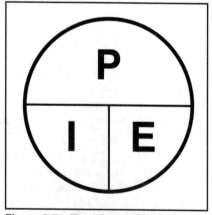

Figure 5-7 – The "Power Circle." Cover the letter representing the unknown quantity to find an equation to calculate that quantity. If you cover the P, you are left with I × E.

5-1). First convert the current to amperes and the resistance to ohms: 7.0 mA = 0.007 A (move the decimal point three places left) and 1.25 kΩ = 1250 Ω (move the decimal point three places right).

$E = I \times R = 0.007 A \times 1250 \Omega = 8.75 V$

Now we can use Equation 5-7:

$P = I \times E = 0.007 A \times 8.75 V = 0.06125 W$

We can easily convert this value to milliwatts by moving the decimal point three places to the right:

$0.06125 W = 61.25 mW.$

[Study questions G5B03 through G5B05 in Chapter 12 before you go on to the next section. Review this section if you have difficulty with any of these questions.]

POWER GAIN, POWER LOSS AND THE DECIBEL

Power gains and losses in electric circuits are often spoken of in terms of **decibels** (one-tenth of a bel). Decibel is abbreviated **dB**. The bel was named for Alexander Graham Bell, and was first used in early audio telephone work to describe a change in loudness levels. The decibel is defined as the change in sound power level that is just perceptible to the human ear. In mathematical terms power gain or loss in decibels is given by the equation:

$$dB = 10 \times \log_{10}\left(\frac{P_2}{P_1}\right)$$

(Equation 5-8)

where:

P_1 = reference power
P_2 = power being compared to the reference value

The $\log_{10}$ in this equation means "the logarithm to the base 10," also called the common logarithm. The common logarithm of a number is defined as the power to which you must raise 10 in order to obtain that number. If $X = 10^A$, then A is the $\log_{10}$ of X. Your scientific calculator probably has keys labeled "log" and "y^x" to help you with these calculations. You won't even need a calculator for a lot of decibel calculations if you learn a few basic relationships, though.

The $\log_{10}$ of 10 is 1, because 10 raised to the first power is 10 ($10^1 = 10$). The $\log_{10}$ of 100 is 2 ($10^2 = 100$); the $\log_{10}$ of 10,000 is 4, and so on. You may notice from these examples that it is very easy to find the common logarithm of a positive whole number consisting of a one and any number of zeros. Simply count the zeros to find the logarithm! The logarithm gives us the answer to the question "10 raised to what power will give us this number?"

Let's look at some sample problems using the power gain and loss relationship. If we increase our transmitter power level from 100 W to 1000 W, we can express this power gain in decibels:

$$dB = 10 \times \log_{10}\left(\frac{P_2}{P_1}\right)$$

$$dB = 10 \times \log_{10}\left(\frac{1000 \text{ W}}{100 \text{ W}}\right)$$

$$dB = 10 \times \log_{10}(10)$$

$$dB = 10 \times 1 = 10 \text{ dB}$$

A power decrease from 1500 W to 15 W would result in a loss of 20 dB:

$$dB = 10 \times \log_{10}\left(\frac{P_2}{P_1}\right)$$

$$dB = 10 \times \log_{10}\left(\frac{15 \text{ W}}{1500 \text{ W}}\right)$$

$$dB = 10 \times \log_{10}(0.01)$$

$$dB = 10 \times -2 = -20 \text{ dB}$$

Notice that the decrease from 1500 W to 15 W can be thought of as one drop of 10 dB from 1500 W to 150 W, and another 10 dB drop from 150 W to 15 W so the total power loss is -10 dB $+ -10$ dB $= -20$ dB. This is a very powerful property of logarithms. For example, if we double our transmitter power from 10 W to 20 W, we have a 3-dB gain:

$$dB = 10 \times \log_{10}\left(\frac{20 \text{ W}}{10 \text{ W}}\right)$$

$$dB = 10 \times \log_{10}(2)$$

$$dB = 10 \times 0.301 \approx 3 \text{ dB}$$

If we then double the power again to 40 watts, we have another 3-dB gain:

$$dB = 10 \times \log_{10}\left(\frac{40 \text{ W}}{20 \text{ W}}\right)$$

$$dB = 10 \times \log_{10}(2)$$

$$dB = 10 \times 0.301 \approx 3 \text{ dB}$$

So if we multiply our power level by a factor of four times, from 10 watts to 40 watts, we would have a total power gain of 3 dB + 3 dB = 6 dB. Checking our calculations:

$$dB = 10 \times \log_{10}\left(\frac{40 \text{ W}}{10 \text{ W}}\right)$$

$$dB = 10 \times \log_{10} (4)$$

$$dB = 10 \times 0.602 \approx 6 \ dB$$

Any time you double the power, there is a 3-dB increase. If you multiply the power by 4, there is a 6-dB increase. If you decrease the power by 3 dB, it means you have cut the power in half.

Receiver signal-strength meters (S meters) are usually marked in decibels above the strength 9 reading. If you receive a signal-strength report of "10 dB over S9," you could reduce your power by a factor of 10 (such as from 1500 W to 150 W) and still have an S9 signal. A report of "20 dB over S9" means you could reduce your power by a factor of 100 (such as from 1500 W to 15 W) and still have an S9 signal!

Power gains and losses expressed in decibels can be added (or subtracted) to find the total system gain or loss. You will learn more about the applications of this principle when you study for your Advanced license. For now, you just need to know the basic ideas presented here.

[Now turn to Chapter 12 and study question G5B01. Review this section if this question gives you any difficulty.]

ALTERNATING CURRENT

It is possible to have a voltage source that periodically reverses polarity. With this kind of voltage the current flows first in one direction and then in the opposite direction. Such a voltage is called an *alternating voltage*. The current produced by this alternating voltage is called an **alternating current** (abbreviated **ac**). The reversals (alternations) may occur at any rate from less than one per second up to

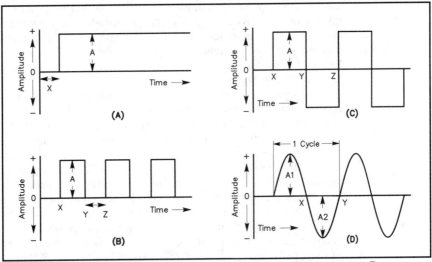

Figure 5-8 — Four types of current are shown. A — direct current; B — intermittent (pulsating) direct current; C — square-wave alternating current; D — sine-wave alternating current.

several billion or more per second.

The difference between alternating current and direct current is shown in Figure 5-8. In these graphs, the horizontal axis indicates time, increasing toward the right. The vertical axis represents the amplitude or strength of the current, increasing either in the up or down direction away from the horizontal axis. If the graph is above the horizontal axis, the current is flowing in one direction through the circuit (indicated by the + sign). If the graph is below the horizontal axis the current is flowing in the opposite direction (indicated by the – sign).

In Figure 5-8A, assume that we close the circuit or make the path for the current complete at the time indicated by X. The current instantly takes the amplitude indicated by the height A. After that, the current continues at the same amplitude as time goes on. This is an ordinary direct current.

In Figure 5-8B, the current starts flowing with the amplitude A at time X, continues at that amplitude until time Y and then instantly ceases. After an interval from Y to Z the current begins to flow again and the same sort of stop-and-start performance is repeated. This is an intermittent direct current (also called a pulsating direct current). We could produce this type of current by alternately opening and closing a switch in the circuit. It is a direct current because the direction of the current does not change; the amplitude is always on the + side of the horizontal axis. This series of current pulses is sometimes called square waves.

The waveform in Figure 5-8C is a little different. The current starts with amplitude A at time X just as the wave in Figure 5-8B, but at time Y the current instantly reverses direction. From time Y to time Z, the current flows in the opposite direction and the voltage has an equal, but opposite polarity. At time Z the current reverses direction again. This is called a square-wave alternating current.

In Figure 5-8D the current starts at zero, smoothly increases in amplitude until it reaches the amplitude A1 while flowing in the + direction, then decreases smoothly until it drops to zero amplitude once more. At that time (X) the direction of the current reverses. As time goes on the amplitude increases, with the current now flowing in the – direction, until it reaches amplitude A2. Then the amplitude decreases until finally it returns to zero (at point Y) and the direction reverses once more. The type of smoothly varying alternating current shown in Figure 5-8D is known as a sine wave.

Looking at the sine wave, the first thing we notice is that the waveform reaches a maximum value (peak) at two points in the ac cycle — once during the positive part and once during the negative part. For the remainder of the cycle, the waveform is constantly varying between these two values. Another interesting characteristic of a sine wave is that the average dc voltage contained in the wave is zero. The positive half of the cycle is a "mirror image" of the negative side — for every positive value, there is a corresponding negative value, and the positive and negative values cancel each other out. This doesn't mean that a sine wave contains no energy, however — it means only that the average dc potential is zero.

So how can we find a value for ac voltage and current? The wave is constantly changing. If we could measure the voltage at one point on the wave at some instant of time, in the next instant the value would be different. There is no one value we can point to and say: "That's the value of the voltage."

We could use the peak value the wave reaches on its positive half-cycle. Or we could measure the voltage from the positive peak to the negative peak, and use this to specify the current or voltage. This value is called the *peak-to-peak* value. We can also use a measuring scale that lets us compare the ac voltage to an equivalent dc voltage.

If we pass dc through a resistor, the resistor will get warm. If we pass ac through the same resistor, it will also get warm. The ac voltage that will heat a resistor to the same temperature as 1 V dc is said to have an **effective voltage** of 1 V ac. If we pass 10 V dc through a resistor and measure its temperature, we can then find an effective ac voltage of 10 V ac that will heat the resistor to the same temperature.

Most ac voltages are specified by their effective values. Your wall outlets provide 120 V effective ac. If we plug a directly heated soldering iron into a source of 120 V dc, it will get just as hot as it will if we plug it into the ac wall outlet.

The effective voltage is also called the **root-mean-square (RMS)** value of the ac wave. The phrase root-mean-square describes the actual process of calculating the effective voltage. The method involves squaring the instantaneous values for a large number of points along the waveform and then finding the average of the squared values. (Another mathematical term for average is *mean*.) We then take the square root of this average (the *root* of the average *[mean]* of the *squares*).

If we know the peak-to-peak value of a sine-wave ac waveform, how do we calculate the RMS value? The RMS value and the peak value are related by a factor of the square root of two. For sine waves, the following relationships are useful:

$$V_{PEAK} = V_{RMS} \times \sqrt{2} = V_{RMS} \times 1.414 \qquad \text{(Equation 5-9)}$$

$$V_{RMS} = \frac{V_{PEAK}}{\sqrt{2}} = V_{PEAK} \times 0.707 \qquad \text{(Equation 5-10)}$$

Remember that the peak value is one-half the peak-to-peak value. Figure 5-9 shows the relationships between peak, peak-to-peak and RMS ac values.

For example, to find the peak-to-peak value of a 120-V RMS ac wave, we use Equation 5-9:

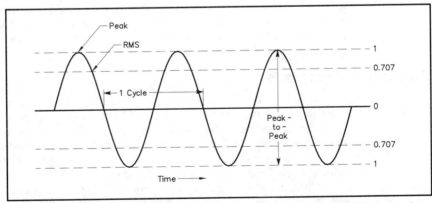

Figure 5-9 — The RMS (effective) value of an ac waveform is 0.707 times the peak value. The peak value is one-half the peak-to-peak value.

$$V_{PEAK} = V_{RMS} \times \sqrt{2}$$

$$V_{PEAK} = 120 \text{ V} \times 1.414 = 169.7 \text{ V}$$

Remember that the peak-to-peak voltage is peak voltage times 2, so:

$$V_{PEAK-TO-PEAK} = 169.7 \text{ V} \times 2 = 339.4 \text{ V}$$

To find the RMS value of a 17 V_{PEAK} ac wave, we use Equation 5-10:

$$V_{RMS} = \frac{V_{PEAK}}{\sqrt{2}} = V_{PEAK} \times 0.707$$

$$V_{RMS} = \frac{V_{PEAK}}{\sqrt{2}} = V_{PEAK} \times 0.707 = 17 \text{ V} \times 0.707 = 12 \text{ V}$$

If you were given the peak-to-peak value, you would divide that by 2 before substituting the value into Equation 5-10.

[Turn to Chapter 12 now and study questions G5B09 through G5B11. Review this section as needed.]

X = REACTANCE

A **capacitor** is an electronics component made of two or more conductive plates separated by an insulating material. A capacitor stores electric energy in an electric field. A capacitor responds to an alternating current by storing and releasing electric energy in an electric field as the current passes through the component.

A **coil** (or inductor) is a component made by winding a conductor into a series of loops. An inductor stores electric energy in a magnetic field. An inductor responds to an alternating current by storing and releasing electric energy in a magnetic field as the current passes through it.

As the amount of stored energy changes, there is an opposition to the current with both capacitors and inductors. This opposition is called **reactance**, and it is measured in **ohms**. In equations, reactance is designated by the letter X. Capacitive reactance is designated X_C and inductive reactance is designated X_L. Unlike resistance, the reactance of a component will vary with the frequency of the applied alternating current.

Capacitive Reactance

A discharged or "empty" capacitor looks like a short circuit. This means that when the circuit is first energized, a lot of current will flow into the capacitor as it charges. Initially, the voltage across the capacitor is zero; as the voltage builds up, the current through the capacitor will drop toward zero. If direct current is applied to a capacitor, the current will drop to zero when the capacitor charges to the applied voltage. See Figure 5-10. A capacitor blocks dc.

When an alternating current is applied to a capacitor, things are a little different. If the frequency of the ac is low, the capacitor has time to charge to the full applied voltage during each half cycle. As the capacitor is charged, it opposes any

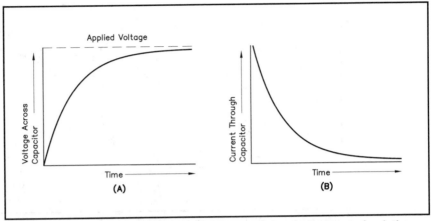

Figure 5-10 — When a circuit containing a capacitor is first energized, the voltage across the capacitor is zero, and the current is very large. As time passes, the voltage across the capacitor increases, as shown at A, and the current drops toward zero, as shown at B.

further increase in voltage. On the next half cycle the capacitor discharges and is then recharged with the opposite polarity. A high-frequency ac wave will not fully charge the capacitor during each half cycle, and the capacitor will pass the full current. We can see from this that for a capacitor, as the frequency of the applied ac *increases*, the opposition to current (the **reactance**) *decreases*.

The reactance of a capacitor is given by the equation:

$$X_C = \frac{1}{2\pi f C}$$ (Equation 5-11)

where:

X_C = capacitive reactance in ohms
f = frequency in hertz
C = capacitance in farads
π = 3.14

You should always use the proper units. If capacitance is given in microfarads, you will have to convert to farads before using Equation 5-11. (To convert microfarads to farads, multiply microfarads by 10^{-6}. This means moving the decimal point 6 places to the left.) The equation shows the inverse relationship between capacitive reactance and frequency; as the *frequency* goes *up*, the *reactance* will go *down*.

Inductive Reactance

An inductor presents opposition to a change in *current*. This means that when a circuit containing an inductor is first energized, no current will flow in the inductor. When a direct current is applied to an inductor, at first the inductor looks like an open circuit. The current will gradually increase to the maximum value, which is determined by the amount of the applied voltage and any circuit resistance. (The word *gradually* is a relative term here. It may only take microseconds or millisec-

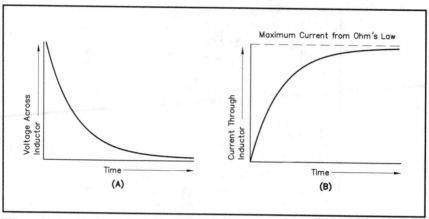

Figure 5-11 — When a circuit containing an inductor is first energized, the initial current is zero and the full applied voltage appears across the inductor. As time passes, the voltage drops toward zero as shown at A, and the current increases, as shown at B.

onds to reach the full current, depending on the value of inductance and other circuit conditions.) At first, all the applied voltage appears across the inductor. Then as the current *increases*, the voltage across the inductor *decreases* toward zero. See Figure 5-11. Inductors pass dc.

When an alternating current is applied to an inductor, as the frequency of the applied ac *increases*, the opposition to the current (the **reactance**) *increases*. Inductors oppose any change in current. The higher the frequency of the applied ac, the more rapidly the current is changing, and the greater the opposition to the current. The equation for inductive reactance is:

$$X_L = 2 \pi f L$$ (Equation 5-12)

where:

X_L = inductive reactance in ohms
f = frequency in hertz
L = inductance in henrys
π = 3.14

Again, the correct units must be used. If the inductance is expressed in units other than henrys (such as millihenrys) you will have to change them to the basic unit. From the equation, we can see that as the frequency of the applied ac *increases*, inductive reactance *increases*.

[Turn to Chapter 12 and study the questions G5A02 through G5A06. Also answer question G5A10. Review this section if you have any difficulty.]

Z = IMPEDANCE

Impedance is a number obtained by dividing the voltage applied to a circuit by the current flowing through it. It represents the opposition to the flow of ac in a circuit that may contain resistance and reactance. See Figure 5-12. Suppose we measure the current, I, flowing into the black box and find it to be 2 A with 250 V ac applied. Dividing 250 V by 2 A results in an impedance of 125. Even though this is not a dc circuit, we say that we have 125 "ohms" since the ohm has already been established as representing the ratio of voltage to current in a dc circuit. So we can say the impedance is 125 Ω. The letter Z is used to represent impedance. The impedance does not tell us what is inside the black box, however.

Figure 5-12 — In this circuit, we know that the box presents 125 Ω of opposition to the current, but we don't know what's in the box.

We could get this result (125 Ω) if we had a 125-Ω resistor in the box. The result would also be the same if we used an inductor (or capacitor) with 125 Ω of reactance at the frequency of the applied voltage. We could also use a combination of resistance and reactance. Such combinations of resistance and reactance not only exist, but are actually more common than either pure resistance or reactance alone.

Impedance Matching

Impedance is an important concept in electronics. Remember that an antenna system operates most efficiently when the SWR (standing-wave ratio) on the feed line is low. The SWR is a measure of how well the impedance of the transmitter, feed line and antenna are matched; that is, the closer the impedances are to the same value, the better the antenna system will operate.

Maximum power transfer occurs when the impedance of the electric load is the same as the impedance of the power source. Some devices (like antennas) require a specific input impedance for proper operation. This input impedance may not be the same as the optimum output impedance for the power source (transmitter). In that case, we use an additional circuit between the two that will match or transform the output impedance of the source (the transmitter) to the input impedance of the load (the antenna). The impedance of the source must be matched to the impedance of the load to ensure that the source can deliver maximum power to the load. This process is called *impedance matching*.

[You should turn to Chapter 12 now and study question G5A01, questions G5A07 through G5A09, and question G5A11. Review this section if you have trouble with any of those questions.]

TRANSFORMERS

When two coils are arranged so that a changing current in one induces a voltage in the other, the combination of windings is called a **transformer**. See Figure 5-13. Every transformer has a primary winding and a secondary winding. The primary winding is connected to the current source, and the secondary winding is connected to the load.

With a transformer, electric energy can be transferred from one circuit to another without direct connection. In the process, the signal voltage can be readily changed from one level to another.

Turns Ratio and Voltage Transformation

For a given magnetic field, the voltage induced in a coil will be proportional to the number of turns in the coil. It follows, therefore, that if the primary and secondary windings of a transformer have the same number of turns and we ignore losses in the coils, we would expect the full primary voltage to be induced into the secondary. If the secondary has fewer turns than the primary, the voltage induced in the secondary will be less than the primary voltage, and the transformer is called a *step-down transformer*. If the secondary has more turns than the primary, the secondary voltage will be greater than the primary, and the transformer is a *step-up transformer*. See Figure 5-14.

If you know the number of turns on the primary and secondary windings of a transformer, and you know the applied voltage, it is easy to calculate the secondary voltage. We use the equation:

$$E_S = \frac{N_S}{N_P} \times E_P$$

(Equation 5-13)

Figure 5-13 — The transformer is an application of mutual inductance between two or more coils or inductors placed close to each other. Both coils of most transformers are wound on the same core material.

Figure 5-14 — The amount of voltage transformation is controlled by the ratio of turns in the primary to turns in the secondary.

where:

E = voltage
N = number of turns
S = secondary
P = primary

For example, a certain transformer has 2250 turns on the primary winding and 500 turns on the secondary winding. If 120 V ac is applied to the primary winding, what will be the secondary voltage?

$$E_S = \frac{N_S}{N_P} \times E_P = \frac{500}{2250} \times 120 \text{ V} = 0.222 \times 120 \text{ V} = 26.7 \text{ V}$$

It is interesting to note that a transformer can't increase the power in a circuit. So if the transformer steps up the voltage, there will be less current in the secondary by the same ratio. If the transformer steps down the voltage, there can be more current in the secondary winding than in the primary winding. Since a transformer changes both the voltage and current between the primary and secondary windings, you can probably guess that we can apply Ohm's Law to find an impedance relationship.

In an ideal transformer — one without losses — the following relationship is true between the primary and secondary impedance and the number of turns in the transformer:

$$Z_P = Z_S \left(\frac{N_P}{N_S} \right)^2 \qquad \text{(Equation 5-14)}$$

where:

Z_P = impedance seen by a device connected to the primary
Z_S = impedance seen by a device connected to the secondary
N_P = number of turns on the primary
N_S = number of turns on the secondary

From this equation, we can derive an equation for the turns ratio necessary to match a given input and output impedance.

$$\frac{N_P}{N_S} = \sqrt{\frac{Z_P}{Z_S}}$$

(Equation 5-15)

In other words, the turns ratio of the transformer must equal the square root of the impedance ratio. So, if we have an audio amplifier with a 600-Ω output impedance to match to a speaker that has a 4-Ω input impedance, the turns ratio of the transformer (N_P to N_S) is:

$$\frac{N_P}{N_S} = \sqrt{\frac{Z_P}{Z_S}} = \sqrt{\frac{600\,\Omega}{4\,\Omega}} = \sqrt{150} = 12.2$$

Therefore, the primary must have 12.2 times the number of turns as the secondary. See Figure 5-15 for another example of how to find the turns ratio for a matching transformer.

Suppose we have an audio amplifier with an output impedance of 2000 Ω, and the matching transformer used to drive a speaker has a turns ratio of 24 to 1. What is the impedance of the speaker for this circuit? To answer this question we must solve Equation 5-14 for the secondary impedance. We will cross multiply the turns ratio term to solve for Z_S. This process results in reversing the positions of the primary and secondary turns in the equation:

Figure 5-15 — To match a 2000-Ω primary impedance to a 4-Ω secondary impedance, we use a transformer with a turns ratio of 24 to 1.

$$Z_P = Z_S \left(\frac{N_P}{N_S} \right)^2$$

$$Z_P \times \left(\frac{N_S}{N_P} \right)^2 = Z_S \qquad \qquad \text{(Equation 5-16)}$$

Now we can substitute the values from our problem into Equation 5-16:

$$Z_P \times \left(\frac{N_S}{N_P} \right)^2 = Z_S = 2000 \ \Omega \times \left(\frac{1}{24} \right)^2 = 2000 \ \Omega \times \left(0.0417 \right)^2$$

$$Z_S = 2000 \ \Omega \times 1.74 \times 10^{-3} = 3.47 \ \Omega$$

Round off this value to about 3.5 Ω. This transformer would be used to drive a 4-Ω speaker with this audio amplifier.

[This completes the material for this chapter. To finish your study, however, you should turn to Chapter 12 and study questions G5B06 through G5B08. Review this section if you have difficulty with any of these questions.]

Capacitor — An electronic component composed of two or more conductive plates separated by an insulating material.

Junction diode — An electronic component formed by placing a layer of N-type semiconductor material next to a layer of P-type material. Diodes allow current to flow in one direction only.

Magnetizing current — A small current that flows in a transformer primary winding, even with no load connected to the secondary.

Maximum average forward current — The highest average forward current that can flow through a diode for a given junction temperature.

Peak-inverse-voltage (PIV) — The maximum voltage a diode can withstand when it is reverse biased (not conducting).

Primary winding — The coil in a transformer that is connected to the energy source.

Resistor — Any material that opposes a current in an electrical circuit. An electronic component specifically designed to oppose current.

Secondary winding — The coil in a transformer that is connected to the load.

Suppressor capacitor — A capacitor (often ceramic) connected across the transformer primary or secondary winding in a power supply. These capacitors are intended to suppress any transient voltage spikes, preventing them from getting through the power supply.

Temperature coefficient — A number used to show whether a component will increase or decrease in value as it gets warm.

Transformer — Mutually coupled coils used to change the voltage level of an ac power source to one more suitable for a particular circuit.

CIRCUIT COMPONENTS

Before you can understand the operation of most complex electronic circuits, you must know some basic information about the parts that make up those circuits. This chapter presents the information about circuit components that you need to know to pass your General written exam. You will find information about resistors, capacitors, inductors and transformers, along with some basic information about semiconductor diodes. These components are combined with other devices to build practical electronic circuits, some of which are described in Chapter 7. Your General exam will have one question from the circuit components group. There is only one syllabus group for this topic:

G6A Resistors; capacitors; inductors; rectifiers and transistors; etc.

As you study the characteristics of the components described in this chapter, be sure to turn to the FCC Element 3B questions in Chapter 12 when you are directed to do so. The questions will help you check on your progress, and will show where you need to do some extra studying. If you thoroughly understand how these components work, you should have no problem learning how they can be connected to make a circuit perform a specific task.

RESISTORS

Current is the flow of electrons from one point to another in a circuit. A perfect insulator would allow no electrons to flow (zero current), while a perfect conductor would allow an infinite number of electrons to flow (infinite current). In practice, however, there is no such thing as a perfect conductor or a perfect insulator. Partial opposition to electron flow occurs when the electrons collide with other electrons or atoms in the conductor. The result is a reduction in current, and heat is produced in the conductor. **Resistors** allow us to control the current in a circuit by controlling the opposition to electron flow. As they oppose the flow of electrons they dissipate electrical energy in the form of heat. The more energy a resistor dissipates, the hotter it will become.

There are several types of resistors, depending on the method used to construct them. For example, a *wire-wound resistor* is made by winding a specific length of wire onto a ceramic form. The length, type and size of the wire determines the resistance of a wire-wound resistor. Another way to form a resistor is to connect leads to both ends of a block or cylinder of material that is a mixture of carbon and clay. The proportions of carbon and clay determine the value of the resistor. This type of resistor is called a *carbon-composition resistor*. Another type of resistor uses a film of metal or carbon deposited onto a form. The conducting metal or carbon film is then trimmed (often into a spiral) to produce the desired resistance. These are called *metal-film* or *carbon-film resistors*. Figure 6-1 shows the construction of several resistor types.

Each resistor type has advantages and disadvantages. Wire-wound resistors, for example can get rid of more heat, and so can be made with higher power ratings than the other types. The coil-shape of the wire winding results in significant inductance. That can be quite a problem in ac circuits, especially at radio frequencies. Some advantages of carbon-composition resistors are the wide range of available values, low inductance and capacitance, good surge-handling capability and the ability to withstand small power overloads without being completely destroyed. The main disadvantage is that the resistance of the composition resistor will vary widely as the operating temperature changes and as the resistor ages. Film-type resistors are replacing carbon-composition types in many applications. It is easier to control the exact resistance during manufacture of film resistors.

As the temperature of a carbon-composition resistor changes, its resistance will change. How the resistance will change is determined by the **temperature coefficient** of the resistor. With a positive temperature coefficient, the resistance will increase as the temperature increases. With a negative coefficient, the resistance will decrease as the temperature increases. Some types of resistors have positive coefficients, and some types have negative coefficients. One thing is certain — as the temperature changes, the value of the resistor will change.

[Now turn to Chapter 12 and study question G6A01.]

CAPACITORS

In Chapter 5 we learned that the basic property of a **capacitor** is the ability to store an electric charge. In an uncharged capacitor, the potential difference between the two plates is zero. As we charge the capacitor, this potential difference increases

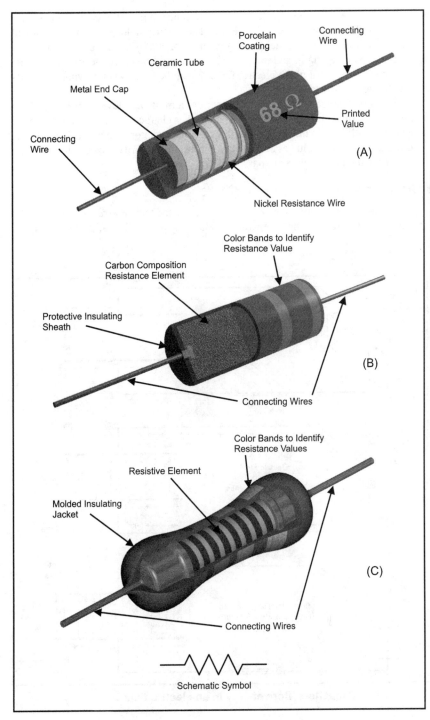

Porcelain
Coating

Connecting
Wire

Ceramic Tube

Metal End Cap

Connecting
Wire

68 Ω

Printed
Value

(A)

Nickel Resistance Wire

Color Bands to Identify
Resistance Value

Carbon Composition
Resistance Element

Protective Insulating
Sheath

(B)

Connecting Wires

Color Bands to Identify
Resistance Values

Resistive Element

Molded Insulating
Jacket

(C)

Connecting Wires

Schematic Symbol

**Figure 6-1 —
Some resistor
construction
types. Part A
shows a
simple wire-
wound
resistor. Part B
is a
composition
resistor. Part C
shows the
construction
of a film
resistor.**

until it reaches the full applied voltage. The difference in potential creates an *electric field* between the two plates. See Figure 6-2. The electric field between the plates of our capacitor is invisible — a field is an invisible force of nature. We put energy into the capacitor by charging it, and until we discharge it or the charge leaks away somehow, the energy is stored in the electric field. When the field is not moving we sometimes call it an electrostatic field.

When a dc voltage is applied to a capacitor, current will flow in the circuit until the capacitor is fully charged. After the capacitor has charged to the full dc voltage, no more current will flow in the circuit. For this reason, capacitors can be used to block dc in a circuit. Because ac voltages are constantly reversing polarity, we can block dc with a capacitor while permitting ac to pass.

Practical Capacitors

Capacitors are described by the material used for their *dielectric*, which is the insulating material used between the conducting plates. Mica, ceramic, mylar,

Figure 6-2 — Capacitors store energy in an electric field.

Figure 6-3 — Some capacitor construction types. Part A shows a mica capacitor, formed by interleaving metal foil with thin sheets of mica. Part B shows how the electrodes are deposited on both sides of a ceramic disc to form a ceramic capacitor. The construction of a plastic-film capacitor is shown in Part C. Part D shows an aluminum electrolytic capacitor and Part E shows a tantalum electrolytic capacitor.

polystyrene, and electrolytic capacitors are in common use today. They each have properties that make them more or less suitable for a particular application.

Mica capacitors consist of strips of metal foil separated by thin strips of mica. (Mica is a mineral that easily separates into thin sheets that are translucent, which means it allows light through the thin sheet, but isn't quite clear, like glass.) Alternate plates are connected, and each set of plates is connected to an electrode. The entire unit is then encased in plastic or ceramic insulating material. An alternative to this form of construction is the "silvered-mica" capacitor. In the silvered-mica type, a thin layer of silver is deposited directly onto one side of the mica, and the plates are stacked so that alternate layers of mica have a layer of silver conductor between them. Figure 6-3A illustrates the construction of a mica capacitor.

Mica has a very high voltage breakdown rating. This means the mica dielectric will withstand several thousand volts on the capacitor plates without allowing a spark to jump through the insulator. Mica capacitors are frequently used in transmitters and high power amplifiers, where the ability to withstand high voltages is important. Mica capacitors also have good temperature stability — their capacitance does not change greatly as the temperature changes. Typical capacitance values for mica capacitors range from 1 picofarad to 0.1 microfarad, and voltage ratings as high as 35,000 are possible.

Ceramic capacitors are constructed by depositing a thin metal film on each side of a ceramic disc. Wire leads are then attached to the metal films, and the entire unit is covered with a protective plastic or ceramic coating. Ceramic capacitors are inexpensive and easy to construct, and they are in wide use today. Figure 6-5B illustrates the construction of a ceramic capacitor. The range of capacitance values available with ceramic capacitors is typically 1 pF to 0.1 µF, with working voltages up to 1000.

Ordinary ceramic capacitors cannot be used where temperature stability is important — their capacitance will change with a change in temperature. Special ceramic capacitors (called NP0 for negative-positive zero) are used for these applications. The capacitance of an NP0 unit will remain substantially the same over a wide range of temperatures.

Ceramic capacitors are often connected across the transformer primary or secondary winding in a power supply. These capacitors, referred to as **suppressor capacitors**, are intended to suppress any transient voltage spikes, preventing them from getting through the power supply.

Plastic-film capacitors use mylar or polystyrene insulation between thin sheets of foil. The unit is rolled into a cylinder, and a protective outer covering is usually added. Figure 6-3C shows this construction technique. The plastic material produces capacitors with a high voltage rating in a physically small package. Plastic-film capacitors also have good temperature stability. Typical values range from 5 pF to 0.47 µF.

In *electrolytic capacitors*, the dielectric is formed after the capacitor is manufactured. The construction of *aluminum electrolytic capacitors* is similar to that of plastic-film capacitors. Two sheets of aluminum foil separated by paper soaked in a chemical solution are rolled up and placed in a protective casing. After assembly, a voltage is applied to the capacitor, causing a thin layer of aluminum oxide to form on the surface of the positive plate next to the chemical. The aluminum oxide acts as the dielectric, and the foil plates act as the electrodes.

Because of the extremely thin layer of oxide dielectric, electrolytic capacitors can be made with a very high capacitance value in a small package. Electrolytic capacitors are polarized — dc voltages must be connected to the positive and negative capacitor terminals with the correct polarity. The positive and negative electrodes in an electrolytic capacitor are clearly marked. Connecting an electrolytic capacitor incorrectly causes gas to form inside the capacitor, and the capacitor may actually explode. This can be very dangerous. At the very least the capacitor will be destroyed by connecting it incorrectly.

Tantalum capacitors are another type of electrolytic capacitor, and they have several advantages over aluminum electrolytic capacitors. Tantalum capacitors can be made even smaller than aluminum electrolytic capacitors for a given capacitance value. They are manufactured in several forms, including small, water droplet-shaped solid-electrolyte capacitors. These are formed on a small tantalum pellet that serves as the anode, or positive capacitor plate. An oxide layer on the outside of the tantalum pellet serves as the dielectric, and a layer of manganese dioxide is the solid electrolyte. Layers of carbon and silver form the cathode, or negative capacitor plate. The entire unit is dipped in epoxy to form a protective coating on the capacitor. Their characteristic shape explains why these tantalum capacitors are often called "tear drop" capacitors.

Electrolytic capacitors are available in voltage ratings of greater than 400 V, and capacitance values from 1 μF to 100,000 μF (0.1 F). Electrolytic capacitors are used in power-supply filters, where large values of capacitance are necessary for good smoothing of the pulsating dc from the rectifier.

[Turn to Chapter 12 now and study questions G6A02 and G6A03. Review this material as necessary.]

INDUCTORS

Just as a capacitor stores energy in an electric field, an inductor stores energy in a magnetic field. Remember from Chapter 5 that inductors oppose any change in current. When a dc voltage is applied across an inductor, there is no current at first. A voltage is induced in the coil that opposes the applied voltage, and tries to prevent a current. Gradually the current will build up to a value that is limited only by any resistance in the circuit (the resistance in the wire of the coil will be very small). In the process of getting this current to flow, energy is stored in the coil in the form of a magnetic field around the wire. While the current is increasing and the magnetic field strength is also increasing, a voltage forms that opposes the changing current. When the current reaches a steady value the inductor no longer opposes the current. An inductor passes direct current with no opposition.

When the applied voltage is shut off, the magnetic field collapses and returns the stored energy to the circuit as a current flowing in the same direction as the original current. This current is produced by the EMF generated by the collapsing magnetic field. Again, this voltage opposes any change in the current already flowing in the coil. The amount of opposition to changes in current, called reactance, depends on the inductance of the coil.

If an alternating voltage is applied across the inductor, energy is stored in the magnetic field as the voltage increases. That energy is returned to the circuit as the voltage decreases to zero. As the voltage reverses direction, the direction of the magnetic field also reverses (the North and South poles reverse positions) and energy is stored again. Then as the voltage decreases to zero again the magnetic field returns the energy to the circuit again. An inductor continually opposes alternating current. The higher the frequency of the applied voltage, the greater is the inductor's opposition to this current. (This opposition is called *reactance*.) Inductors can be used to pass direct current and block alternating current. Inductors and capacitors are helpful in directing ac and dc to various parts of a circuit, so the proper type of signal reaches the appropriate circuit sections.

TRANSFORMERS

When coils are positioned close to each other, so the magnetic field of one coil goes through another coil, we say the coils have *mutual inductance*. A changing current in one coil can induce a voltage in the other. Therefore, two coils having mutual inductance form a **transformer**. The coil connected to the source of energy is called the **primary winding**, and the coil connected to the load is called the **secondary winding**. See Figure 6-4.

With a transformer, electrical energy can be transferred from one circuit to another without direct connection. In the process, the signal voltage can be readily changed from one level to another. Common house current is 120 V ac. If you need 240 V ac, you would use a transformer that has twice as many turns on the secondary coil as it does on its primary coil. The induced voltage in the secondary would then be double the primary voltage, or 240 V. A transformer can only be used with alternating current, because no voltages will be induced in the secondary if the magnetic field is not changing.

The primary and secondary coils of a transformer may be wound on a *core* of a magnetic material, such as iron. This increases the coupling of the coils so that practically all of the field set up by the current in the primary coil will cut the turns of the secondary coil. A small amount of current, called the **magnetizing current**, flows in a transformer primary winding, even with no load connected to the secondary. This magnetizing current is necessary to overcome losses in the iron core and the resistance of the primary winding. The magnetizing current represents energy lost in the transformer.

Transformers have power ratings, just as other components do. Usually, the primary and secondary voltages are specified, along with the maximum current that can be drawn from the secondary winding. Sometimes the secondary voltage and current are combined into a "volt-ampere" (VA) rating. A transformer with a 12-V, 1.5-A secondary would have a volt-ampere rating of 18 VA.

[At this point, you should turn to Chapter 12 and study questions G6A04 and G6A05. Review this section if you have any difficulty with those questions.]

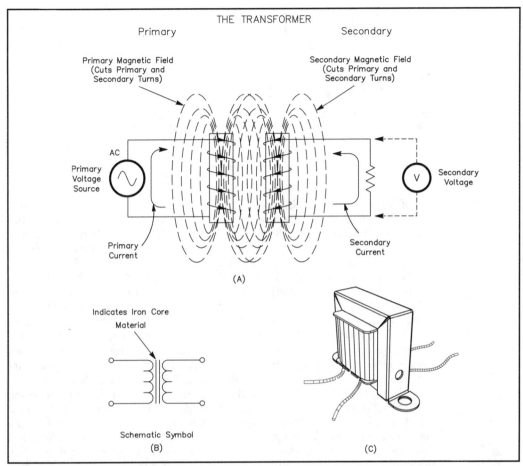

Figure 6-4 — Part A illustrates the operation of a transformer. Part B shows the schematic symbol used to represent an iron-core transformer. Part C shows what a typical small transformer might look like.

DIODES

Semiconductor material exhibits properties of both metallic and nonmetallic substances. Generally, the layers of semiconductor material are made from germanium or silicon. To control the conductive properties of the material, impurities are added as the semiconductor crystal is "grown." This process is called doping. If a material with an excess of free electrons is added to the structure, N-type material is produced. This type of material is sometimes referred to as *donor material*. When an impurity that results in an absence of electrons is introduced into the crystal structure, you get P-type material. The result in this case is a material with positive charge carriers, called holes. P-type material is also called *acceptor material*.

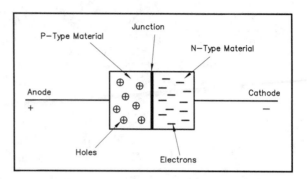

Figure 6-5 — A PN junction consists of P-type and N-type material separated by a barrier.

The **junction diode**, also called the PN-junction diode, is made from two layers of semiconductor material joined together. One layer is made from P-type material and the other layer is made from N-type material. The name PN junction comes from the way the P and N layers are joined to form a semiconductor diode. Figure 6-5 illustrates the basic concept of a junction diode.

The P-type side of the diode is called the *anode*, while the N-type side is called the *cathode*. (The anode connects to the positive supply lead and the cathode connects to the negative supply lead.) Current flows from the cathode to the anode. The excess electrons from the N-type material flow to the P-type material, which has holes (an electron deficiency). Electrons and holes are called charge carriers because they carry current from one side of the junction to the other. When no voltage is applied to a diode, the junction between the N-type and P-type material acts as a barrier that prevents carriers from flowing between the layers.

When voltage is applied to a junction diode as shown at A in Figure 6-6, however, carriers will flow across the barrier and the diode will conduct (electrons will flow through it). When the diode anode is positive with respect to the cathode, electrons are attracted across the barrier from the N-type material, through the P-type material and onto the positive battery terminal. As the electrons move through the P-type material, they fill some holes and leave other holes behind as they move, so the holes appear to move in the opposite direction, toward the negative battery terminal. When the diode is connected in this manner it is said to be *forward biased*.

If the battery polarity is reversed, as shown in Figure 6-6B, the excess electrons in the N-type material are attracted away from the junction by the positive battery terminal. Electrons in the P-type material are forced toward the junction by the negative charge from the battery, and the electrons leave holes that appear to move toward the negative battery terminal. Because there are no holes in the N-type material to accept electrons, no conduction takes place across the junction. When the anode is connected to a negative voltage source and the cathode is connected to a positive source, the diode does not conduct, and it is said to be *reverse biased*.

Junction diodes are used as rectifiers because they allow current to flow in one direction only. (We will discuss rectifier circuits in Chapter 7.) When an ac signal is applied to a diode, the diode will be forward biased during one half of the cycle, so it will conduct, and current will flow to the load. During the other half of the cycle, the diode is reverse biased, and there is no current. The diode output is pulsed dc, and the current always flows in the same direction.

Figure 6-6 — At A, the PN junction is forward biased and is conducting. At B, the junction is reversed biased and it does not conduct.

Diode Ratings

Junction diodes have maximum voltage and current ratings that must be observed, or damage to the junction will result. The voltage rating is called the **peak inverse voltage (PIV)** and the current rating is called the **maximum average forward current**. PIV is sometimes called reverse breakdown voltage or peak reverse voltage (PRV). With present technology, diodes are commonly available with ratings up to 1000 PIV and 100 A forward current.

Peak inverse voltage is the voltage a diode must withstand when it isn't conducting. Although a diode is normally used in the forward direction, it will conduct in the reverse direction if enough voltage is applied. A few hole/electron pairs are thermally generated at the junction when a diode is reverse biased. These pairs cause a very small reverse current, called leakage current. Semiconductor diodes can withstand some leakage current, but if the inverse voltage reaches a high enough value the leakage current will rise abruptly, resulting in a heavy reverse current. The point at which the leakage current rises abruptly is called the *avalanche point*. A large reverse current usually damages or destroys the diode.

The maximum average forward current is the highest average current that can flow through the diode in the forward direction for a specified junction temperature. This specification varies from device to device, and it depends on the maximum allowable junction temperature and on the amount of heat the device can dissipate. As the forward current increases, the junction temperature will increase. If the diode is allowed to get too hot, it will be destroyed.

Impurities at the PN junction cause some resistance to current. This resistance results in a voltage drop across the junction. For silicon diodes, this drop is approximately 0.6 to 0.7 V; for germanium diodes, the drop is 0.2 to 0.3 V. When current flows through the junction, some power is dissipated in the form of heat. The amount of power dissipated depends on the current through the diode. For example, it

Figure 6-7 — The schematic symbol for a diode is shown at A. Diodes are typically packaged in one of the case styles shown at B.

would be approximately 6 W for a silicon rectifier with 10 A flowing through it:

$$P = I \times E \hspace{3cm} \text{(Equation 6-1)}$$

$$P = 10 \text{ A} \times 0.6 \text{ V} = 6 \text{ W}$$

If the junction temperature exceeds the safe level specified by the manufacturer, the diode is likely to be damaged or destroyed.

Diodes designed to safely handle forward currents in excess of 6 A generally are packaged so they may be mounted on a heat sink. These diodes are often referred to as stud-mount devices, because they are made with a threaded screw attached to the body of the device. This screw is attached to the heat sink so that the heat from the device will be effectively transferred to the heat sink. The heat sink helps the diode package dissipate heat more rapidly, thereby keeping the junction temperature at a safe level. The metal case of a stud-mount diode is usually one of the contact points, so it must be insulated from ground.

Figure 6-7 shows some of the more common diode-case styles, and the general schematic symbol for a diode. The line or spot on a diode case indicates the cathode lead. On a high-power stud-mount diode, the stud may either be the anode or the cathode. Check the case or the manufacturer's data sheet for the correct polarity.

[Before proceeding to Chapter 7, turn to Chapter 12 and study questions G6A06 and G6A07. Review this section as needed. The remaining questions in the G6A section will be covered by material in Chapter 7.]

Balanced modulator — A mixer circuit that combines an audio input signal with a carrier-oscillator signal. The output signal contains the two sidebands produced by this mixing, but does not include the original carrier-oscillator signal or the pure audio signal. A modulated RF signal contains some information to be transmitted.

Band-pass filter — A circuit that allows signals to go through it only if they are within a certain range of frequencies, and attenuates signals above and below this range.

Bleeder resistor — A large-value resistor connected to the filter capacitor in a power supply to discharge the filter capacitors when the supply is switched off.

Detector — A mixer circuit used to recover the information signal from a modulated RF signal.

Filter — A circuit that will allow some signals to pass through it but will greatly reduce the strength of others. In a power-supply circuit, a filter smoothes the ac ripple.

Full-wave bridge rectifier — A full-wave rectifier circuit that uses four diodes and does not require a center-tapped transformer.

Full-wave rectifier — A circuit basically composed of two half-wave rectifiers. The full wave rectifier allows the full ac waveform to pass through; one half of the cycle is reversed in polarity. This circuit requires a center-tapped transformer.

Half-wave rectifier — A circuit that allows only half of the applied ac waveform to pass through it.

High-pass filter — A filter that allows signals above the cutoff frequency to pass through, and attenuates signals below the cutoff frequency.

Local oscillator (LO) — A receiver circuit that generates a stable, pure signal used to mix with the received RF to produce a signal at the receiver intermediate frequency (IF).

Low-pass filter — A filter that allows signals below the cutoff frequency to pass through and attenuates signals above the cutoff frequency.

Mixer — A circuit that takes two or more input signals, and produces an output that is the sum or difference of those signal frequencies.

Power supply — A device used to convert the available voltage and current source (often the 120-V ac household supply) to a form that is required for a specific circuit requirement. This will often be a higher or lower dc voltage.

Pulsating dc — The output from a rectifier before it is filtered. The polarity of a pulsating dc source does not change, but the amplitude of the voltage changes with time.

Rectifier — An electronic component that allows current to pass through it in only one direction.

Ripple — The amount of change between the maximum voltage and the minimum voltage in a pulsating dc waveform.

Single-sideband, suppressed-carrier signal — A radio signal in which only one of the two sidebands generated by amplitude modulation is transmitted. The other sideband and the RF carrier signal are removed before the signal is transmitted.

Superheterodyne receiver — A receiver that converts RF signals to an intermediate frequency before detecting them (converting the signals to audio).

PRACTICAL CIRCUITS

Now that you have studied some basic electrical principles, and have learned about the properties of some simple components, you are ready to learn how to apply those ideas to practical Amateur Radio circuits. This chapter will lead you through examples and explanations to help you gain that knowledge.

In this chapter, we will look at how power supplies operate, and we will discuss band-pass, high-pass and low-pass filter circuits. You will be directed to turn to Chapter 12 at appropriate points, and to use the General question pool as a study aid to review your understanding of the material.

Keep in mind that there have been entire books written on each topic covered in this chapter. If you do not understand some of the circuits from our brief discussion, it would be a good idea to consult some other reference books. ARRL's *Understanding Basic Electronics* is a good starting point. *The ARRL Handbook for Radio Amateurs* contains much more detailed information, but even that won't tell you everything about a topic. The discussion in this chapter will help you understand the circuits well enough to pass your General license exam, however. There will be one question from the practical circuits subelement. The syllabus point for that topic is:

G7A Power supplies and filters; single-sideband transmitters and receivers.

POWER SUPPLIES

One circuit that is common to just about every type of radio circuit is the **power supply**. The 120 V ac available at your wall outlet isn't exactly what we mean by a power supply. The current at the outlet is an alternating current, and most electronic components require direct current. Additionally, circuits may require voltage levels other than the 120 V available at the wall outlet. A power supply is used to increase or decrease the value of the voltage and to convert ac to dc.

An ac power supply consists of three sections: the transformer, the diode **rectifier** and the **filter**. A power transformer is used to raise or lower the voltage. It transforms the input-voltage level (120 or 240 V) to the level required by the equipment. Power transformers normally operate at 60 hertz, the household-current frequency.

Many power transformers have multiple secondary windings to provide several different output voltages. The power transformer used in a vacuum-tube amateur transmitter or amplifier might have three secondaries: one delivering 6.3 V for the tube filaments, one 12-V winding for the solid-state circuits and one supplying high voltage for the plates of the final-amplifier tubes.

Rectifiers

The diode rectifier section of a power supply converts ac to dc. (Remember that diodes conduct only in one direction.) Figures 7-1 and 7-2 show several common rectifier circuits. Let's examine the operation of the simplest type, the **half-wave rectifier**.

To understand diode-rectifier action, we'll consider a diode connected to a secondary winding of a power transformer, as shown in Figure 7-1A. During half of the ac cycle, the applied voltage makes the anode positive with respect to the cathode. The diode is *forward biased* and will conduct during this half cycle. Current flows through the diode and any load attached to the rectifier output. The current passing through the load will vary with time, because the diode allows current to pass only during one half of the cycle. During the other half of the cycle, the anode is not positive with respect to the cathode, so no current passes through the diode. In this case the diode is *reverse biased*. The action of the diode in permitting the current to flow only in one direction is called *rectification*.

The output of the rectifier is also shown in Figure 7-1A. The half-wave rectifier circuit takes its name from the fact that only half the ac wave passes through the circuit. One complete cycle of an ac wave goes from zero to 360° and the half-wave rectifier uses only 180° (one half) of the wave. The half-wave rectifier conducts during 180° of each cycle. There is one output pulse for every complete cycle of the input voltage. The output waveform of a half-wave rectifier has a frequency equal to the ac input waveform.

If another diode is connected to the opposite end of the transformer secondary, the second diode will conduct during the portions of the ac cycle that the first diode cannot. A connection (called a center tap) is made in the center of the transformer winding and connected through the load to the cathodes of the diodes. The rectifier circuit that has diodes working on both halves of the cycle is called a **full-wave rectifier**. This particular full-wave rectifier is known as a *full-wave, center-tap*

Figure 7-1 — Fundamental rectifier circuits are shown. (A) Half-wave.
(B) Full-wave center-tap. These rectifier circuits are discussed in the text.

rectifier. The advantage of the full-wave rectifier can be seen from the output waveform in Figure 7-1B — output is produced during the entire 360° of the ac cycle.

There are two output pulses for every full cycle of the input voltage. This means the output waveform from a full-wave rectifier has a frequency equal to twice the ac input frequency.

A third type of rectifier circuit is the **full-wave bridge rectifier** shown in Figure 7-2. The output current or voltage waveshape is the same as for the full-wave center-tap rectifier. The important difference is in the output voltage from the rectifier compared to the transformer-secondary output voltage. In the center-tap circuit, each side of the center-tapped secondary must develop a peak voltage high enough to supply the desired dc output voltage, so the total transformer peak output voltage must be twice the power-supply output voltage (for a 6.3-V rectifier output we must use a center-tapped transformer with a peak output of 12.6 volts). In the bridge circuit, no center tap is necessary — we can get 12.6-V output from a 12.6-V transformer. We can't get something for nothing, however — the elimination of the center tap requires the use of two additional rectifiers in the bridge-rectifier circuit. The bridge is another full-wave rectifier, and it uses the full 360° of the ac wave.

In the bridge circuit, two rectifiers are connected to the transformer secondary in the same way as the two rectifiers in the center-tap circuit shown in Figure 7-1B. The second pair of rectifiers is also connected in series between the ends of the

$E_{PEAK} = 1.4\ E_{RMS}$
$E_{AVG} = 0.9\ E_{RMS}$
$E_{PIV} = 1.4\ E_{RMS}$
$Ripple = 48\%/120\ Hz$

Figure 7-2 — The operation of a full-wave, bridge-rectifier circuit is shown. The basic circuit is illustrated at A. Diodes D_1 and D_3 conduct on one-half of the input cycle, while diodes D_2 and D_4 conduct on the other half. The nonconducting diodes have the full transformer output voltage across them in the reverse direction.

transformer winding, but in reverse. See Figure 7-2. When the upper end of the transformer secondary is positive, Diode D_1 conducts. The current then flows through the load and back to D_3, which also conducts. This completes the circuit from one side of the transformer, through the load and back to the other side of the transformer. Diodes D_2 and D_4 are reverse biased during this time, so they do not conduct. During the second half of the ac cycle, diodes D_2 and D_4 are forward biased so they conduct. Diodes D_1 and D_3 are reverse biased, so they do not conduct.

Diode Ratings

Remember that diodes are rated with regard to their current-handling capability and the maximum voltage that may be applied in the reverse direction. These ratings must not be exceeded. For example, when one diode in a bridge rectifier is conducting, the two diodes connected to it are not. These diodes must each withstand the full transformer secondary voltage in the reverse direction. Since the peak value of the voltage is 1.41 times the RMS value, the diodes must withstand a peak inverse voltage (PIV) of 1.41 times the RMS value of the transformer secondary. A safe design practice is to use diodes rated for at least twice the transformer output voltage.

A full-wave center-tap rectifier has the full transformer output voltage across the reverse-biased diode. The diodes must be able to withstand a PIV equal to twice the peak output voltage. (The output voltage is only half the full transformer voltage because of the center-tapped transformer. See Figure 7-1B.) It is also a good design practice to select diodes with a peak inverse voltage rating (PIV) of two or more times the normal peak output voltage of the supply for full-wave rectifier circuits.

The diode in a half-wave rectifier circuit must withstand the full transformer peak output voltage. It is good design practice to select a diode with a PIV rating of one to two times the normal peak output voltage of the supply.

In full-wave rectifier circuits, each diode carries one-half the average output current, so the diodes must be rated to pass at least this much current without becoming too warm. Using diodes able to handle the full average current (instead of half) is a safer design practice. In addition, when a capacitor-input filter is used, the capacitor appears as a dead short to the rectifier when the supply is first switched on. This means that the diodes may pass as much as 10 to 100 times the average current in one brief burst. The diodes used with a capacitor-input filter must be able to handle this surge current.

Diodes in Series and Parallel

Suppose we're building a power supply, and we need rectifiers rated at 1000 PIV, but we only have 500-PIV diodes on hand. How can we use the 500-PIV diodes? If we connect two 500-PIV diodes in series, the pair will withstand 1000 PIV ($2 \times 500 = 1000$). With modern silicon rectifier diodes, you can safely wire them in series to increase the effective PIV rating.

Diodes can also be placed in parallel to increase total forward current-handling capability. When diodes are in parallel, a resistor should be placed in series with each diode to ensure that each takes the same

Figure 7-3 — Use equalizing resistors when connecting diodes in parallel to increase the forward current-handling capability. The resistor value should be selected to provide a few tenths of a volt drop at the expected forward current.

current. This is illustrated in Figure 7-3. Without a resistor in series with each diode, one diode may take most of the current, and that could destroy the diode. The resistor value should be chosen to provide a few tenths of a volt drop at the expected forward current. Be sure to select resistors with sufficient power rating.

[Turn to Chapter 12 now and study questions G6A09 through G6A11. Also study questions G7A04 and G7A05. Review this section if you have trouble with any of these questions.]

Power-Supply Filters

The output from a rectifier is not like dc from a battery. It's neither pure nor constant. It's actually what's known as **pulsating dc** — flowing only in one direction but not at a steady value. Figure 7-4A shows a full-wave rectifier connected to a resistive load. The output waveform is a series of pulses at twice the frequency of the ac input, because there are two output pulses for every ac cycle. Using this type of current as a replacement for a battery in a transmitter or receiver would introduce a strong hum on all signals. To smooth out the pulsations (called **ripple**) and eliminate the hum and its effects, a **filter** is used between the rectifier and the load.

Figure 7-4 — The circuit shown at A is a simple full-wave rectifier with a resistive load. The waveform shown to the right shows the output voltage and diode current for this circuit. B illustrates how diode current and output voltage change with the addition of a capacitor filter. The diodes conduct only when the rectified voltage is greater than the voltage stored in the capacitor. Since this time is usually only a short portion of a cycle, the peak current through each diode will be quite high.

Figure 7-5 — Shown at A is a choke-input power-supply filter circuit. B shows a capacitor-input, multisection filter.

The simplest type of filter is a large-value capacitor across a load (Figure 7-4B). If the capacitance is high enough and the current drawn by the load is not excessive, the capacitor will charge during voltage peaks. The *filter capacitor* discharges as the pulse decreases, smoothing out the ripple. During the peaks in the pulsating dc waveform, the capacitor stores energy. As the value of the dc waveform decreases, the capacitor releases some of its energy, and supplies current to the load. This cycle occurs over and over, resulting in a smooth dc output waveform, with minimum ripple.

We can design a more effective filter if we place an inductor, or *filter choke*, between the rectifier and the load, as shown in Figure 7-5A. The series inductor opposes changes in the circuit current the way the capacitor opposes changes in circuit voltage. We can connect several series-choke/parallel-capacitor sections one after another to improve the filtering action even more. The two basic filters are called *choke-input filters* and *capacitor-input filters*, depending on which component comes immediately after the rectifier. A capacitor-input multisection filter is shown in Figure 7-5B. In either case, capacitors and inductors are used to form the power-supply filter network.

The Bleeder Resistor

It's a good design practice to connect a high-value resistor across the filter capacitor in a power supply, as shown in Figure 7-6. Such a resistor, called a **bleeder resistor**, is used to discharge the capacitor when the power-supply primary voltage is

Figure 7-6 — A bleeder resistor connected to the output of a power supply will discharge the filter capacitor(s) when the supply is switched off.

turned off. It drains the charge from the capacitors and decreases the chances for accidental electrical shock when the power supply is turned off.

[Turn to Chapter 12 now and study question G6A08 and questions G7A01 through G7A03. Review this section as needed.]

FILTERS

We've already discussed one type of filter used in Amateur Radio: the power-supply filter. You should also be familiar with three others: the low-pass filter, the high-pass filter and the band-pass filter.

A **low-pass filter** is one that passes all frequencies below a certain frequency, called the *cutoff frequency*. Frequencies above the cutoff frequency are *attenuated*, or significantly reduced in amplitude. See Figure 7-7A. The cutoff frequency depends on the design of the low-pass filter. One common use for a low-pass filter in an amateur station is to connect one between the transmitter and the antenna, preferably as close to the transmitter as possible. It is important that the filter have the same source and load impedance as the feed line into which it is inserted. This ensures that the filter won't introduce an impedance mismatch that could increase the SWR on the feed line.

The low-pass filter cutoff frequency has to be higher than the highest frequency used for transmitting. A filter with a 45-MHz cutoff frequency would be fine for the "low bands" (1.8 through 29.7 MHz), but the filter would significantly attenuate 6-meter (50 MHz) signals.

A **high-pass filter** passes all frequencies above the cutoff frequency, and attenuates those below it. See Figure 7-7B. A high-pass filter is often connected to a television set, stereo receiver or other home-entertainment device that is receiving interference. The filter will attenuate the lower-frequency signals from an amateur HF station while allowing the higher-frequency television or FM broadcast signals to pass through to the receiver. This is useful in reducing the amount of lower-frequency radiation (at the ham's operating frequency) that might overload a television set, causing disruption of reception. For best effect, the filter should be connected as close to the television set's tuner as possible — inside the TV if it is your own set and you don't mind opening it up, or directly to the antenna terminals on the back of the television. If the set belongs to your neighbors, have them contact a qualified service technician to install the filter, so you are not blamed if something goes wrong with the set later on. Again, it is important that the filter have the same source and load impedance as the feed line into which it is inserted.

A **band-pass filter** is a combination of a high-pass and low-pass filter. It passes a desired range of frequencies while rejecting signals above and below the pass-band. This is shown in Figure 7-7C. Band-pass filters are commonly used in receivers to provide different degrees of rejection — very narrow filters are used for CW reception, wider filters for single-sideband voice (SSB) and AM double-side-band reception.

[Now it is time to turn to Chapter 12 again. Study question G7A06. Review the material in this section if needed.]

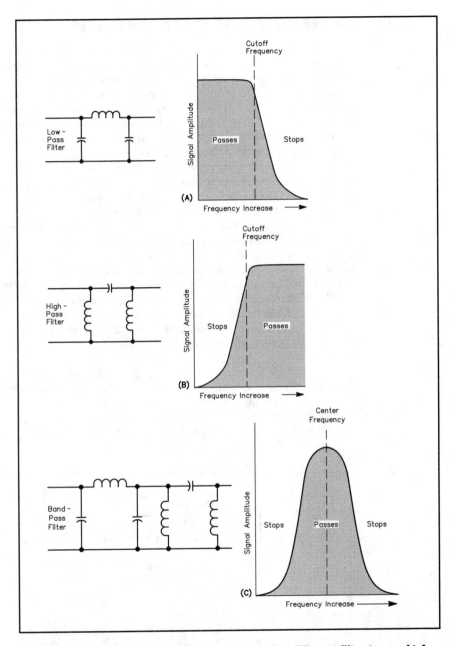

Figure 7-7 — Output-versus-frequency curves for different filter types. At A, the low-pass filter passes signals below the cutoff frequency, and attenuates signals above the cutoff. At B, the high-pass filter attenuates only those signals below the cutoff. The band-pass filter has a response curve like (C), and passes only those signals within the passband.

SINGLE-SIDEBAND VOICE TRANSMITTERS

When you speak into the microphone of your single-sideband voice transmitter, the magic of radio converts your voice to radio signals. These radio signals come out of the transmitter and travel to the antenna. Then they radiate off into the air as they make their way to who knows where. This process of changing your voice into a radio signal is not as complicated as it may seem. Figure 7-8 shows the block diagram of a basic transmitter that produces a **single-sideband, suppressed-carrier signal**. When we refer to this type of signal, we usually abbreviate it to single sideband, or SSB. You can compare this type of signal to those used by stations on the AM, Standard Broadcast band. There the transmitters use *double-sideband, full-carrier signals*. From the names, you can tell that SSB is just a standard AM signal with one sideband and the carrier removed. Let's follow the signals as they move through the various stages in our SSB transmitter.

When you speak, your vocal chords cause air molecules to vibrate. The vibrating air molecules bump into the microphone, which changes the air-pressure variations of your voice into a changing electrical signal. This electrical signal is usually quite weak, so it is normally amplified before being passed on to the **balanced modulator**. The balanced modulator has a second input, this one from the carrier oscillator. The carrier oscillator produces a signal at the intermediate frequency, or IF of the transmitter circuit. The system shown in Figure 7-8 uses two crystals to switch the carrier-oscillator frequency to select the upper sideband or the lower sideband. It is also possible to use a single-frequency oscillator and switch band-pass filters.

The balanced modulator processes signals from the speech amplifier and the carrier oscillator, and sends them on to a band-pass filter. The modulator is a mixer stage, which adds the two input signals and passes the sum along to the output. It also subtracts the audio from the carrier, and passes that difference along to the output. Because the modulator is *balanced*, however, it does not pass either the

Figure 7-8 — This block diagram shows a basic single-sideband, suppressed-carrier (SSB) transmitter. The text explains the operation of the various stages in this circuit.

audio or the carrier signals to the output. The balanced modulator takes two input signals and produces two different output signals. The output signals are the two *sidebands*, but the carrier is suppressed.

The next stage of our transmitter completes the process of generating an SSB signal by removing one of the sidebands. This is the job of the band-pass filter. The filter must have a bandwidth that is narrow enough to pass one of the sidebands but reject the opposite one. After the band-pass filter there is often an amplifier stage to boost the strength of the signal before it is processed further.

Next is the **mixer** stage, which is similar to the balanced modulator. The mixer has two inputs and one output. The second input is from the RF heterodyne oscillator, which is set to a frequency that will add to or subtract from the signal coming from the modulator, to produce an output at the desired transmit frequency.

The output signal from the mixer is ready to be transmitted. The signal is often amplified by one or more amplifier stages before it is passed to the antenna and transmitted. In most transmitters, the modulation and mixing processes are carried out at low power levels. Any amplifier stages after the balanced modulator must be linear, so the signal does not become distorted.

[Turn to Chapter 12 now and study questions G7A07 and G7A08. Review this section if you do not understand either of those questions.]

SINGLE-SIDEBAND VOICE RECEIVERS

An SSB receiver reverses the processes carried out in the transmitter. The received radio signal is processed, and the speaker reproduces the air-molecule vibrations necessary to recreate the sound of the transmitting operator's voice. Figure 7-9 illustrates the primary stages of a **superheterodyne receiver** suitable for SSB reception.

The received signal coming in from the antenna is usually quite weak. Many

Figure 7-9 — This block diagram shows a simple superheterodyne SSB receiver. The operation of the various stages is explained in the text.

receivers have an amplifier stage before any further signal processing takes place. There may be one or more resonant networks at the input also. This is a tuned circuit used to select the range of frequencies that the receiver will process. If the receiver is to cover more than one band, it will have a bandswitch to select the proper tuned circuits for the desired operating band.

The mixer stage has two inputs and one output, just like the modulator and mixer in our transmitter circuit. The first input signal comes from the input filter and RF amplifier stage just discussed. The second input for the receive mixer is from the **local oscillator**, which generates a signal to mix with the received signal to produce an output at the receiver intermediate frequency (IF). The LO frequency is variable, so this oscillator is often called a variable-frequency oscillator, or VFO. As the frequency changes different RF signals are converted to the IF. This frequency-conversion technique allows the IF stages to operate over a relatively narrow frequency range. The IF filters can be designed to provide a high degree of selectivity without the need to adjust the filter operating frequency.

The IF filter sets the overall receiver selectivity. Many receivers use several selectable filters for different modes. A narrow filter provides the needed selectivity for CW and RTTY reception, and a 2.4-kHz filter for SSB operation. After filtering, there are usually one or more stages of amplification before the signal is passed on to the product **detector**. This amplifier operates at the intermediate frequency (IF) so it is usually called the IF amplifier.

The detector is another mixer stage, so it has two inputs and one output. The first input is from the IF amplifier. The second input this time is from the *beat-frequency oscillator*, or *BFO*. Notice that like the transmitter carrier oscillator, the BFO can change frequency to select either the upper sideband or the lower sideband for reception. The IF and BFO signals mix in the detector, giving an output signal that matches the original transmitted audio. After one or more amplification stages, this audio signal is ready to be fed to a speaker or headphones, where the electrical signals produce variations in air pressure again, creating sound.

[This completes the material for Chapter 7. Now turn to Chapter 12 and study questions G7A09 through G7A11. Review this section as needed before proceeding to Chapter 8.]

CHAPTER 8 KEYWORDS KEYWORDS KEYWORDS

Amplitude modulation (AM) — A method of combining an information signal and an RF carrier wave in which the amplitude of the RF envelope (carrier and sidebands) is varied in relation to the information signal strength.

Audio-frequency shift keying (AFSK) — A method of transmitting radioteletype information by switching between two audio tones fed into an FM transmitter microphone input. This is the RTTY mode most often used on VHF and UHF.

Balanced modulator — A circuit used in a single-sideband suppressed-carrier transmitter to combine a voice signal and the RF signal. The balanced modulator isolates the input signals from each other and the output, so that only the difference of the two input signals reaches the output.

Bandwidth — The frequency range (measured in hertz) over which a signal is stronger than some specified amount below the peak signal level. For example, if a certain signal is at least half as strong as the peak power level over a range of +3 kHz, the signal has a 3-dB bandwidth of 6 kHz.

Deviation ratio — The ratio between the maximum change in RF-carrier frequency and the highest modulating frequency used in an FM transmitter.

Flattopping — A distorted audio signal produced by an SSB transmitter with the microphone gain set too high. The peaks of the voice waveform are cut off in the transmitter because of overmodulation. Also called *clipping*.

Frequency deviation — The amount the carrier frequency in an FM transmitter changes as it is modulated.

Frequency modulation (FM) — The process of varying the frequency of an RF carrier in response to the instantaneous changes in an audible signal.

Frequency-shift keying (FSK) — A method of transmitting radioteletype information by switching an RF carrier between two separate frequencies. This is the RTTY mode most often used on HF.

Image response — A form of interference to received signals that is produced when a mixer responds to a signal frequency equal to the LO – the IF when the desired signal frequency is equal to the LO + the IF. Also when the mixer responds to a signal frequency equal to the LO + IF when the desired signal frequency is the LO – IF.

Mixer — A circuit that takes two or more input signals, and produces an output that includes the sum and difference of those signal frequencies.

Modulation — The process of varying some characteristic (amplitude, frequency or phase) of an RF carrier for the purpose of conveying information.

Modulation Index — The ratio between the maximum carrier frequency deviation and the audio modulating frequency at a given instant in an FM transmitter.

Peak envelope power (PEP) — The average power of the RF cycle having the greatest amplitude. (This occurs during a modulation peak.)

Phase — The time interval between one event and another in a regularly recurring cycle.

Phase modulation — Varying the phase of an RF carrier in response to the instantaneous changes in an audio signal.

Reactance modulator — An electronic circuit whose capacitance or inductance changes in response to an audio input signal.

RF envelope — The shape of an RF signal as viewed on an oscilloscope.

Sideband — The sum or difference frequencies generated when an RF carrier is mixed with an audio signal.

Single-sideband, suppressed-carrier, amplitude modulation (SSB) — A technique used to transmit voice information in which the amplitude of the RF carrier is modulated by the audio input, and the carrier and one sideband are suppressed.

Splatter — Interference to adjacent signals caused by overmodulation of a transmitter.

Varactor diode — A component whose capacitance varies as the reverse bias voltage is changed.

SIGNALS AND EMISSIONS

One of the most exciting aspects of Amateur Radio is that it offers so many different ways to participate. This chapter will introduce the modes and emission types you will need to understand for your General exam. There will be two questions from this subelement on your exam, and these will come from two groups of questions:

G8A Signal information; AM; FM; single and double sideband and carrier; bandwidth; modulation envelope; deviation; overmodulation
G8B Frequency mixing; multiplication; bandwidths; HF data communications

SIGNAL QUALITY

The quality of the signal your station produces reflects on you! As a radio amateur and control operator, you are responsible (legally and otherwise) for all the signals emanating from your station. Your signals are the only way an amateur on the other side of the country or the world will get to know you.

Communication is the transfer of information from one place to another. We can derive information from a radio signal just by its presence and its strength, as in the case of a beacon. By switching the signal on and off in some prescribed manner we can transmit more information. Finally, we can modify the signal in other ways to convey still more information. An important consideration *and* limitation, however, is the amount of space in the radio-frequency spectrum that a signal occupies. This space is called **bandwidth**. The bandwidth of a transmission is determined by the information rate. Thus, a pure, continuous, unmodulated carrier has a very small bandwidth, while a television transmission, which contains a great deal of information, is several megahertz wide.

MODULATION

Modulation is the process of varying some characteristic (amplitude, frequency or phase) of a radio frequency (RF) wave in accordance with the instantaneous variations of some external signal, for the purpose of conveying information. Almost every amateur will think of phone transmission when the word modulation is mentioned. The subject of modulation, however, is much broader than that. The principles are the same whether the radio transmission is modulated by speech, audio tones or the on-off keying that modulates a CW transmitter with Morse code.

The sound of your voice consists of physical vibrations in the air, called sound waves. The range of audio frequencies (AF) generated by a person's voice may be quite large; the normal range of human hearing is from 20 to 20,000 Hz. All the information necessary to make your voice understood, however, is contained in a narrower band of frequencies. In amateur communications, your audio signals are usually filtered so that only frequencies between about 300 and 3000 Hz are transmitted. This filtering is done to reduce the bandwidth of the phone signal.

Amplitude Modulation

Amplitude modulation is a method of combining an information signal and an RF carrier so the amplitude of the **RF envelope** (carrier and sidebands) varies in relation to the information signal strength. An amplitude modulation (AM) system changes the amplitude of an RF wave for the purpose of conveying information. For phone transmissions, the audio (information) signal is constantly changing in frequency and amplitude, or strength. The instantaneous amplitude of the RF signal envelope varies in accordance with the modulating audio.

On the high-frequency amateur bands, **single-sideband, suppressed-carrier, amplitude modulation** (usually called **SSB**) is the most widely used radiotelephone mode. Since SSB is a sophisticated form of amplitude modulation, it is worthwhile to take a look at some fundamentals of amplitude modulation.

Modulation is a mixing process. When RF and AF signals combine in a standard double-sideband, full-carrier, AM transmitter (such as one used for commercial broadcasting) four output signals are produced: the original RF signal, the original AF signal, and two **sidebands**, whose frequencies are the sum and difference of the original RF and AF signals. See Figure 8-1. The amplitude of the sidebands varies with the amplitude of the audio signal.

For higher-frequency modulating tones, the sideband frequencies will be further from the carrier frequency, and for lower-frequency tones the sideband will be closer to the carrier frequency. The sum component is called the upper sideband, and increasing the frequency of the modulating audio causes a corresponding increase in the frequency of the RF output signal. The difference frequency is called the lower sideband, and is inverted, meaning that an increase in the frequency of the modulating AF causes a decrease in the frequency of the output signal. The amplitude and frequency of the carrier are unchanged by the modulation process. The resulting RF envelope, as viewed on an oscilloscope, has the shape of the modulating waveform, as Figure 8-2 shows. The modulating waveform is mirrored above and below the zero axis of the RF envelope.

The amount of spectrum space occupied by the sidebands in a properly operating double-sideband phone transmitter depends on the bandwidth of the audio modulating signal. This is why most amateur transmitters limit the maximum audio-frequency component of your voice that is transmitted to about 3000 Hz. There is one emission type that does not produce sideband frequencies. That emission is an unmodulated carrier signal, which the FCC calls a test emission. [See §97.3(c)(9) of the FCC Rules.]

Figure 8-1 — A 10-MHz carrier modulated by a 1-kHz sine wave has sidebands at 9.999 MHz and 10.001 MHz.

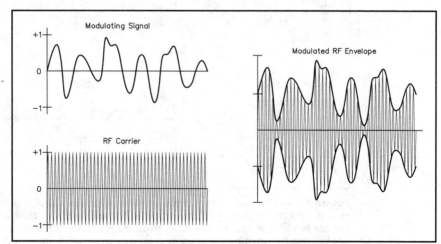

Figure 8-2 — This drawing illustrates the relationship between the modulating audio waveform, the carrier and the resulting RF envelope in a double-sideband, full-carrier AM signal.

Modulation Percentage

One of the concepts that is easy to visualize by looking at the RF envelope is percentage of modulation. Figure 8-3A is a sine-wave signal used to modulate an RF carrier. In Figure 8-3B, we see that the modulating signal has just the right value to make the RF-envelope amplitude go to zero on the audio downswing and to twice the unmodulated value at the peak of the upswing. This is called 100% modulation. The percent of modulation is the ratio of the peak-to-peak voltage of

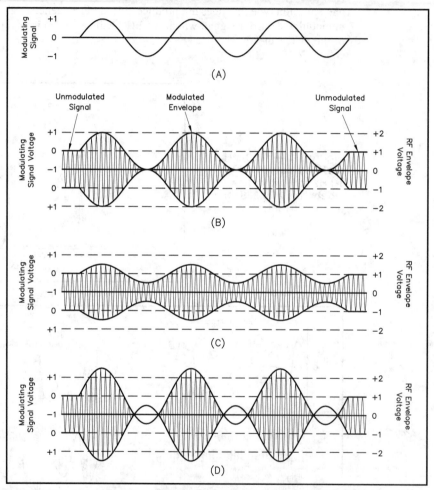

Figure 8-3 — The audio-frequency waveform at A is superimposed on an RF signal, and the resulting RF envelope is shown by the outline at B. The RF carrier is 100% modulated — the envelope just barely reaches zero between peaks. The RF envelope shown at C is less than 100% modulated because the maximum amplitude of the audio signal was decreased from the amplitude shown at A. At D, the audio-signal strength was increased, and the RF envelope is modulated more than 100%.

the modulating signal to the peak-to-peak voltage of the unmodulated RF envelope. With voice modulation, the percentage is continually varying, because speech contains many variations in volume. If the modulating signal were only half as strong, so its peak-to-peak voltage was 1 instead of 2 as shown in Figure 8-3A, the modulated envelope would look like the one shown in part C. This represents a condition of 50% modulation.

Occasionally the envelope may be held at zero for longer than an instant, as shown in Figure 8-3D. This produces a gap in the RF output that distorts the shape of the modulation envelope so it differs greatly from the modulating signal. This situation is called overmodulation, since the carrier is modulated more than 100%. The distorted signal introduces harmonics and can cause **splatter** — a signal with excessive bandwidth that results in interference to nearby signals. The signal from an overmodulated single-sideband or double-sideband phone transmitter is distorted and occupies more bandwidth than it should.

[Study the following questions in Chapter 12 before you go on to the next section: G8A01, G8A05 and G8A09. Review this section if you have difficulty with any of these questions.]

SINGLE-SIDEBAND, SUPPRESSED-CARRIER SIGNALS

When the carrier signal is modulated, sidebands are generated in proportion to the strength of the modulating signal, as shown in Figure 8-4A. The carrier amplitude is not affected by the modulation. Since the carrier is never changed, it contains no information. All the information is contained in the sidebands, which are mirror images of each other. The only purpose of the carrier is to provide a reference signal for demodulation by an envelope detector.

Suppose we remove or suppress the carrier and amplify only the sidebands, as shown in Figure 8-4B. Removing the carrier means we can increase the power in the sidebands by using the power that was required to amplify the carrier in the final stages. The total power dissipation in the transmitter final amplifier remains the same. Taking this even further, since both sidebands contain the same information, we really need only one. If we remove one of the sidebands we can use the power that would have amplified that sideband to increase the power in the remaining sideband. See Figure 8-4C.

Single-sideband phone is the most popular form of voice modulation in use on the amateur HF bands. FCC rules require that the carrier be reduced to a level at least 40 dB below the **peak envelope power (PEP)** output of the desired sideband in a single-sideband phone transmitter.

A **balanced modulator** is used to suppress the carrier in a single-sideband phone transmitter. A band-pass filter placed after the modulator removes the unwanted sideband. In a typical single-sideband phone transmitter a 2.5-kHz band-pass filter is used.

By now, you probably realize that by removing one of the sidebands and the carrier, the range of radio frequencies is reduced quite a bit as compared to a double-sideband, full-carrier transmission. In fact, SSB signals have the narrowest bandwidth of any of the popular phone emissions.

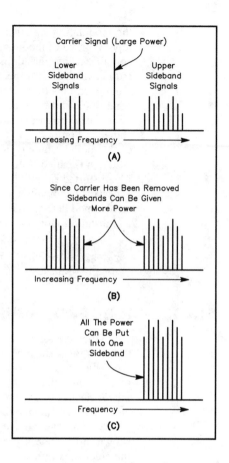

Figure 8-4 — This drawing shows the frequency spectrum of amplitude-modulated radio signals. Part A shows a double-sideband, full-carrier signal. If the carrier is removed, as shown at B, the sidebands can be given more power without increasing the total transmitter power. Going further, if one sideband is suppressed, as shown at C, the full transmitter power can be concentrated in one sideband. The suppressed parts of the signal are not needed for intelligibility.

Adjusting Microphone Gain

Always make sure your transmitter is operating properly and adjust your microphone gain correctly. Generally speaking, if your rig has an automatic level control (ALC) meter, you should adjust the microphone gain until you see a slight movement of the ALC meter on modulation peaks. (Most transceivers have one meter, with several scales to indicate received signal strength, output power and sometimes SWR in addition to ALC. With an ALC indicator light, adjust the microphone gain until the indicator just lights on voice peaks.

Start with the MIKE GAIN control set to minimum. Speak into the mike and begin increasing the control until the meter moves slightly, but does not exceed the "ALC" zone on the meter scale, even on voice peaks. If you have a monitor oscilloscope, you can observe the effects of adjusting the MIKE GAIN, and see when it is set too high. Proper voice waveforms have rounded peaks. Peaks with flat tops indicate **flattopping** (also called *clipping*), caused by an excessive microphone gain control setting. See Figure 8-5. When the audio input is too high, this excessive drive causes a distorted output. Consult the owner's manual for your rig for instructions on proper operation and gain control settings.

Why is proper operation important? If your microphone gain is set too high, your transmitted signal will be distorted. Distortion can cause splatter, resulting in interference to stations on other frequencies. Speak clearly into the microphone, while remaining a constant, close distance away from it. This will reduce background noise, raising the signal-to-background-noise ratio. If you use a speech processor, use the minimum necessary processing level to limit distortion. An over-processed, distorted signal is more difficult to copy than an unprocessed one.

Speech is the primary element of radiotelephone operation. For effective voice communication, your speech should be clearly enunciated, delivered directly into the microphone at a speed suitable for the purpose and conditions at hand. To be efficient, the operator must use the microphone and other speech equipment properly.

Microphones vary in design and purpose, but generally it is best to speak close to the microphone, holding it a few inches away from you. This will improve the signal-to-noise ratio by making your voice louder than any background noises, such as the kids, the TV set or traffic noise when you are in your car.

Pay attention to your mike technique to keep average speech levels high without overdoing it. Automatic level controls (ALC) help, but operator care is also needed to maintain relatively constant speech levels.

[Now turn to Chapter 12 and study questions: G8A06, G8A07, G8A08, G8A10 and G8A11. Review this section as needed.]

Mixer Operation

The **mixer** stages in a transmitter and receiver change the frequency of a signal that is being processed. A **mixer** takes two or more input signals, and produces an output that includes the sum and difference of those signal frequencies. One of the input signals is the signal being processed. This could be the audio from a transmitter microphone, an intermediate-frequency (IF) signal being changed to the final transmitter frequency, a received RF signal or an IF signal in a receiver. (The IF stages in transmitters and receivers provide a convenient way to filter and

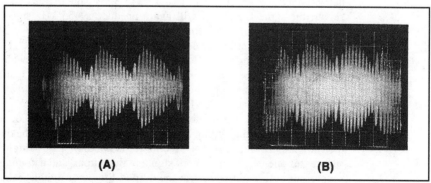

Figure 8-5 — The waveform of a properly adjusted SSB transmitter is shown at A. B shows a severely clipped signal.

process the signals. All such filtering and processing can be done at a single frequency — or narrow range of frequencies — while the transmitter or receiver can be set to operate on one of several bands.

The second mixer input signal comes from an oscillator in the transmitter or receiver. This oscillator may be called the *local oscillator* (LO), *variable-frequency oscillator* (VFO), *beat-frequency oscillator* (BFO) or several other names. The frequency of this signal is selected to change the processed signal to the desired output frequency.

When the input signals are combined in the mixer they add and subtract. We will have four output signals with two input signals. Two of the output signals are the same as the original input signals. The other two output signals consist of the sum of the two input signals and the difference between the input signals. Usually there will be a filter at the output to select only the desired signal. An example will make this easier to understand.

Suppose you have a transmitter that processes signals at an IF of 5.3 MHz. You want to convert this signal to 14.3 MHz to transmit on the 20-meter band. A 9.0-MHz oscillator signal mixed with the 5.3 MHz IF will produce the desired output.

5.3 MHz + 9.0 MHz = 14.3 MHz

You could also use a 19.6-MHz oscillator to produce the desired output signal.

19.6 MHz – 5.3 MHz = 14.3 MHz

Suppose you want to receive a 14.25-MHz signal. What frequency will the VFO in your receiver be set to if the receiver uses an IF of 455 kHz? We need a VFO frequency that is either the sum or difference of these two frequencies. (First convert 455 kHz to 0.455 MHz, so both frequencies are expressed in the same units.)

14.25 MHz + 0.455 MHz = 14.705 MHz

The oscillator could also be set to the difference frequency:

14.25 MHz – 0.455 MHz = 13.795 MHz

For any given oscillator signal, there are two possible signal frequencies to produce the same output frequency. For example, you might have a receiver that is designed to use a 13.800-MHz LO signal to mix with a 14.255-MHz received signal, producing a 455-kHz IF. If a 13.345-MHz signal finds its way into the receiver, the same LO signal will again produce a 455-kHz signal, which will be processed by the receiver. You might be listening to the 13.345-MHz signal even though your receiver indicates it is tuned to 14.255 MHz! The 13.345-MHz signal would produce interference to any 14.225-MHz signals you were receiving. This type of interference is known as **image response**, and is a result of the mixing process. If the desired signal has a frequency of LO + IF, the *image frequency* is at LO – IF, and vice versa. See Figure 8-6.

Mixer circuits can be designed to prevent one or more of the input signals from appearing at the output. If both input signals appear at the output, along with the sum and difference signals, the mixer is *unbalanced*. A *single-balanced mixer* suppresses one or the other input signal at the output, and a *double-balanced mixer* suppresses both input signals at the output. Single or double-balanced mixers can simplify the filtering task at the output. They also improve other receiver-performance characteristics.

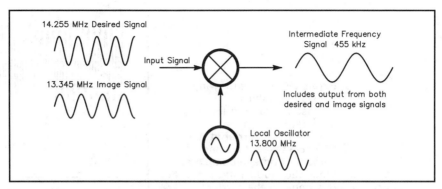

Figure 8-6 — A mixer combines two signals (usually an input signal being processed and an oscillator signal) and produces an output signal that includes the sum and difference of the input signals.

[Now turn to Chapter 12 and study questions G8B01 through G8B03. Review this section if these questions give you difficulty.]

FREQUENCY MODULATION (FM)

We can transmit information by modulating any property of a carrier. We have already studied amplitude modulation. We can also modulate the *frequency* or the *phase* of the carrier. **Frequency modulation** and **phase modulation** are closely related, since the phase of a signal cannot be varied without also varying the frequency, and vice versa. Phase modulation and frequency modulation are especially suited for channelized local UHF and VHF communication because they feature good audio fidelity and high signal-to-noise ratio, as long as the signals are stronger than a minimum, or threshold, level.

In FM systems, when a modulating signal is applied, the carrier frequency is increased during one half of the audio cycle and decreased during the other half of the cycle. The change in the carrier frequency, or **frequency deviation**, is proportional to the instantaneous amplitude of the modulating signal. Figure 8-7 shows a representation of a frequency-modulated signal. The deviation is slight when the amplitude of the modulating signal is small and greatest when the modulating signal reaches its peak amplitude. The amplitude of the envelope does not change with modulation. This means that an FM receiver is not sensitive to amplitude variations caused by impulse-type noise, and this feature makes it popular for mobile communication.

Practical FM Transmitters

The simplest type of FM transmitter we could design is shown in Figure 8-8. Remember that a circuit containing capacitance and inductance will be resonant at some frequency. If we use a resonant circuit in the feedback path of an oscillator, we can control the oscillator frequency by changing the resonant frequency of the tuned circuit. A capacitor microphone is nothing more than a capacitor with one

Figure 8-7 — This drawing shows a graphical representation of frequency modulation. In the unmodulated carrier at A, each RF cycle takes the same amount of time to complete. When the modulating signal at B is applied, the carrier frequency is increased or decreased according to the amplitude and polarity of the modulating signal, as shown by Part C.

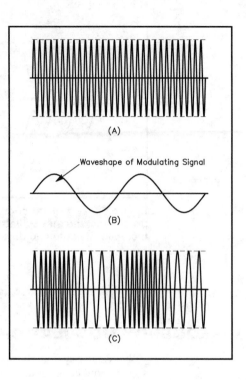

Figure 8-8 — This diagram shows a simple FM transmitter. The frequency of the oscillator is changed by changing the capacitance in the resonant circuit.

movable plate (the diaphragm). When you speak into the microphone, the diaphragm vibrates and the spacing between the two plates of the capacitor changes. When the spacing changes, the capacitance value changes. If we connect the microphone to the resonant circuit in our oscillator, we can vary the oscillator frequency by speaking into the microphone. If we add frequency multipliers to bring the oscillator frequency up to our operating frequency, and amplifiers to bring up the power, we have a simple FM transmitter.

Another way to shift the frequency of the oscillator would be to use a circuit called a **reactance modulator**. This is a vacuum tube or transistor wired in a circuit so that it changes either the capacitance or inductance of the oscillator resonant circuit in response to an audio input signal.

Modern FM transmitters may use a **varactor diode** to modulate the oscillator. A varactor diode is a special diode that changes capacitance when its bias voltage is changed. Connected to a crystal oscillator as shown in Figure 8-9, the varactor diode will "pull" the oscillator frequency slightly when the audio input changes.

PHASE MODULATION (PM)

One problem with early direct-modulated FM transmitters was frequency stability. Using a capacitive microphone or a reactance modulator means that a crystal oscillator cannot be used. Frequency multiplication also multiplies any drift or other instability problems in the oscillator. With phase modulation, however, the modulation takes place after the oscillator, so a crystal oscillator can be used. For this reason phase modulation is used in most FM transmitters built for mobile applications, where stability may be a serious problem because of shocks and temperature

Figure 8-9 — A varactor diode can also be used to frequency-modulate an oscillator. The capacitance of the varactor diode changes when the bias voltage is varied.

variations. Phase modulation produces what is called indirect-modulated FM. The most common method of generating a phase-modulated telephony signal is to use a reactance modulator.

The term **phase** essentially means "time," or the time interval between the instant when one thing occurs and the instant when a second related thing takes place. The later event is said to *lag* the earlier, while the one that occurs first is said to *lead*. When two waves of the same frequency start their cycles at slightly different times, the time difference (or phase difference) is measured in degrees. This is shown in Figure 8-10. In phase modulation, we shift the phase of the output wave in response to the audio-input-signal amplitude.

The output from an RF oscillator is an unmodulated wave, as shown in Figure 8-11A. The phase-modulated wave is shown in Figure 8-11B. At time 0 and again 168 microseconds later the two waves are in phase. The phase modulation has shifted cycle X' so that it reaches its peak value at time 39 microseconds as compared with 52 microseconds for the unmodulated wave. (Cycle X' leads cycle X.)

The number of cycles in both waveforms is the same, so the center frequency of the wave has not been changed. All the cycles to the left of cycle X' have been compressed, and all the cycles to the right of cycle X' have been spread out. The frequency of the wave to the left is greater than the center frequency, and the frequency to the right is less — the wave has been *frequency modulated*.

Figure 8-10 — When two waves of the same frequency start their cycles at slightly different times, the time difference (or phase difference) is measured in degrees. In this diagram wave B starts 45 degrees (one-eighth cycle) later than A, and so lags wave A by 45°. (We can also say that wave A leads wave B by 45°.)

Figure 8-11 — This diagram shows a graphical representation of phase modulation. The unmodulated wave is shown at A. After modulation, cycle X lags cycle X', and all the cycles to the left of cycle X' are compressed. To the right, the cycles are spread out.

Frequency Deviation

With direct FM, frequency deviation is proportional to the amplitude of the audio modulating signal. With phase modulation, the frequency deviation is proportional to both the amplitude and the frequency of the modulating signal. Frequency deviation is greater for higher audio frequencies. This is actually a benefit, rather than a drawback, of phase modulation. In radiocommunication applications, speech frequencies between 300 and 3000 Hz need to be reproduced for good intelligibility. In the human voice, however, the natural amplitude of speech sounds between 2000 and 3000 Hz is low. Something must be done to increase the amplitude of these frequencies when a direct FM transmitter is used. A circuit called a *preemphasis network* amplifies the sounds between 2000 and 3000 Hz. With phase modulation, the preemphasis network is not required, because the deviation already increases with increasing audio input frequency.

Modulation Index

The sidebands that occur from FM or PM differ from those resulting from AM. With AM, only a single set of sidebands is produced for each modulating frequency. FM and PM sidebands occur at integral *multiples* of the modulating frequency on either side of the carrier, as shown in Figure 8-12. Because of these multiple sidebands, FM or PM signals inherently occupy a greater bandwidth. The additional sidebands depend on the relationship between the modulating frequency and the frequency deviation. The ratio between the peak carrier frequency deviation and the audio modulating frequency is called the **modulation index**.

Given a constant input level to the modulator, in phase modulation, the modulation index is constant regardless of the modulating frequency. For an FM signal, the modulation index varies with the modulating frequency. In an FM system, the ratio of the maximum carrier-frequency deviation to the highest modulating frequency used is called the **deviation ratio**. Whereas modulation index is a variable that depends on a set of operating conditions, deviation ratio is a constant. The deviation ratio for narrow-band FM is 5000 Hz (maximum deviation) divided by 3000 Hz (maximum modulation frequency) or 1.67.

[Now turn to Chapter 12 and study questions G8A02, G8A03 and G8A04. Review this section as needed.]

Frequency Multiplication and Amplification

Since there is no change in the amplitude with modulation, an FM or PM signal can be amplified in a nonlinear amplifier without producing distortion. This has the advantage that modulation can be introduced in a low-level stage and the signal can then be amplified efficiently.

It is not usually practical to have an oscillator operating in the VHF range or higher, because such an oscillator would not be as stable as one operating at lower frequencies. Common practice is to use an oscillator operating at some submultiple of the desired operating frequency, and then to use *frequency multiplication* to obtain the proper output frequency. A frequency multiplier is an amplifier that produces harmonics of the input signal. A filter selects the desired harmonic for the output frequency.

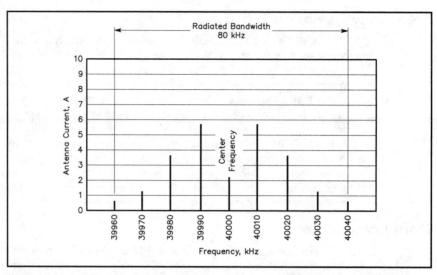

Figure 8-12 — When an RF-carrier is frequency-modulated by an audio signal, multiple sidebands are produced. This diagram shows a 40-MHz carrier modulated by a 10-kHz sinusoidal audio signal. Additional sidebands exist above 40.04 MHz and below 39.96 MHz, but their amplitude is too low to be significant.

When the modulation is applied to the oscillator in such a system, care must be taken to set the proper deviation ratio. When the modulated signal is multiplied to the output frequency, the deviation ratio will also be multiplied by the same factor.

For example, suppose we are using a 12.21-MHz reactance-modulated oscillator in our FM transmitter operating at 146.52 MHz. We want the maximum frequency deviation to be 5 kHz for the transmitted signal. What is the maximum deviation of the oscillator frequency? First we need to know how much multiplication the transmitter is using. We find this by dividing the output frequency by the oscillator frequency:

$$\text{Multiplication Factor} = \frac{\text{Transmitter Output Frequency}}{\text{Oscillator Frequency}} \qquad \text{(Equation 8-1)}$$

$$\text{Multiplication Factor} = \frac{146.52 \text{ MHz}}{12.21 \text{ MHz}} = 12$$

This means we are multiplying the oscillator frequency by a factor of 12 to bring it up to the operating frequency. So the deviation in the oscillator will also be multiplied by 12.

$$\text{Oscillator deviation} \times \text{Multiplication factor} = \text{Transmitter deviation} \qquad \text{(Equation 8-2)}$$

$$\text{Oscillator deviation} \times 12 = 5 \text{ kHz}$$

$$\text{Oscillator deviation} = \frac{5 \text{ kHz}}{12} = 0.4167 \text{ kHz} = 416.7 \text{ Hz}$$

Frequency multiplication offers a means for obtaining any desired amount of frequency deviation, whether or not the modulator is capable of that much deviation. Overdeviation of an FM transmitter causes **splatter** — out-of-channel emissions that can cause interference to adjacent frequencies.

A frequency-multiplier stage is an amplifier that produces harmonics of the input signal. By using a filter to select the desired harmonic, the proper output frequency can be obtained. A frequency multiplier is not the same as a mixer stage, which is used to obtain the desired output frequency in an SSB or CW rig. A mixer simply mixes two input signals to provide an output at some new frequency.

Bandwidth in FM and PM

With frequency deviation defined as the instantaneous change in frequency for a given signal, we can now define the total bandwidth of the signal. Since the frequency actually swings just as far in both directions, the total frequency swing is equal to twice the deviation. In addition, there are sidebands that increase the bandwidth still further. A good estimate of the bandwidth is twice the maximum frequency deviation plus the maximum modulating audio frequency:

$$Bw = 2 \times (D + M) \qquad\qquad \text{(Equation 8-3)}$$

where:

Bw = bandwidth

D = maximum frequency deviation

M = maximum modulating audio frequency

With a transmitter using 5-kHz deviation and a maximum audio frequency of 3 kHz, the total bandwidth is approximately 16 kHz.

$$Bw = 2 \times (5 \text{ kHz} + 3 \text{ kHz}) = 2 \times 8 \text{ kHz}$$

$$Bw = 16 \text{ kHz}$$

The actual bandwidth is somewhat greater than this, but it is a good approximation.

Frequency modulated phone is not used below 29.5 MHz because the bandwidth of such signals would exceed FCC limits. Between 29.5 and 29.7 MHz on the 10-meter band, and on the VHF bands and higher frequencies, the allowable bandwidth is greater, so FM (and PM) phone are permitted.

[Now study these questions in Chapter 12: G8B04 through G8B07. Review this section as needed.]

DIGITAL COMMUNICATIONS

Digital communications refers to the type of coding used to transmit information. Any signal that has separate, distinct conditions, and switches between those conditions to form the pattern of a code, is a digital communications method. Usually there are only two different conditions used to form the code. The on-off keying of a Morse code signal is one simple example of digital communications. Morse code is designed to be copied by ear, but other digital codes are designed to be copied by machine. Baudot radioteletype (RTTY), AMTOR, PACTOR and packet radio are examples of codes designed to be copied by machine. They are all *digital communications*.

Instead of switching a carrier on and off to send information as in CW, the carrier can be left on continuously and switched between two different frequencies. This is called **frequency-shift keying (FSK)**. This is the type of keying used to produce RTTY, AMTOR and packet radio signals below 50 MHz. FSK has the advantage over on-off keying that it gives definite signals for both the on and off states used for digital communication. These *on* and *off* states are referred to as "mark" and "space," respectively.

FSK can be produced in two ways. The first method is to change the oscillator frequency back and forth between two frequencies so the carrier also shifts between two frequencies. The second method makes use of the fact that there is no output from an SSB transmitter when there is no modulation. Only when an audio tone is applied to the microphone input is there a corresponding RF signal emitted from the transmitter. By switching between two fixed audio tones, the RF signal is shifted between the mark and space frequencies. The difference in the two RF signals is equal to the difference in frequency of the audio tones.

When using FSK emissions below 50 MHz, no more than 1000 Hz is permitted between the mark and space signals. Above 50 MHz, the frequency shift, in hertz, must not exceed the sending speed, in bauds, of the transmission, or 1000 Hz, whichever is greater. As the sending speed of an RTTY transmission is increased, the frequency shift between the mark and space tones must also be increased.

The electronic device that goes between the RTTY terminal (keyboard and display unit) and the transmitter is called a *modem*, which is short for *mo*dulator/*dem*odulator. As the sending speed is increased, it becomes more difficult for the modem to distinguish between the two frequencies used to represent mark and space. Increasing the shift between mark and space helps to solve this problem. This also increases the bandwidth of the signal, so the FCC bandwidth restrictions impose practical limits on the keying speed of an RTTY signal. At higher frequencies, where wider bandwidths are permitted, higher keying speeds can be used. Below 28 MHz, the sending speed may not exceed 300 bauds. Between 28 and 50 MHz you may use speeds up to 1200 bauds, between 50 and 220 MHz the speed limit is 19,600 bauds (19.6 kilobauds) and above 220 MHz you may use speeds up to 56 kilobauds. A baud is the unit used to describe transmission speeds for digital signals. For a single-channel transmission, a baud is equivalent to one digital bit of information transmitted per second. So a 300-baud signaling rate represents a transmission rate of 300 bits of digital information per second in a single-channel transmission.

Another way to transmit digital communication is to feed audio tones into the microphone input of an FM transmitter. These emissions are called **audio-frequency shift keying (AFSK)** emissions.

The audio frequencies used for AFSK have been standardized in the US at 2125 Hz and 2295 Hz for 170-Hz shift and 2125 Hz and 2975 Hz for 850-Hz shift.

Most amateur operation uses 170-Hz shift. These tones were selected because they are close to the upper limit of the audio passband of most transmitters. This is important because harmonics produced in the tone generator will fall outside the audio passband and, therefore, will be attenuated in the transmitter. When lower-frequency audio tones are used, care must be taken to ensure that harmonics are eliminated from the signal produced by the tone generator. If the audio input to the transmitter contains harmonics, the RF output from the transmitter may contain signals at frequencies other than the desired fundamental. These extra signals can cause interference to other amateur stations, as well as producing RFI and TVI to consumer electronics devices.

It is important to consider the duty cycle of your transmitter when transmitting digital communications. For Morse code, your transmitter is producing the full output power every time you close the key. Each dot or dash is short, however, so your transmitter is actually on only a short time, and then turned off for a short time while you are "transmitting."

When transmitting Baudot RTTY your transmitter is producing full output power the entire time, because it just switches between the two transmitted frequencies. This is called 100% duty cycle. If your transmitter is not rated for 100% duty cycle it may overheat and be destroyed. It is common practice to reduce the transmitter power to about 50% of maximum for RTTY operation to protect the transmitter.

Mode A AMTOR transmission has a duty cycle of about 50%, because your transmitter sends three characters, then turns off to await an acknowledgment. Your transmitter has a 100% duty cycle to transmit Mode B AMTOR, however. Packet radio has a duty cycle less than 100% because it stops transmitting after each "packet" to await an acknowledgment. PACTOR also has a duty cycle of less than 100% because the station transmits a block of data and then waits for an acknowledgment.

Most AMTOR and PACTOR operation takes place near the low-frequency end ("bottom") of the RTTY segment on each band. On 20 meters, most AMTOR and PACTOR activity is found near 14.075 MHz. HF packet radio operation is usually found at the high-frequency end ("top") of the RTTY segment on each band.

[This completes the material for this chapter. You should now turn to Chapter 12 and study questions G8B08 through G8B11. Review any material in the chapter that you had difficulty with.]

CHAPTER 9
KEYWORDS
KEYWORDS
KEYWORDS

Balanced line — Feed line with two conductors having equal but opposite voltages, with neither conductor at ground potential.

Balun — A transformer used between a *bal*anced and an *un*balanced system, such as for feeding a balanced antenna with an unbalanced feed line.

Coaxial cable — Feed line with a central conductor surrounded by plastic, foam or gaseous insulation, which in turn is covered by a shielding conductor and the entire cable is covered with vinyl insulation.

Cubical quad antenna — A full-wavelength loop antenna built with its elements in the shape of squares.

Delta loop antenna — A full-wavelength loop antenna built with its elements in the shape of equilateral triangles.

Director — A parasitic element in "front" of the driven element in a multielement antenna.

Driven element — The element connected directly to the feed line in a multielement antenna.

Feed line — The wire or cable used to connect an antenna to the transmitter and receiver. (Also called *transmission line*.)

Front-to-back ratio — The energy radiated from the front of a directive antenna divided by the energy radiated from the back of the antenna.

Gain — An increase in the effective power radiated by an antenna in a certain desired direction, or an increase in received signal strength from a certain direction. This is at the expense of power radiated in, or signal strength received from, other directions.

Ground-plane antenna — A vertical antenna built with a central radiating element one-quarter-wavelength long and several radials extending horizontally from the base. The radials are slightly longer than one-quarter wave, and may droop toward the ground.

Half-wavelength dipole antenna — A fundamental antenna one-half wavelength long at the desired operating frequency, and connected to the feed line at the center. This is a popular amateur antenna.

Horizontally polarized wave — An electromagnetic wave with its electric lines of force parallel to the ground.

Main lobe — The direction of maximum radiated field strength from an antenna. (Also called *major lobe.*)

Parallel-conductor feed line — Feed line constructed of two wires held a constant distance apart; either encased in plastic or constructed with insulating spacers placed at intervals along the line.

Parasitic element — Part of a directive antenna that derives energy from mutual coupling with the driven element. Parasitic elements are not connected directly to the feed line.

Polarization — The orientation of the electric lines of force in a radio wave, with respect to the surface of the Earth.

Quarter-wavelength vertical antenna — An antenna constructed of a quarter-wavelength-long radiating element placed perpendicular to the Earth. (See **Ground-plane antenna**.)

Random-length wire antenna — A multiband antenna consisting of any convenient length of wire, connected directly to a transmitter or impedance-matching network without the use of feed line.

Reflector — A parasitic element placed "behind" the driven element in a directive antenna.

Standing-wave ratio (SWR) — The ratio of maximum voltage to minimum voltage along a feed line. Also the ratio of antenna impedance to feed line impedance when the antenna is a purely resistive load.

Unbalanced line — Feed line with one conductor at ground potential, such as coaxial cable.

Vertically polarized wave — A radio wave that has its electric lines of force perpendicular to the surface of the Earth.

Yagi antenna — A directive antenna made with a half-wavelength driven element, and two or more parasitic elements arranged in the same horizontal plane.

ANTENNAS AND FEED LINES

An *antenna system* includes the actual antenna (the part that actually radiates the signal), the feed line, and any coupling devices or matching networks used for transferring power from the transmitter to the line and from the line to the antenna. In some simple systems the feed line may be part of the antenna, and coupling devices may not be used. An applicant for the General license should know the basic design and operation of commonly used Amateur Radio antennas, and the principles of feed lines and standing wave ratio (SWR). There are four questions from this material on the General exam, and these questions come from the four syllabus groups:

G9A Yagi antennas — physical dimensions; impedance matching; radiation
 patterns; directivity and major lobes

G9B Loop antennas — physical dimensions; impedance matching; radiation
 patterns; directivity and major lobes

G9C Random wire antennas — physical dimensions; impedance matching;
 radiation patterns; directivity and major lobes; feed-point impedance of
 $1/2$-wavelength dipole and $1/4$-wavelength vertical antennas

G9D Popular antenna feed lines — characteristic impedance and impedance
 matching; SWR calculations

WAVE CHARACTERISTICS AND POLARIZATION

An electromagnetic wave consists of moving electric and magnetic fields. Remember that a field is an invisible force of nature. We can't see radio waves — the best we can do is to show a representation of where the energy is in the electric and magnetic fields. We can visualize a traveling radio wave as looking something like Figure 9-1. The lines of electric and magnetic force are at right angles to each other, and are also perpendicular to the direction of travel. These fields can have any position with respect to the Earth.

Polarization is defined by the direction of the electric lines of force in a radio wave. If the electric lines of force are parallel to the surface of the Earth, the wave is called a **horizontally polarized wave**. Similarly, if the electric lines of force are perpendicular to the Earth, the wave is called a **vertically polarized wave**.

The polarization of a radio wave as it leaves the antenna is determined by the orientation of the antenna. For example, a half-wavelength dipole parallel to the surface of the Earth transmits a wave that is horizontally polarized. A whip antenna, mounted vertically on an automobile, transmits a wave that is vertically polarized.

After radio waves have traveled some distance from the transmitting antenna

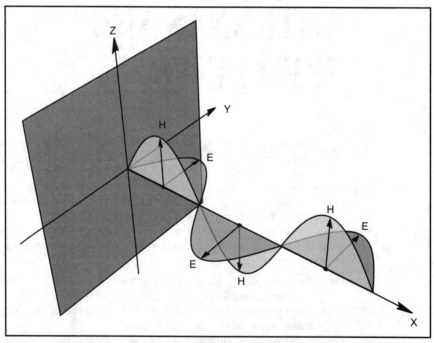

Figure 9-1 — This diagram illustrates the electric and magnetic field components of an electromagnetic wave. The polarization of a radio wave is the same as the plane of the electric field. In this example the electrical lines of force are parallel to the ground. This is a horizontally polarized electromagnetic wave.

and have interacted with their surroundings and with the ionosphere, the polarization may change. Longer wavelengths will typically retain their polarization, while shorter wavelengths will often change polarization as they interact with the ionosphere. These changes can occur quite rapidly. Most man-made noise tends to be vertically polarized; thus, a horizontally polarized antenna will receive less noise of this type than will a vertical antenna.

RANDOM WIRE ANTENNA

One of the simplest antenna types is the **random-length wire antenna**, also known as the *random-wire antenna*. As the name implies, the length of this antenna is not related to the wavelength of the desired signals. The random-wire antenna is a multiband antenna. The antenna impedance will vary from band to band, and so requires the use of some type of impedance-matching network.

A random-wire antenna does not require a feed line. The antenna is a single wire, which connects directly to the impedance-matching network output. Because the antenna has no feed line, it comes right into the radio shack. This causes one of the greatest disadvantages of the random-wire antenna. You may experience RF feedback in your station if you use this type of antenna. RF feedback may result in radio-frequency interference of various types. Your radio or other station equipment may cause RF burns when you touch the equipment.

[You should turn to Chapter 12 now, and study questions G9C01, G9C02 and G9C03. Review this section if you have difficulty with any of these questions.]

VERTICAL ANTENNAS

Another popular antenna is the **quarter-wavelength vertical antenna**. It is often used to obtain low-angle radiation when a beam or dipole antenna cannot be placed far enough above ground. Low-angle radiation refers to signals that travel closer to the horizon, rather than signals that are high above the horizon as they leave the antenna. Low-angle radiation is usually advantageous when you are attempting to contact distant stations.

You might also want to use a vertical antenna if you don't have two supports separated by an appropriate distance to hold the ends of a dipole antenna. As shown in Figure 9-2, the quarter-wavelength vertical antenna is half of a half-wavelength antenna, mounted vertically. Conductivity in the ground produces an "image" of the missing quarter wavelength. An excellent ground connection is necessary for the most effective operation of a vertical antenna.

In most installations, ground conductivity is inadequate, so an artificial ground must be made from wires placed along the ground near the base of the antenna, as shown in Figure 9-2C. These wires, called *radials*, are usually one-quarter wavelength long or longer. Depending on ground conductivity, 8, 16, 32 or more radials may be required to form an effective ground. The radial wires of a ground-mounted vertical antenna should be placed on the ground surface or buried a few inches below the ground.

For best results, the vertical radiator should be located away from nearby con-

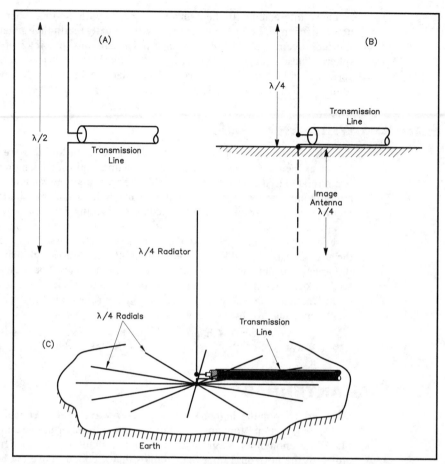

Figure 9-2 — A half-wavelength vertical antenna is shown at A. At B is its grounded quarter-wavelength counterpart. In ground with good conductivity, we consider the missing quarter wavelength to be supplied by the image. A practical quarter-wave vertical antenna installation will require the use of several ground radials, as shown at C.

ductive objects. Nearby conductive objects may distort, or *skew*, the antenna radiation pattern. Such objects may also cause the antenna feed-point impedance to change. You should ensure that no people can come near your antenna while you are transmitting because they may also skew the radiation pattern and cause the feed-point impedance to vary. Of course you should always take steps to keep people away from your antennas to avoid exposure to RF radiation. Radiation exposure is the most important reason to keep people away from your transmitting antenna.

Vertical antennas can be combined to form arrays in which each element is fed with a signal from the transmitter. By controlling the phase relationships of the signals fed to each element, you can obtain a variety of radiation patterns.

The radiation resistance of a quarter-wavelength antenna over a perfect ground is about 36 Ω. The feed-point impedance of a real quarter-wavelength antenna may vary between 30 and 100 Ω, depending on ground resistance.

The Ground-Plane Antenna

The **ground-plane antenna** is a vertical antenna that uses an artificial metallic ground consisting of metal rods or wires either perpendicular to, or sloping from, the antenna base and extending outward, as shown in Figure 9-3. The entire antenna, including the radials, is mounted above the ground. This permits the antenna to be mounted at a height clear of surrounding obstructions such as trees and buildings. The ground plane also requires only 3 or 4 radials to operate properly, as opposed to the large number required for some ground-mounted installations.

With the radials perpendicular to the antenna, the feed-point impedance is around 35 Ω. Sloping the radials downward raises the feed-point impedance of the antenna somewhat. If the radials are angled down at about a 45° angle, the feed-point impedance is around 50 Ω, which makes it easier to match the antenna to available coaxial-cable feed lines. Unlike other quarter-wavelength vertical antennas without an artificial ground, the ground-plane antenna will give low-angle radiation regardless of the height above actual ground. The radials should be slightly longer than the radiating element.

[Turn to Chapter 12 and study questions G9C04, G9C05 and G9C11 now. Review the material in this section if you have difficulty with any of these questions.]

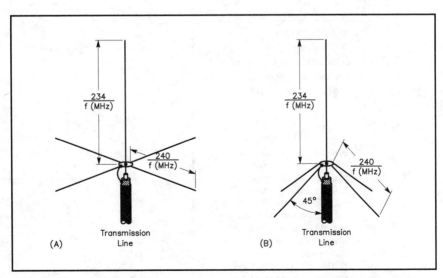

Figure 9-3 — This drawing illustrates a ground-plane antenna. Dropping the radials (as shown at B) raises the feed-point impedance closer to 50 Ω.

THE HALF-WAVELENGTH DIPOLE ANTENNA

The radiation from an ideal dipole antenna in free space is not uniform in all directions. It is strongest in directions perpendicular to the wire, and nearly zero along the axis of the wire, as shown in Figure 9-4. The plane radiation pattern for an ideal **half-wavelength dipole antenna** is a figure-eight at right angles to the antenna.

When placed over real ground, this ideal pattern is modified. The antenna height above ground, the conductivity of the ground and other nearby objects all affect the pattern. A half-wavelength dipole exhibits excellent directivity when placed at least one-half wavelength above the ground, as shown by the pattern in Figure 9-5A. This is approximately a figure-eight pattern, with the maximum radiation at right angles to the antenna. A dipole cut for the 40-meter band must be mounted at least 20 meters (about 65 feet) above ground to exhibit such directivity. If the antenna is lower, the directivity effects are reduced. Figure 9-5B shows the radiation pattern for a dipole mounted only one-quarter wavelength above the ground. Notice that the pattern is more nearly circular. This pattern is nearly omnidirectional, meaning there is no directional advantage. Waves reflected from the ground significantly distort the ideal pattern.

Despite this apparent disadvantage, the dipole is the most common and practical antenna for the 80 and

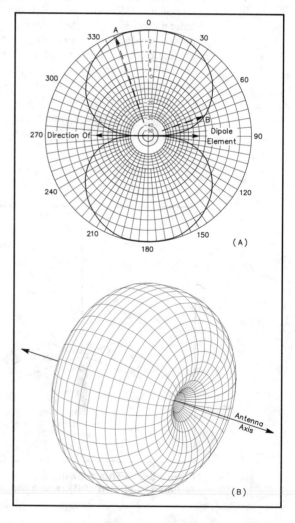

Figure 9-4 — Part A shows the solid (three-dimensional) directive pattern of an ideal dipole in free space. Part B shows the plane directive diagram of a dipole. The solid line shows the direction of the wire. Note that the pattern is bidirectional; the ideal dipole radiates equally well in two directions.

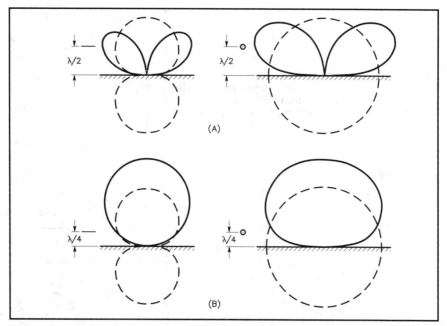

Figure 9-5 — The effect of ground on the radiation from a horizontal half-wavelength antenna, for heights of one-half (A) and one-quarter (B) wavelength is shown. The dashed lines show what the pattern would be if there were no reflection from the ground.

40-meter bands. The impedance at the feed point of a half-wavelength dipole suspended horizontally at least one-quarter wavelength above ground is close to 70 Ω, so a dipole can be fed directly with 75-Ω coaxial cable. The feed-point impedance will be less than 70 Ω if the antenna is mounted less than one-quarter wavelength above the ground, as shown in Figure 9-6. Coaxial cable with a characteristic impedance of 50 Ω is often used as the feed line to dipole antennas.

[Now turn to Chapter 12 and study questions G9C06 and G9C07. Review this section as needed.]

MULTIPLE-ELEMENT ARRAYS

The radiation pattern of the ideal half-wavelength dipole antenna is described as bidirectional — it radiates equally well in two directions. A unidirectional pattern (maximum radiation in one direction) can be produced by coupling the half-wavelength antenna to additional elements. The additional elements may be made of wire or metal tubing.

Parasitic Excitation

In most multiple-element antennas, the additional elements are not directly

Figure 9-6 — The radiation resistance of a horizontal half-wavelength antenna varies depending on how high above ground the antenna is mounted.

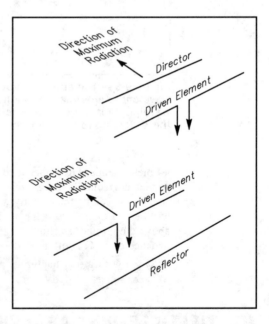

Figure 9-7 — In a directive antenna, the reflector element is placed "behind" the driven element. The director goes in "front" of the driven element.

connected to the feed line. They receive power by mutual coupling from the **driven element** (the element connected to the feed line). They then reradiate it in the proper phase relationship to achieve gain or directivity over a simple half-wavelength dipole. These elements are called **parasitic elements**.

There are two types of parasitic elements. A **director** is generally shorter than the driven element and is located at the "front" of the antenna. A **reflector** is generally longer than the driven element and is located at the "back" of the antenna. See Figure 9-7. The direction of maximum radiation from a parasitic antenna travels from the reflector through the driven element and the director. The term **main lobe** refers to the region of maximum radiation from a directional antenna. The main lobe is also sometimes referred to as the *major lobe*. If communication in different directions is desired, provision must be made to rotate the array in the *azimuth*, or horizontal plane. The minimum practical spacing between the elements of such an antenna is 0.1 wavelength.

A parasitic element that is slightly shorter than the driven element, placed 0.1 λ from a dipole antenna will produce a horizontal radiation pattern with a main lobe *toward* the parasitic element. A parasitic element that is slightly longer than the driven element, placed 0.1 λ from a dipole antenna will produce a horizontal radiation pattern with a main lobe *away* from the parasitic element.

[Turn to Chapter 12 and study questions G9C09 and G9C10 before going on to the next section. Review this text as needed.]

Yagi Arrays

An antenna that uses a half-wavelength dipole antenna and at least one parasitic element parallel to it is called a *Yagi-Uda antenna*, named for its developers. This name is normally shortened to **Yagi antenna**. The Yagi arrays in Figure 9-8 are examples of antennas that make use of parasitic elements to produce a unidirectional radiation pattern. Though typical HF antennas of this type have three elements, some may have six or more. Multiband Yagi antennas may have many elements. Some designs use several elements on one frequency range and other elements that are used for different frequencies. Other multiband designs use traps in the elements, so one set of elements will work on several bands.

The length of the driven element in the most common type of Yagi antenna is

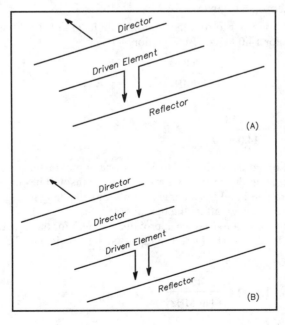

Figure 9-8 — Part A shows a three-element Yagi. Part B shows a four-element Yagi with two directors.

approximately one-half wavelength. This means that Yagi antennas are most often used for the 20-meter band and higher frequencies. For frequencies below 20 meters, the physical dimensions become so large that the antennas require special construction techniques and heavy-duty supporting towers and rotators. Yagis for 30 and 40 meters are fairly common, but 80-meter rotatable Yagis are few and far between. To overcome the mechanical difficulties, some amateurs build nonrotatable Yagi antennas for 40 and 80 meters, with elements made of wire supported on both ends.

In a three-element beam, the director will be approximately 5% (0.05) shorter than one-half wavelength, and the reflector will be approximately 5% longer than one-half wavelength. We can derive a set of equations to calculate these element lengths.

The driven element length is about the same as the length of a half-wavelength dipole antenna. The length is a bit shorter than a "free-space" half wavelength because of "end effects," the element diameter, and other factors. To calculate the length of a half-wavelength dipole antenna (or the driven element of a Yagi antenna) use:

$$\text{(Yagi)} \quad L_{DRIVEN} \left(\text{in ft}\right) = \frac{468}{f \left(\text{in MHz}\right)} \qquad \text{(Equation 9-1)}$$

To find the length of a director element for a Yagi antenna, we shorten this length by about 5%:

$$L_{DIRECTOR} = L_{DRIVEN} \left(1 - 0.05\right)$$

$$\text{(Yagi)} \quad L_{DIRECTOR} = L_{DRIVEN} \times 0.95 \qquad \text{(Equation 9-2)}$$

To find the length of a reflector element for a Yagi antenna, we increase this length by about 5%:

$$L_{REFLECTOR} = L_{DRIVEN} \left(1 + 0.05\right)$$

$$\text{(Yagi)} \quad L_{REFLECTOR} = L_{DRIVEN} \times 1.05 \qquad \text{(Equation 9-3)}$$

Suppose you want to find the approximate length of the driven element of a Yagi antenna for 14.0 MHz. Use Equation 9-1:

$$\text{(Yagi)} \quad L_{DRIVEN} \left(\text{in ft}\right) = \frac{468}{f \left(\text{in MHz}\right)}$$

$$L_{DRIVEN} \left(\text{in ft}\right) = \frac{468}{14.0 \text{ MHz}} = 33.4 \text{ ft}$$

You can round this value off to 33 ft as an approximate answer. Any values you calculate using the equations for antenna lengths will be subject to some adjustment when you build the antenna. Conditions like height, nearby objects and element diameter can all affect the optimum length.

Suppose you want to find the approximate length for the director element of a Yagi antenna for 21.1 MHz. First, use Equation 9-1 to calculate the driven-element length:

$$\text{(Yagi)} \quad L_{DRIVEN} \left(\text{in ft}\right) = \frac{468}{f \left(\text{in MHz}\right)}$$

$$L_{DRIVEN} \left(in\ ft \right) = \frac{468}{21.1\ MHz} = 22.2\ ft$$

Next, use Equation 9-2 to calculate the approximate director length:

(Yagi) $L_{DIRECTOR} = L_{DRIVEN} \times 0.95$

$L_{DIRECTOR} = 22.2\ ft \times 0.95 = 21.1\ ft$

This is approximately 21 ft.

Now suppose you want to find the approximate length for the reflector element of a Yagi antenna for 28.1 MHz. First, use Equation 9-1 to calculate the driven-element length:

(Yagi) $L_{DRIVEN} \left(in\ ft \right) = \frac{468}{f \left(in\ MHz \right)}$

$$L_{DRIVEN} \left(in\ ft \right) = \frac{468}{28.1\ MHz} = 16.7\ ft$$

Next, use Equation 9-3 to calculate the approximate reflector length:

(Yagi) $L_{REFLECTOR} = L_{DRIVEN} \times 1.05$

$L_{REFLECTOR} = 16.7\ ft \times 1.05 = 17.5\ ft$

There can be considerable variation on these lengths, however. The actual lengths depend on factors, such as the spacing between elements, the diameter of the elements, and whether the elements are made from tapered or cylindrical tubing.

The director element is usually the shortest parasitic element on a three-element Yagi antenna. The reflector element is usually the longest parasitic element on a three-element Yagi antenna.

[Now turn to Chapter 12 and study examination questions G9A02 through G9A05. Review the material in this section as needed.]

Front-to-Back Ratio

A typical Yagi-antenna radiation pattern is shown in Figure 9-9. This pattern indicates that the antenna will reject signals coming from the sides and back, selecting mainly those signals from a desired direction. This helps explain why Yagi antennas are so popular for use on crowded HF bands like the 20-meter band. The antenna helps reduce interference from other stations in directions off to the side of the desired station, or from behind the receiving station. Transmitted signals are concentrated in the desired direction, reducing potential interference to stations in directions other than the desired one. The **main lobe** of a Yagi antenna radiation pattern is the direction of maximum radiated field strength from the antenna. If the antenna has higher **gain**, more of the transmitted signal energy is in the direction of the main lobe. One way to increase the gain of a Yagi antenna is by increasing the boom length and adding more directors to the antenna. In general, directors added in front of the driven element are shorter as you move away from the driven element. In other words, a second director added to the

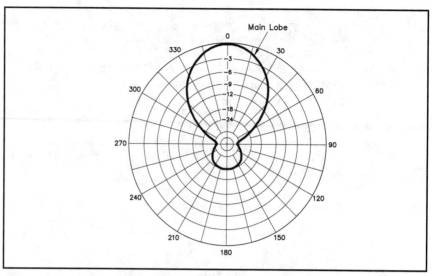

Figure 9-9 — This diagram represents the directive pattern for a typical, three-element Yagi. Note that this pattern is essentially unidirectional, with most of the radiation in the direction of the main lobe. There is also a small *minor lobe* at 180° from the direction of the main lobe, however.

antenna will be shorter and farther from the driven element. Additional reflectors are not generally added to a Yagi antenna.

Front-to-back ratio is the ratio between the power radiated in the major radiation lobe (the direction of maximum radiation — the "front" of the antenna) compared to the power radiated in exactly the opposite direction (the "back" of the antenna). (Sometimes this is also called the *front-to-rear ratio* and is taken to mean the ratio of power radiated in the major lobe compared to power radiated generally behind the antenna rather than just 180° from the maximum radiation lobe.) If you point your antenna directly at a receiving station and transmit, and then turn the antenna 180° and transmit again, the difference in the received signal strength is the front-to-back ratio, which is usually expressed in decibels. An increase in the front-to-back ratio is brought about by adjusting the length of the parasitic elements or their position relative to the driven element and each other. The tuning condition that gives maximum attenuation to the rear is considerably more critical than the condition for maximum forward gain.

In addition to the main radiation lobe, there will usually be one or more *minor* radiation lobes. For a Yagi antenna, there will be a minor lobe at about 180° from the direction of the main lobe, as shown in Figure 9-9. There may also be side lobes at various other angles. For example, suppose an antenna pattern shows a main lobe of radiation at 0° and a minor lobe at 180°. You might describe the radiation pattern by saying most of the signal would be radiated toward 0° and a smaller amount would be radiated toward 180°.

Gain versus Spacing

When we speak of antenna **gain**, we mean gain referenced to another antenna, used for comparison. One common reference antenna is an ideal half-wavelength dipole in free space. The gain of an antenna with parasitic elements varies with the boom length of the antenna, the spacing between elements, and the length and the number of parasitic elements. The maximum front-to-back ratio seldom, if ever, occurs at the same conditions that yield maximum forward gain, and it is frequently necessary to sacrifice some forward gain to get the greatest front-to-back ratio, or vice versa. To obtain maximum performance from a Yagi antenna the lengths and spacing of the elements must be optimized.

Changing the tuning and spacing of the elements also affects the impedance of the driven element. The impedance will vary as the operating frequency changes. The **standing-wave ratio (SWR)** will increase as you move higher and lower than the design operating frequency. The antenna *SWR bandwidth* is the frequency range over which the antenna will have less than some particular SWR, such as the 2:1 SWR bandwidth. The most effective method to increase the SWR bandwidth of a parasitic beam antenna is to use larger-diameter elements.

Theoretically, an optimized three-element (director, driven element and reflector) Yagi antenna has a gain of slightly more than 7 dB over a half-wavelength dipole in free space. Wide element spacing results in an antenna with high gain, wider bandwidth and less critical tuning.

The design of a Yagi antenna is generally optimized for forward gain, front-to-rear gain ratio and SWR bandwidth. You can use computer software to model the antenna and predict how changes to the various parameters will affect your design. One parameter that won't affect the design is whether you plan to orient the antenna elements either horizontally or vertically. (With the elements oriented horizontally the antenna will produce horizontally polarized radiation and with the elements oriented vertically the antenna will produce vertically polarized radiation.)

[Turn to Chapter 12 and study question G9A01 and questions G9A06 through G9A11. Also study question G9C08. Review this material as needed.]

Loop Antennas

There is another type of antenna that uses a parasitic element to produce a directional radiation pattern. The elements of this antenna are full-wavelength loops. The elements of a **cubical quad antenna** (or *quad*) are full-wavelength loops. A typical quad, shown in Figure 9-10, has two elements — a driven element and a reflector. A two-element quad could also use a driven element with a director. More elements, such as a reflector and one or more directors, can be added to increase the directivity of the antenna. By installing additional loops of the right dimensions, we can work different frequency bands with the same antenna. This is commonly done as a modification to a 20-meter quad to provide 15- and 10-meter coverage. The elements of the quad are arranged as a square, with each side a quarter-wavelength long. The total lengths of the elements are calculated as follows:

Figure 9-10 — This drawing shows the construction of a cubical quad antenna. The total length of the driven element can be found using Equation 9-4, and the antenna can be fed directly with coaxial cable.

Circumference of driven element:

$$\text{(Quad) Driven Element Length} \left(\text{in ft} \right) = \frac{1005}{f \left(\text{in MHz} \right)} \qquad \text{(Equation 9-4)}$$

Circumference of director element:

$$\text{(Quad) Director Element Length} \left(\text{in ft} \right) = \frac{975}{f \left(\text{in MHz} \right)} \qquad \text{(Equation 9-5)}$$

Circumference of reflector element:

$$\text{(Quad) Reflector Element Length} \left(\text{in ft} \right) = \frac{1030}{f \left(\text{in MHz} \right)} \qquad \text{(Equation 9-6)}$$

So for a 21.4-MHz cubical quad, the element lengths would be:

$$\text{Driven Element Length} \left(\text{in ft} \right) = \frac{1005}{21.4 \text{ MHz}} = 47.0 \text{ ft}$$

$$\text{Director Element Length} \left(\text{in ft} \right) = \frac{975}{21.4 \text{ MHz}} = 45.6 \text{ ft}$$

$$\text{Reflector Element Length (in ft)} = \frac{1030}{21.4 \text{ MHz}} = 48.1 \text{ ft}$$

These equations give the total length of the elements. To find the length of each side of the antenna, we must divide the total lengths by 4:

$$\text{Driven Element Side (in ft)} = \frac{\text{Driven Element Length (in ft)}}{4} = \frac{47.0 \text{ ft}}{4} = 11.7 \text{ ft}$$

$$\text{Director Element Side (in ft)} = \frac{\text{Director Element Length (in ft)}}{4} = \frac{45.6 \text{ ft}}{4} = 11.4 \text{ ft}$$

$$\text{Reflector Element Side (in ft)} = \frac{\text{Reflector Element Length (in ft)}}{4} = \frac{48.1 \text{ ft}}{4} = 12.0 \text{ ft}$$

Use Equations 9-4, 9-5 and 9-6 to calculate the length of wire needed for a quad antenna on any frequency. Divide these lengths by 4 to calculate the length of one side for each element.

The polarization of the signal from a quad antenna is determined by where the feed point is located on the driven element, as shown in Figure 9-11. With the feed point located in the center of a side parallel to the Earth's surface, the transmitted wave will be horizontally polarized; fed in the center of a perpendicular side, the transmitted wave will be vertically polarized. If we turn the antenna 45°, so it looks like a diamond, and feed it at the bottom corner, the transmitted wave will be horizontally polarized. If the antenna is fed at a side corner, the transmitted wave will be vertically polarized.

Polarization is especially important when building antennas for use at VHF and UHF. Propagation at these frequencies is generally line of sight, and the polarization of a signal does not change from transmitting antenna to receiving antenna. Best signal reception will occur when both transmitting and receiving stations use the same polar-

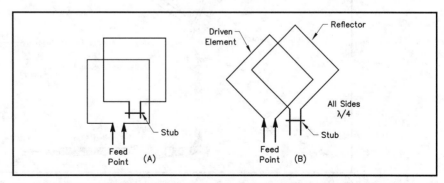

Figure 9-11 — The feed point of a quad antenna determines the polarization. Fed in the middle of the bottom side (as shown at A) or at the bottom corner (as shown at B), the antenna produces a horizontally polarized wave. Vertical polarization is produced by feeding the antenna at the side in either case.

ization. On the HF bands, the polarization of the signal may change many times as it passes through the ionosphere, so antenna polarization is not as important.

A **delta loop antenna** also uses full-wavelength elements, as shown in Figure 9-12. In a delta loop, the elements are triangular rather than square. Equations 9-4, 9-5 and 9-6 also work to calculate the full element lengths for the delta loop. To find the length of each side of the delta loop antenna, the total length is divided by 3, because of the triangular shape of the elements.

For example, suppose you want to design a delta loop antenna for 24.9 MHz. Calculate the loop lengths and the lengths of each side as follows:

Circumference of driven element:

$$\text{(Quad) Driven Element Length (in ft)} = \frac{1005}{f \text{ (in MHz)}} \qquad \text{(Equation 9-4)}$$

Circumference of director element:

$$\text{(Quad) Director Element Length (in ft)} = \frac{975}{f \text{ (in MHz)}} \qquad \text{(Equation 9-5)}$$

Circumference of reflector element:

$$\text{(Quad) Reflector Element Length (in ft)} = \frac{1030}{f \text{ (in MHz)}} \qquad \text{(Equation 9-6)}$$

Figure 9-12 — A delta loop antenna uses full-wavelength loops arranged as triangles with equal sides. The total length of the driven element can be found using the same equation as used for a quad antenna. This antenna is fed with a gamma match.

$$\text{Driven Element Length} \left(\text{in ft}\right) = \frac{1005}{24.9 \text{ MHz}} = 40.46 \text{ ft}$$

$$\text{Director Element Length} \left(\text{in ft}\right) = \frac{975}{24.9 \text{ MHz}} = 39.2 \text{ ft}$$

$$\text{Reflector Element Length} \left(\text{in ft}\right) = \frac{1030}{24.9 \text{ MHz}} = 41.4 \text{ ft}$$

These equations give the total length of the elements. To find the length of each side of the antenna, we must divide the total lengths by 3:

$$\text{Driven Element Side} \left(\text{in ft}\right) = \frac{\text{Driven Element Length} \left(\text{in ft}\right)}{3} = \frac{40.46 \text{ ft}}{3} = 13.45 \text{ ft}$$

$$\text{Director Element Side} \left(\text{in ft}\right) = \frac{\text{Director Element Length (in ft)}}{3} = \frac{39.2 \text{ ft}}{3} = 13.1 \text{ ft}$$

$$\text{Reflector Element Side} \left(\text{in ft}\right) = \frac{\text{Reflector Element Length} \left(\text{in ft}\right)}{3} = \frac{41.4 \text{ ft}}{3} = 13.8 \text{ ft}$$

The radiation pattern of a typical quad is similar to that of the Yagi shown in Figure 9-9. A typical two-element quad or two-element delta loop has a gain of about 6.5 dB over a half-wavelength dipole. This compares favorably with the gain of a three-element Yagi, which is approximately 7 dB. Compared to a dipole antenna, a quad or delta loop antenna has more directivity in both the horizontal and vertical planes. These antennas have a radiation pattern that includes a main lobe, which is the direction of maximum radiated field strength from the antenna. They also exhibit a front-to-back ratio, with more power radiated in the direction of the major lobe compared to the power radiated in exactly the opposite direction.

[Now turn to Chapter 12 and study questions G9B01 through G9B11. Review this section as necessary.]

FEED LINES

A **feed line** (or *transmission line*) is used to transfer power from the transmitter to the antenna. The two basic types of feed lines generally used — **parallel-conductor feed line** and **coaxial cable** — can be constructed in a variety of forms. Both types can be divided into two classes: those in which the majority of the space between the conductors is air, and those in which the conductors are embedded in and separated by a solid plastic or foam insulation (dielectric).

Air-insulated feed lines have the lowest loss per-unit length (usually expressed in dB / 100 ft). Adding a solid dielectric between the conductors increases the losses in the feed line, and decreases the maximum voltage the feed line can withstand before arcing. In general, as frequency increases, feed-line losses become greater. If a 160-meter signal and a 2-meter signal pass through the same coaxial cable, the 2-meter signal will be attenuated a greater amount than the 160-meter signal.

The characteristic impedance of parallel-conductor line depends on the distance between the centers of the conductors and the radius of the conductors. The greater the spacing between the conductors, the higher the characteristic impedance of the feed line. The impedance decreases, however, as the size of the conductors increases. The characteristic impedance of a feed line is not affected by the length of the line.

Solid-Dielectric Feed Lines

Feed lines in which the conductors are separated by a flexible dielectric have several advantages over air-dielectric line: They are less bulky, maintain more uniform spacing between conductors, are generally easier to install and are neater in appearance. Both parallel-conductor and coaxial lines are available with this type of insulation.

One disadvantage of these types of lines is that the power loss per unit length is greater than air-insulated lines because of the dielectric. As the frequency increases, the dielectric losses become greater. The power loss causes heating of the dielectric. If the heating is great enough — as may be the case with high power or a high SWR — the dielectric may actually melt, or arcing may occur inside the line.

One common parallel-conductor feed line has a characteristic impedance of 300 Ω. This type of line is used for TV antenna feed line, and is usually called twin lead. Twin lead consists of two number 20 wires that are molded into the edges of a polyethylene ribbon about a half-inch wide. The presence of the solid dielectric lowers the characteristic impedance of the line as compared to the same conductors in air. Figure 9-13 shows the construction of some common twin lead feed line.

Part of the electric and magnetic fields between the conductors exists outside the solid dielectric. This leads to several operating disadvantages. Dirt or moisture on the surface of the ribbon tends to change the characteristic impedance and increase the line losses. Weather effects can be minimized, however, by coating the feed line with silicone grease or car wax. In any case, the changes in the impedance will not be very serious if the line is terminated in its characteristic impedance (Z_0). If there is a considerable standing-wave ratio, however, then small changes in Z_0 may cause wide fluctuations of the input impedance.

Conductors

Dielectric (Insulator)

Figure 9-13 — This drawing shows the construction of common 300-Ω twin lead.

Coaxial Cable

Coaxial cables are available in flexible and semiflexible formats, but the fundamental design is the same for all types. Some coaxial cables have stranded-wire center conductors, while others employ a solid copper conductor. Figure 9-14 shows the typical construction of coaxial cable. Coaxial cables commonly used by radio amateurs have a characteristic impedance of 50 or 75 Ω. The outer conductor or shield may be a single layer of copper braid, a double layer of braid (more effective shielding), or solid copper or aluminum (most effective shielding). An outer insulating jacket (usually vinyl) provides protection from dirt, moisture and chemicals. Exposure of the dielectric to moisture and chemicals will cause it to deteriorate over time and increase the electrical losses in the line.

The outer conductor or shield serves to contain the electric and magnetic fields inside the cable. This means the impedance of a coaxial line is not affected by weather or other nearby conductors. This is one advantage of coaxial feed lines over parallel conductor feed lines.

The characteristic impedance of a coaxial line depends on the diameter of the center conductor, the inside diameter of the shield braid and the distance between them. The characteristic impedance of coaxial cables increases for larger-diameter shield braids, but it decreases for larger-diameter center conductors.

The larger the diameter, the higher the power-handling capability of the line because of the increased dielectric thickness and conductor size. In general, losses decrease as the cable diameter increases, because there is less power lost in the conductor. As the frequency increases, the conductor and dielectric losses become greater, causing more attenuation of the signal in the cable. Attenuation is not affected by the characteristic impedance of the line, at least if the spacing between the conductors in the coaxial cable is a small fraction of a wavelength at the operating frequency. If the spacing between conductors is a significant portion of a wavelength, the line will begin to act as a waveguide. At frequencies below about 1.5 GHz this is not a problem.

[Turn to Chapter 12 and study the following questions: G9D01, G9D02, G9D03, G9D07 and G9D08. Review this section as needed.]

Figure 9-14 — Coaxial cables consist of a conductor surrounded by insulation. The second conductor, called the shield, goes around the insulation. A plastic insulation goes around the entire cable.

STANDING-WAVE RATIO (SWR)

In a perfect antenna system, all the power put into the feed line would be radiated by the antenna. A practical antenna system will behave most like this ideal when the feed-line impedance is matched to the antenna feed-point impedance. Some power will always be lost in the feed line, but you should select a low-loss line to minimize this. Power lost in the feed line is converted to heat.

If the antenna feed-point impedance does not exactly match the characteristic impedance of the feed line, some power will be reflected back down the feed line from the antenna. A mismatch is said to exist — the greater the mismatch, the more power will be reflected by the antenna. Some of the reflected power is dissipated as heat. In a lossy line more heat is produced than in a lower-loss line. The reflected power is reflected again at the transmitter, and goes back to the antenna. There, some power will be radiated, and some reflected back to the transmitter. This process continues until, eventually, all the power is either radiated by the antenna or lost as heat in the feed line.

The reflected power creates what is called a standing wave. If we measure either the voltage or current at several points along the feed line, we find that it varies from a maximum value to a minimum value at intervals of one-quarter wavelength, as shown in Figure 9-15. The standing wave is created when energy reflected from the antenna meets the forward energy from the transmitter — the two waves alternately cancel and reinforce each other.

The **standing-wave ratio** or **SWR** is defined as the ratio of the maximum voltage to the minimum voltage in the standing wave:

$$SWR = \frac{E_{MAX}}{E_{MIN}}$$

(Equation 9-7)

An SWR of 1:1 means you have no reflected power. The voltage and current are constant at any point along the feed line, and the line is said to be "flat." If the load is completely resistive, then the SWR can be calculated by dividing the line

Figure 9-15 — The standing-wave ratio is the ratio of the voltage amplitude at point A to the voltage amplitude at point B, or the ratio of the current amplitude at point B to the current amplitude at point A.

characteristic impedance by the load resistance, or vice versa — whichever gives a value greater than one:

$$SWR = \frac{Z_0}{R} \text{ or } SWR = \frac{R}{Z_0}$$

(Equation 9-8)

where:

Z_0 = characteristic impedance of the feed line

R = load resistance (not reactance)

For example, if you feed a 50-Ω antenna with a 50-Ω feed line, the impedances are matched, and you will have an SWR of 50 / 50 or 1:1. Similarly if the antenna impedance is 10 Ω and you feed it with 50-Ω feed line, the SWR is 50 / 10 or 5:1. If you feed a 200-Ω antenna with 50-Ω feed line, the SWR is 200 / 50 or 4:1.

When a high SWR condition exists, losses in the feed line are increased. This is because of the multiple reflections of the signal between the antenna and transmitter. Each time the transmitted power has to travel up and down the feed line, a little more energy is lost as heat. This effect is not as great as some people believe, however. If the line loss is less than 2 dB (such as for 100 feet of RG-8 or RG-58 cables up to about 30 MHz), the SWR would have to be greater than 3:1 to add an extra decibel of loss because of the SWR.

When a feed line is terminated in a resistance equal to its characteristic impedance, maximum power is delivered to the antenna, and feed line losses are minimized. This would be an ideal condition, although such a perfect match is seldom realized in a practical antenna system.

IMPEDANCE MATCHING

Most currently manufactured Amateur Radio transmitters are designed to be connected to antenna systems with impedances of 50 to 75 Ω. Some transmitters with vacuum-tube power amplifiers that have a tunable output circuit, however, can be adjusted to match impedances over a greater range. Depending on the type of antenna you are using, you may have to improve the match between the feed line and the antenna. A matching network (often called a *Transmatch*) can be used near the transmitter to match the transmitter 50-Ω output impedance to the antenna-system impedance.

When a coaxial cable is used to feed a half-wave dipole, a transformer, called a **balun** (*bal*anced to *un*balanced), can be used to decouple the feed line from the antenna. This prevents the feed line from radiating a signal, which could distort the antenna radiation pattern.

Many amateurs prefer to use parallel-conductor feed line because of its lower loss than coaxial cable. This type of feed line is a **balanced line**, and so will not disturb the balanced nature of a dipole antenna. Modern amateur transceivers use a coaxial-cable connector for the antenna, however. Parallel-conductor feed line requires the use of a balun to change the balanced line condition of the parallel-conductor feed line to the **unbalanced line** condition of the coaxial cable.

An inductively coupled impedance-matching network transforms the unbalanced line output (one side grounded to the chassis) at the transceiver to a balanced line output for use with a parallel-conductor feed line. Figure 9-16 shows such a

Figure 9-16 — A link-coupled impedance-matching network is suitable for use with balanced lines.

Transmatch circuit, which *tunes* the balanced feed line to allow the antenna to be used on several bands. The coil taps and capacitor settings are adjusted for lowest SWR. Higher impedance loads are tapped farther out from the center of the coil. The split-stator capacitor (C_1 and C_2) is used because it provides two symmetric sections that are tuned simultaneously with a single control. Normally, a short length of coaxial cable connects the transmitter to an inductively coupled impedance-matching network. Parallel-conductor feed line then connects the matching network to the antenna. An inductively coupled matching network is not normally used when a coaxial-cable feed line goes all the way to a center-fed resonant dipole antenna.

It is important to note that even though a transmitter may "see" a pure 50-Ω load, and the SWR between the transmitter and matching device is 1:1, the SWR measured in the feed line between the matching device and the antenna may not be 1:1. Inserting a matching device between the feed line and the transmitter does not affect the SWR in the feed line between the matching device and the antenna; the matching device only provides a 50-Ω resistive load for the transmitter. The SWR meter should be placed between the transmitter and the Transmatch to adjust the matching network properly.

[Now complete your study of this chapter by turning to Chapter 12 and studying questions G9D04 through G9D06 and questions G9D09 through G9D11. Review this section as needed. That completes your study of the material in this chapter for your General examination.]

Athermal effects of RF radiation — Biological effects of RF radiation not directly related to heating effects in exposed body tissue. While research is ongoing, no conclusive evidence has been found to demonstrate that such fields cause serious health effects at low-level energy exposure.

Duty cycle — The ratio between the actual RMS value of an RF signal and the RMS value of a continuous signal having the same PEP value, expressed as a percentage. A duty cycle of 100% corresponds to a continuous carrier, such as a test signal.

Electric field strength — This is the field resulting from the electric charge distribution present on a radiating element. Electric field strength is expressed in volts per meter (V / m).

Far field of an antenna — That region of the electromagnetic field surrounding an antenna where the field strength as a function of angle (the antenna pattern) is essentially independent of the distance from the antenna. In this region (also called the free-space region), the field has a predominantly plane-wave character. That is, locally uniform distributions of electric field strength and magnetic field strength are in a plane perpendicular to the direction of propagation.

Magnetic field strength — This is the field resulting from the currents on a radiating element. Magnetic field strength is expressed in amperes per meter (A / m).

Maximum Permissible Exposure (MPE) limits — The electric field strength, magnetic field strength and plane-wave equivalent power density associated with a radiated electromagnetic wave to which a person may be exposed without harmful effect, and with an acceptable safety factor.

Near field of an antenna — That region of the electromagnetic field immediately surrounding an antenna where the reactive field dominates and where the field strength as a function of angle (the antenna pattern) depends upon the distance from the antenna. It is a region in which the electric and magnetic fields do not have a substantial plane-wave character, but vary considerably from point to point.

Power density — A measure of the power flow through a unit area normal (perpendicular) to the direction of propagation. It is usually expressed in watts per square meter (W / m^2)

Routine RF evaluation — A procedure required of some Amateur Radio stations, to determine that the station meets the maximum permissible exposure (MPE) limits established by FCC Rules.

Specific absorption rate (SAR) — A measure of the rate at which RF energy is absorbed in body tissue. SAR is expressed in units of watts per kilogram (W / kg). The SAR depends on the frequency of the energy, the power density of the RF field that strikes the body and factors such as the polarization of the wave.

Thermal effects of RF radiation — Body tissue changes that are directly related to heat production when RF energy is absorbed. For example, in extreme cases at high levels of SAR, hyperthermia and tissue damage can occur. It has been demonstrated that in extreme cases, RF-induced heating in the eyes of laboratory animals can result in cataract formation.

Time averaging — Transmitter power is averaged over times of 6 minutes for controlled RF environments or 30 minutes for uncontrolled RF environments for power density calculations to determine exposure levels.

RF SAFETY

In August 1996, the FCC announced new rules governing exposure to radio frequency (RF) radiation. These new rules set limits on the amount of RF energy to which people may be exposed. The rules also require that some stations be evaluated to determine if they are in compliance with these rules. (Almost all Amateur Radio operation is already in compliance with the rules, but amateurs must be familiar with the requirements.) The new FCC Rules also added a new exam topic with 5 additional exam questions to the Novice (Element 2), Technician (Element 3A) and General (Element 3B) examinations.

The Novice and Technician question pools put into use on July 1, 1997 included that new topic and questions. This General question pool, put into use on July 1, 1998 also includes the RF Safety topic and questions. Your General license exam will include 5 questions, based on these 5 exam topics:

G0A   RF safety principles
G0B   RF safety rules and guidelines
G0C   Routine station evaluation and measurements (FCC Part 97 refers to RF radiation evaluation)
G0D   Practical RF-safety applications
G0E   RF-safety solutions

The material in this chapter will help you begin to understand the issues involved with RF radiation safety. ARRL's *RF Exposure and You* is a book written to provide you with much more detailed information about the FCC Rules related to

RF exposure. That book will also help you understand the process of performing an RF environmental evaluation and includes step-by-step instructions and tables to help you determine that your station meets the maximum permissible exposure requirements. You can order the book directly from the ARRL or purchase a copy from a local ARRL dealer.

RF SAFETY PRINCIPLES

Amateur Radio is basically a safe activity. In recent years, however, there has been considerable discussion and concern about the possible hazards of electromagnetic radiation (EMR), including both RF energy and power-frequency (50-60 Hz) electromagnetic (EM) fields. FCC regulations set **maximum permissible exposure (MPE) limits** allowed from the operation of radio transmitters. These regulations do not take the place of RF-safety practices, however. This section deals with the topic of RF safety.

This section was prepared by members of the ARRL RF Safety Committee and coordinated by Dr Robert E. Gold, WBØKIZ. It summarizes what is now known and offers safety precautions based on the research to date.

All life on Earth has adapted to survive in an environment of weak, natural, low-frequency electromagnetic fields (in addition to the Earth's static geomagnetic field). Natural low-frequency EM fields come from two main sources: the sun and thunderstorm activity. But in the last 100 years, man-made fields at much higher intensities and with a very different spectral distribution have altered this natural EM background in ways that are not yet fully understood. Researchers continue to look at the effects of RF exposure over a wide range of frequencies and levels.

The energy from both RF and 60-Hz fields are classified as *nonionizing radiation*, because the frequency is too low for there to be enough photon energy to ionize atoms. (*Ionizing radiation*, such as X-rays, gamma rays and even some ultraviolet radiation has enough energy to knock electrons loose from their atoms. When this happens, positive and negative ions are formed.) Still, at sufficiently high power densities, EMR poses certain health hazards. It has been known since the early days of radio that RF energy can cause injuries by heating body tissue. (Anyone who has ever touched an improperly grounded radio chassis or energized antenna and received an *RF burn* will agree that this type of injury can be quite painful.) It has been demonstarted that in extreme cases, RF-induced heating in the eyes of laboratory animals can result in cataract formation and can even cause blindness. Excessive RF heating of the reproductive organs can cause sterility. Other health problems also can result from RF heating. These heat-related health hazards are called **thermal effects of RF radiation**. A microwave oven is a positive application of this thermal effect.

There also have been observations of changes in physiological function in the presence of RF energy levels that are too low to cause measurable body heating. These functions return to normal when the field is removed. Although research is ongoing, no harmful health consequences have been linked to these changes.

In addition to the ongoing research, much else has been done to address this issue. For example, FCC regulations set limits on exposure from radio transmitters. The Institute of Electrical and Electronics Engineers (IEEE), The American

National Standards Institute (ANSI) and the National Council for Radiation Protection and Measurement, among others, have recommended voluntary guidelines to limit human exposure to RF energy. The ARRL has established the RF Safety Committee, consisting of concerned medical doctors and scientists, serving voluntarily to monitor scientific research in the fields and to recommend safe practices for radio amateurs.

Thermal Effects of RF Energy

Body tissues that are subjected to *very high* levels of RF energy may suffer serious heat damage. These effects depend upon the frequency (or wavelength) of the energy, the power density of the RF field that strikes the body, and even on factors such as the polarization of the wave.

For a given exposure level at frequencies near the body's natural resonant frequency, RF energy is absorbed more efficiently, and an increase in heating occurs. In adults, this frequency usually is about 35 MHz if the person is grounded, and about 70 MHz if the person's body is insulated from the ground. Individual body parts may be resonant at different frequencies. The adult head, for example is resonant around 400 MHz, while a baby's smaller head resonates near 700 MHz. Human eyes have a free-space resonance in the 1270-MHz range. This resonance may be modified by the presence of other tissues surrounding the eye. Body size and structure thus determine the frequency at which most RF energy is absorbed. As the frequency is moved further from resonance, less RF heating generally occurs at a given exposure level. **Specific absorption rate (SAR)** is a term that describes the rate at which RF energy is absorbed into the human body tissue. This quantity, expressed in watts per kilogram (W / kg) best associates the RF energy absorption with the biological effects of RF fields on the human body.

Maximum permissible exposure (MPE) limits are based on whole-body averaged SAR values, with additional safety factors included as part of the standards and regulations. This helps explain why these safe exposure limits vary with frequency. The MPE limits define the maximum **electric field strength** and **magnetic field strength** or the plane-wave equivalent **power density** associated with these fields, that a person may be exposed to without harmful effect — and with an acceptable safety factor. The regulations assume that a person exposed to a specified (safe) MPE level will also experience a safe SAR.

Nevertheless, thermal effects of RF energy should not be a major concern for most radio amateurs, because of the power levels we normally use and the intermittent nature of most amateur transmissions. Amateurs spend more time listening than transmitting, and many amateur transmissions such as CW and SSB have a low **duty cycle**. Duty cycle takes into account the reduced average transmitted power that results because the transmitter is not operating at full power continuously. This means greater short-term exposure levels can be permitted with low-duty-cycle emissions. (With FM or RTTY, though, the RF is present continuously at its maximum level during each transmission. These high-duty-cycle modes require lower short-term exposure levels.) In any event, it is rare for radio amateurs to be subjected to RF fields strong enough to produce thermal effects unless they are fairly close to an energized antenna or unshielded power amplifier. Specific suggestions for avoiding excessive exposure are offered later in this chapter.

The frequency of the radio signal, the power density (and electric and magnetic field strengths) of the energy and the duty cycle of the transmission mode are all important in estimating the effects of RF energy on body tissue. *Critical angle* is a property of the radiation that is related to how the wave interacts with the ionosphere, but is *not* a factor in determining the effects of RF energy.

Athermal Effects of RF Radiation

Athermal effects of RF radiation have become a concern for exposures to lower-level energy fields that are believed to be too weak to cause either ionization or heating effects. Research about possible athermal health effects resulting from exposure to the lower level energy fields has been of two basic types: epidemiological research and laboratory research.

Scientists conduct laboratory research into biological mechanisms by which EMR may affect animals including humans. Epidemiologists look at the health patterns of large groups of people using statistical methods. These epidemiological studies have been inconclusive. By their basic design, these studies do not demonstrate cause and effect, nor do they postulate mechanisms of disease. Instead, epidemiologists look for associations between an environmental factor and an observed pattern of illness. For example, in the earliest research on malaria, epidemiologists observed the association between populations with high prevalence of the disease and the proximity of mosquito infested swamplands. It was left to the biological and medical scientists to isolate the organism causing malaria in the blood of those with the disease and identify the same organisms in the mosquito population.

In the case of athermal effects, some studies have identified a weak association between exposure to EMF at home or at work and various malignant conditions including leukemia and brain cancer. A larger number of equally well designed and performed studies, however, have found no association. A risk ratio of between 1.5 and 2.0 has been observed in positive studies (the number of observed cases of malignancy being 1.5 to 2.0 times the "expected" number in the population). Epidemiologists generally regard a risk ratio of 4.0 or greater to be indicative of a strong association between the cause and effect under study. For example, men who smoke one pack of cigarettes per day increase their risk for lung cancer tenfold compared to nonsmokers, and two packs per day increase the risk to more than 25 times the nonsmokers' risk.

Epidemiological research by itself is rarely conclusive, however. Epidemiology only identifies health patterns in groups — it does not ordinarily determine their cause. And there are often confounding factors: Most of us are exposed to many different environmental hazards that may affect our health in various ways. Moreover, not all studies of persons likely to be exposed to high levels of EMR have yielded the same results.

There has also been considerable laboratory research about the biological effects of EMR in recent years. For example, it has been shown that even fairly low levels of EMR can alter the human body's circadian rhythms, affect the manner in which cancer-fighting T lymphocytes function in the immune system, and alter the nature of the electrical and chemical signals communicated through the cell membrane and between cells, among other things. Although these studies are intriguing, they do not demonstrate any effect of these low-level fields on the overall organism.

Much of this research has focused on low-frequency magnetic fields, or on RF fields that are keyed, pulsed or modulated at a low audio frequency (often below 100 Hz). Several studies suggested that humans and animals can adapt to the presence of a steady RF carrier more readily than to an intermittent, keyed or modulated energy source.

The results of studies in this area, plus speculations concerning the effect of various types or modulation, were and have remained somewhat controversial. None of the research to date conclusively proves that low-level EMR causes adverse health effects.

Given the fact that there is a great deal of ongoing research to examine the health consequences of exposure to EMF, the American Physical Society (a national group of highly respected scientists) issued a statement in May 1995 based on its review of available data pertaining to the possible connections of cancer to 60-Hz EMF exposure. This report is exhaustive and should be reviewed by anyone with a serious interest in the field. Among its general conclusions were the following:

1. The scientific literature and the reports of reviews by other panels show no consistent, significant link between cancer and power line fields.

2. No plausible biophysical mechanisms for the systematic initiation or promotion of cancer by these extremely weak 60-Hz fields has been identified.

3. While it is impossible to prove that no deleterious health effects occur from exposure to any environmental factor, it is necessary to demonstrate a consistent, significant, and causal relationship before one can conclude that such effects do occur.

A National Cancer Institute epidemiological study of residential exposure to magnetic fields and acute lymphoblastic leukemia in children was published in the *New England Journal of Medicine* in July 1997. The exhaustive seven-year study concludes that if there is any link at all, it is far too weak to be concerned about.

Readers may want to follow this topic as further studies are reported. Amateurs should be aware that exposure to RF and ELF (60 Hz) electromagnetic fields at all power levels and frequencies has not been fully studied under all circumstances. Most amateur operations are well within the MPE limits. If any risk does exist, it will almost surely fall well down on the list of causes that may be harmful to your health (on the other end of the list from your automobile). It does mean, however, that hams should be aware of the potential for exposure from their stations, and take whatever reasonable steps they can take to minimize their own exposure and the exposure of those around them.

[Turn to Chapter 12 now and study questions G0A01 through G0A06 and G0B03. Review this section as needed.]

SAFE EXPOSURE LEVELS

How much EM energy is safe? Scientists and regulators have devoted a great deal of effort to deciding upon safe RF-exposure limits. This is a very complex problem, involving difficult public health and economic considerations. The recommended safe levels have been revised downward several times in recent years

— and not all scientific bodies agree on this question even today. An Institute of Electrical and Electronics Engineers (IEEE) standard for recommended EM exposure limits went into effect in 1991. It replaced a 1982 American National Standards Institute (ANSI) standard. In the new standard, most of the permitted exposure levels were revised downward (made more stringent), to better reflect the current research. The new IEEE standard was adopted by ANSI in 1992.

The IEEE standard recommends frequency-dependent and time-dependent maximum permissible exposure levels. Unlike earlier versions of the standard, the 1991 standard recommends different RF exposure limits in *controlled environments* (that is, where energy levels can be accurately determined and everyone on the premises is aware of the presence of EM fields) and in *uncontrolled environments* (where energy levels are not known or where some persons present may not be aware of the EM fields). FCC regulations also include controlled/occupational and uncontrolled/general population exposure environments.

The graph in Figure 10-1 depicts the 1991 IEEE standard. It is necessarily a complex graph, because the standards differ not only for controlled and uncontrolled environments but also for electric (E) fields and magnetic (H) fields. Basically, the lowest E-field exposure limits occur at the very high frequency (VHF) range, between 30 and 300 MHz. The lowest H-field exposure levels occur at 100-300 MHz. The ANSI standard sets the maximum E-field limits between 30 and 300 MHz at a power density of 1 mW/cm^2 (61.4 V/m) in controlled environments — but at one-fifth that level (0.2 mW/cm^2 or 27.5 V/m) in uncontrolled environments. The H-field limit drops to 1 mW/cm^2 (0.163 A/m) at 100-300 MHz in controlled environments and 0.2 mW/cm^2 (0.0728 A/m) in uncontrolled environments. Higher power densities are permitted at frequencies below 30 MHz (below 100 MHz for H fields) and above 300 MHz, based on the concept that the body will

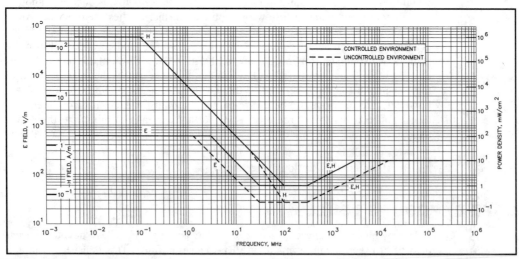

Figure 10-1 — 1991 RF protection guidelines for body exposure of humans. It is known officially as the "IEEE Standard for Safety Levels with Respect to Human Exposure to Radio Frequency Electromagnetic Fields, 3 kHz to 300 GHz."

not be resonant at those frequencies and will therefore absorb less energy.

In general, the 1991 IEEE standard requires averaging the power level over time periods ranging from 6 to 30 minutes for power-density calculations, depending on the frequency and other variables. The ANSI exposure limits for uncontrolled environments are lower than those for controlled environments, but to compensate for that the standard allows exposure levels in those environments to be averaged over much longer time periods (generally 30 minutes). This long averaging time means that an intermittently operating RF source (such as an Amateur Radio transmitter) will show a much lower power density than a continuous-duty station — for a given power level and antenna configuration. **Time averaging** takes into account the total RF exposure averaged over a certain specified time.

Time averaging is based on the concept that the human body can withstand a greater rate of body heating (and thus, a higher level of RF energy) for a short time than for a longer period. Time averaging may not be appropriate, however, when considering nonthermal effects of RF energy.

The IEEE standard excludes any transmitter with an output below 7 W because such low-power transmitters would not be able to produce significant whole-body heating. (Recent studies show that hand-held transceivers often produce power densities in excess of the IEEE standard within the head.)

There is disagreement within the scientific community about these RF exposure guidelines. The IEEE standard was based on an assessment procedure of the peer-reviewed literature where classifications of findings were made without prejudgment of the mechanisms of the effects. The standards committee observed that no reliable scientific data exist indicating that athermal (other than shock) or modulation specific characteristics of exposure may be meaningfully related to human health. A small but significant number of researchers now believe that athermal effects should be given more attention. Several European countries and localities in the United States have adopted stricter standards than the recently updated IEEE standard.

Another national body in the United States, the National Council for Radiation Protection and Measurement (NCRP), also has adopted recommended exposure guidelines. NCRP urges a limit of 0.2 mW/cm^2 for nonoccupational exposure in the 30-300 MHz range. The NCRP guideline differs from IEEE in two notable ways: It takes into account the effects of modulation on an RF carrier, and it does not exempt transmitters with outputs below 7 W.

The FCC MPE regulations are based on parts of the 1992 IEEE/ANSI standard and recommendations of the National Council for Radiation Protection and Measurement (NCRP). The MPE limits under the regulations are slightly different than the IEEE/ANSI limits. Note that the MPE levels apply to the FCC Rules put into effect for radio amateurs on January 1, 1998. These MPE requirements do not reflect and include all the assumptions and exclusions of the IEEE/ANSI standard.

[Turn to Chapter 13 and study questions G0A07 and G0A08. Review this section as needed.]

THE RF EXPOSURE RULES

The rules and guidelines set **maximum permissible exposure (MPE) limits** for humans who are near radio transmitters. The regulations control *exposure* to RF fields, not the *strength* of RF fields. There is no limit to how strong a field can be as long as no one is being exposed to it, although FCC regulations require that amateurs use the minimum necessary power at all times (§97.313(a)). If the operation of your station resulted in exposure over the limits in areas where there are no people *at the time you are operating*, the station is still in compliance.

All radio stations must comply with the requirements for MPEs; even QRP stations running only a few watts or less! The MPEs vary with frequency, as shown in Table 10-1.

MPEs are derived from the Specific Absorption Rate (SAR) — the rate at which tissue absorbs RF energy, usually expressed in watts per kilogram (W/kg). The FCC MPEs are not based strictly on IEEE/ANSI C95.1-1992, but rather on a hybrid between that standard and the report written by the NCRP (the National Council on Radiation Protection and Measurements). NCRP is a body commissioned to develop recommendations for federal agencies. In terms of exposure levels, the NCRP report recommends lower MPE levels over some frequency ranges than are found in the IEEE/ANSI standard. The most stringent requirements are from 30 to 300 MHz, because various human-body resonances fall in that frequency range.

MPE limits are specified in maximum electric and magnetic fields for frequencies below 30 MHz, in power density for frequencies above 300 MHz and all three ways for frequencies from 30 to 300 MHz. For compliance purposes, all these limits must be

Table 10-1
Limits for Maximum Permissible Exposure (MPE)

Frequency Range (MHz)	Controlled Exposure (6-Minute Average)			Uncontrolled Exposure (30-Minute Average)		
	Electric Field Strength (V/m)	Magnetic Field Strength (A/m)	Power Density (mW/cm^2)	Electric Field Strength (V/m)	Magnetic Field Strength (A/m)	Power Density (mW/cm^2)
0.3-3.0	614	1.63	(100)*			
3.0-30	1842/f	4.89/f	(900/f^2)*			
0.3-1.34				614	1.63	(100)*
1.34-30				824/f	2.19/f	(180/f^2)*
30-300	61.4	0.163	1.0	27.5	0.073	0.2
300-1500	—	—	f/300	—	—	f/1500
1,500-100,000	—	—	5	—	—	1.0

f = frequency in MHz
* = Plane-wave equivalent power density

Note 1: Occupational/controlled limits apply in situations in which persons are exposed as a consequence of their employment provided those persons are fully aware of the potential for exposure and can exercise control over their exposure. Limits for occupational/controlled exposure also apply in situations when an individual is transient through a location where occupational/controlled limits apply provided he or she is made aware of the potential for exposure.

Note 2: General population/uncontrolled exposures apply in situations in which the general public may be exposed, or in which persons that are exposed as a consequence of their employment may not be fully aware of the potential for exposure or can not exercise control over their exposure.

considered separately — if any one is exceeded, the station is not in compliance.

For example, if a 144-MHz amateur station had an H-field exposure level of 0.08 A/m (amperes/meter) and an E-field exposure of 22 V/m (volts/meter), the station is not in compliance for exposure to the general public because the H field limit has been exceeded, even though the E field is below the limits.

MPEs Vary with Frequency

The MPE limits vary with frequency, as shown in Table 10-1. The human body is roughly resonant (for different body sizes and under differing conditions) at frequencies between 30 and 300 MHz. The MPEs are the most stringent over this frequency range. In Table 10-1, there are separate limits for the electric field (E field), the magnetic field (H field) and power density. The electric field is specified in volts per meter (V/m), the magnetic field is specified in amperes per meter (A/m) and the power density is specified in milliwatts per square centimeter. In addition, for some frequencies the term "plane-wave equivalent power density" is used.

Average Exposure

Table 10-1 shows the MPE limits for various frequency ranges. MPEs assume continuous-duty and operation at the average rate. The levels shown assume that the exposure will be continuous over the exposure period. The regulations, however, average the total exposure over 6 minutes for controlled environments and 30 minutes for uncontrolled environments. This average includes both the duty factor of the operating mode and the actual on and off times over the worst-case averaging period. In most cases, the average power of an amateur station is considerably less than its peak power, and the ratio of transmit time to nontransmit time is less than 100%.

Thus, it is permissible to exceed the MPE limits for some time, as long as that is offset by a corresponding reduction in the exposure limits for other times within the averaging period. For example, in an uncontrolled environment, if one is in a field that is 10 times the limit for 3 minutes, this is acceptable as long as one has no exposure for the preceding 27 minutes *and* the following 27 minutes. The 30-minute window is not based on arbitrary half-hour segments by the clock, but is a "sliding" window, such that in *any* 30-minute period, the total exposure must be below the limits. It would not be acceptable to have no exposure for 15 minutes, twice the exposure for 15 minutes, then be exposed at the limit for the next 15 minutes because the total exposure in the worst-case window (the last 30 minutes) exceeds the average MPE levels. There are a number of ways to calculate the time-averaged exposure.

Who Must Comply

All Amateur Radio stations must comply with the MPE limits, regardless of power, operating mode or station configuration. Even a 10-milliwatt station must comply. It is unlikely that low-power stations would exceed the limits, but the rules apply equally to all.

Routine Environmental Evaluations

The FCC RF safety rules are designed to control the maximum permissible human exposure to all RF radiated fields. The core of the requirements under these regulations, then, are the MPE levels. The core of the specific actions that need to be taken by Amateur Radio operators, however, is the requirement for some amateurs to perform a "routine environmental evaluation" for RF exposure. This will establish that the station is being operated in compliance with the FCC RF-Exposure guidelines.

A **routine RF evaluation** is not nearly as onerous as it sounds! This subject is covered in detail in ARRL's *RF Exposure and You*, but it is summarized here, as part of the discussion about the rules. Doing an evaluation will help ensure a safe operating environment for amateurs, their families and neighbors.

The FCC is relying on the demonstrated technical skill of Amateur Radio operators to *evaluate their own stations* (although it is perfectly okay for an amateur to rely on another amateur or skilled professional to perform the evaluation).

Most evaluations will not involve measurements, but will be done with comparisons against typical charts developed by the FCC, relatively straightforward calculations or computer modeling of near-field signal strength. The FCC encourages flexibility in the analysis, and will accept any technically valid approach.

It is not difficult to do the necessary station evaluation. The FCC guidance is contained in *OET Bulletin No. 65: Evaluating Compliance With FCC-Specified Guidelines for Human Exposure to Radio Frequency Radiation* and an Amateur Radio supplement to that bulletin, *Supplement B to OET Bulletin 65: Additional Information for Amateur Radio Stations*. The FCC material contains the basic information hams need to evaluate their stations, including a number of tables showing compliance distances for typical amateur power levels and antennas. The ARRL also publishes a book, *RF Exposure and You*, which includes more information and extensive tables listing common amateur station configurations. Generally, hams will use tables like these to evaluate their stations.

In most cases, hams will be able to use a table that best describes their station's operation to determine the minimum compliance distance for their specific operation. These tables show the compliance distances for uncontrolled environments for a particular type of antenna at a particular height. (The power levels shown in the tables are average power levels, adjusted for the duty cycle of the operating mode being used, and operating on and off time, averaged over 6 minutes for controlled environments or 30 minutes for uncontrolled environments.)

What should you do if you perform the routine RF evaluation on your station and determine that the RF fields exceed the FCC exposure limits in human-accessible areas? Simply take action to prevent human exposure to the excessive RF fields! There are many ways to accomplish that task, and the FCC allows you great latitude to decide what steps are appropriate. For example, you can move your antennas farther away, restrict access to the areas where the exposure would exceed the limits, or reduce power to reduce the field strengths in those areas.

Categorical Exemptions

Some types of amateur stations do not need to be evaluated (but these stations must still comply with the MPE limits!) The FCC has exempted these stations from the evaluation requirement because their output power, operating mode, use, frequency or antenna location are such that they are presumed to be in compliance

Table 10-2

Power Thresholds for Routine Evaluation of Amateur Radio Stations

Wavelength Band	Evaluation Required if Power* (watts) Exceeds:
MF	
160 m	500
HF	
80 m	500
75 m	500
40 m	500
30 m	425
20 m	225
17 m	125
15 m	100
12 m	75
10 m	50
VHF (all bands)	50
UHF	
70 cm	70
33 cm	150
23 cm	200
13 cm	250
SHF (all bands)	250
EHF (all bands)	250
Repeater stations (all bands)	*non-building-mounted antennas*: height above ground level to lowest point of antenna < 10 m *and* power > 500 W ERP *building-mounted antennas*: power > 500 W ERP

*Transmitter power = Peak-envelope power input to antenna. For repeater stations **only**, power exclusion based on ERP (effective radiated power).

with the rules. These stations are *not* exempt from the rules, but are presumed to be in compliance without the need for an evaluation.

• Stations using the peak-envelope power levels or less to the antenna as shown in Table 10-2.
• Amateur repeaters using 500-W ERP or less.
• Amateur repeaters with antennas not mounted on buildings if the antenna is located more than 10 meters (32.8 feet) high above ground.
• Amateur mobile and portable hand-held stations using push-to-talk or equivalent operation.

Note that Table 10-2 cites power to the antenna. This is not the same as your transmitter output power, although you can conservatively use your transmitter output power to decide if you need to do an evaluation, if you wish. As an example, if you are running 90 W PEP and have a feed line loss of 3 dB, you are losing approximately 50% of your power in the feed line, so you have approximately 45 W PEP to the antenna.

This part of your operation would not have to be evaluated on any band. Note, too, that unlike the MPE, the levels in this table are *not* average-power levels, but are peak-envelope powers (PEP). If you transmit only one short dit per 30-minute period, and that dit is transmitted at levels above those in the chart, you will still have to do an evaluation. When you did the evaluation, however, you could use average power. Admittedly, this sounds a bit complex, but it is explained in detail in ARRL's *RF Exposure and You*.

Table 10-2 is taken from §97.13(c)(1). That table forms the guideline used to determine if a routine RF evaluation must be performed. Stations that use more power than the power levels to the antenna shown in Table 10-2 must be evaluated. Most HF transceivers are rated at 100-W PEP output; on 15 meters and below, stations using this power level need not be evaluated. In fact, stations operating on frequencies lower than 21 MHz can operate with even higher power without being required to perform an evaluation. On 17 meters, the threshold is 175 W PEP and on 20 meters it jumps to 225 W PEP. Although amateurs are only permitted to use 200 W PEP on the 30-meter band, the RF evaluation threshold is 425 W PEP on that band! On the 40, 80 and 160-meter bands, the threshold is 500 W PEP.

Operators who wish to use 12 and 10 meters with a 100-watt transceiver could either perform an evaluation for those two bands, or they could reduce power to 75 W PEP on 12 meters and 50 W PEP on 10 meters and forego the evaluation altogether. Most VHF transceivers are rated at 50-W PEP output or less; stations using this power level on VHF (the 6, 2 and 1.25 meter bands) need not be evaluated.

The power levels used to determine if an RF environmental evaluation is required vary with frequency. Compare the MPE levels in Table 10-1 for the various frequencies with the evaluation threshold levels shown in Table 10-2. You will see that the evaluation thresholds vary in much the same way as the MPE limits. Where higher exposure is permitted, the evaluation threshold is higher and where the MPE is lower, so is the evaluation threshold.

Repeater Operation

All amateur repeaters operating at a power of 500 W ERP or less are generally categorically exempt from evaluation. All amateur repeaters whose antennas are not mounted on buildings and that have all parts of their radiating antenna located at least 10 meters (32.8 feet) above ground also are exempt. Amateur repeaters with antennas located on buildings (presumably buildings where people could be located) must be evaluated if they use more than 500 W ERP. ERP is derived by multiplying the power to the antenna by the numerical gain of the antenna over a dipole (6 dBd, for example, represents a numerical equivalent of 3.98). This categorical exemption from evaluation will probably cover many repeater stations.

Multitransmitter Sites

The rules are intended to ensure that operation of transmitters regulated by the FCC doesn't result in exposure in excess of MPE limits. It is fairly easy to make this determination for single transmitters, when there are no other sources of RF to complicate things. However, many transmitters operate in proximity to other transmitters, and it is entirely possible for two or more transmitters to all be below their own limit, but the total exposure from them all operating together to be greater than the permitted MPEs. Amateur repeaters are the most likely stations to be located at a site with multiple transmitters operating in several radio services. The multitransmitter rules aren't limited to repeater stations, however.

The FCC regulations and other FCC documents cover the likely situation of multiple transmitters. The bottom line is that, in most cases, all the *significant* RF transmitters operating at multitransmitter sites generally must be considered when determining if the site's total exposure is in compliance. In addition, all significant emitters are jointly responsible for overall site compliance.

The rules stipulate that in a multi-transmitter environment, a single transmitter operator is jointly responsible with other operators at the site for all areas at the site where the exposure from that transmitter is greater than 5% *of what is permitted for that transmitter.* (This is 5% of the permitted power density or 5% of the square of the E or H-field value.) Note that this is *not* the same as 5% of the total exposure, which could sometimes be unknown.

In many cases involving Amateur Radio transmitters, only a relatively small area would be encompassed by that 5% exposure threshold, so joint responsibility might only exist in the immediate vicinity of the amateur antenna. A repeater trustee, for example, might have that 5% level extend only to those areas to 10 feet above and below the antenna up the tower, and thus be responsible for overall site compliance only to that area on the tower. In this case, the responsibility may be only to radio service personnel climbing the tower (generally a controlled exposure environment would apply) or tower maintenance people (who may or may not be trained about RF exposure, so an uncontrolled environment may be more appropriate).

Often, you may not know much about the other transmitters on your site. In that case, you should make the best assumptions you can about the other stations' power, antenna gains and operating duty cycles, and conduct your assessment of site compliance accordingly.

[Turn to Chapter 12 and study questions G0A09, G0A10, G0A11, G0B01, G0B02 and G0B04 through G0B11. Review the material in this section if you have difficulty with any of those questions.]

Paperwork and Proof of Evaluation

Performing a routine RF exposure evaluation is the most important step you can take to ensure that your station is in compliance with the FCC RF safety regulations. Even if your station is exempt from the requirement to perform such an evaluation, you might want to do a simple evaluation. As a minimum, it will be good practice for the time that you make a station change that might require evaluation. The results of your evaluation will certainly demonstrate to yourself, and possibly to your neighbors, that your station operation is well within the guidelines, and is no cause for concern.

Once you determine that your Amateur Radio station complies with the regulations, you may begin operating. There's no need for FCC approval before operating. Other than a short certification on Form 610 station applications when applying for a new license or a license renewal, the regulations do not normally require hams to file proof of evaluation with the FCC. The Commission recommends that each amateur keep a record of the station evaluation procedure and its results, in case questions arise.

When you make changes to your station, you may need to perform a new RF safety evaluation. You should carefully consider the changes and decide if you may have done anything to increase the RF exposure to any area. In many cases you will not have to perform a new evaluation. For example, suppose your station is in compliance and then you decrease your transmitter power from 1000 watts to 500 watts. You should not need to perform a new evaluation when you make this change, unless you made some other changes at the same time that could result in stronger radiated fields. Although your station may not be exempt from the evaluation requirement, since it was in compliance at the higher power, it will also be in compliance at the lower level. If you decrease your transmitter power from 500 watts to 40 watts, your station is even exempt from the requirement to perform an evaluation. Always keep in mind that your station must *comply* with the RF safety rules, however.

If you use a calibrated field-strength meter to measure the RF fields in your station, and those measurements indicate that people might be exposed to more than the MPE limits, there are many steps you can take to reduce the exposure. For example, you should ensure that all of your station equipment is properly grounded and that all equipment covers are tightly fastened. If a piece of equipment is not properly grounded or the cover is off a radio or amplifier, this could be a good source of excessive radiation. You should also be sure to use the minimum transmitter power necessary.

Suppose your station uses an indoor 20-meter dipole. If the calculations in your routine RF evaluation indicate that you or your family might be receiving more radiation exposure than the MPE limits allow, one good step would be to move the antenna to a safe outdoor environment.

In another example, your station evaluation might show that your neighbors could be receiving more than the MPE limits from your Yagi or Quad antenna when it is pointed at their house. One simple solution to this problem is to take steps to ensure that you can't point your antenna at their house while you are transmitting. This could be as simple as a few marks on the rotator control to remind you not to transmit with the antenna pointed in a certain direction. Another step you could take would be to reduce your transmitter power to a level that reduces their exposure to a value that is below the MPE limit.

These examples point out one of the main advantages and also one of the main disadvantages of a high-gain, narrow-beamwidth antenna. From an RF exposure point of view, the main advantage of such an antenna is that it allows you to focus in a direction away from populated areas. That will reduce the possible exposure of people to the RF fields from your signal. The disadvantage of a high-gain, narrow-beamwidth antenna is that individuals in the main beam will receive a greater exposure than when a low-gain antenna is used.

By installing your antenna as high as possible you will maximize the distance from your antenna to any nearby people. That will generally help reduce the RF exposure that your station produces to your neighbors or other people who may be nearby.

[Turn to Chapter 12 and study questions G0C07, G0C10 and G0C11 Also study questions G0E02, G0E03, G0E05, G0E06, G0E09, G0E10 and G0E11. Review this section as needed.]

SOME RF AWARENESS GUIDELINES

The following text was derived from guidelines developed by the ARRL RF Safety Committee. The guidelines represent good common sense anytime you are working with RF circuits. They are especially important safety steps to help you minimize your exposure to the dangers of RF fields.

• Although antennas on towers (well away from people) pose no exposure problem, make certain that the RF radiation is confined to the antenna radiating elements themselves. Provide a single, good station ground (earth), and eliminate radiation from transmission lines. Use good coaxial cable or other feed line properly. Avoid serious imbalance in your antenna system and feed line. For high-powered installations, avoid end fed antennas that come directly into the transmitter area near the operator.

Considering RF exposure, install antennas as high and as far away from populated areas as possible. This is true whether you are installing the antenna outdoors or indoors. In the case of an indoor antenna, you should locate the antenna as far away as possible from any living spaces that will be occupied while you are operating. Minimize feed line radiation into populated areas and if the antenna is a gain antenna, consider keeping it pointed away from populated areas when you are transmitting.

If you must make adjustments to your transmitter while it is operating, it is generally best to use a dummy antenna. In addition to allowing you to make transmitter adjustments without putting a signal on the air, a dummy antenna helps provide a safer test environment because the energy is converted to heat rather than being radiated.

One sure sign that you don't have a good RF ground system is if you feel a tingling sensation or receive minor burns every time you touch your microphone while you are transmitting. Commonly called "RF in the shack," this condition indicates that there is unwanted RF in your station. You and others in the station may be exposed to more than the maximum permissible level of RF radiation. Take steps to provide a better RF ground for your station in that case.

• No person should ever be near any transmitting antenna while it is in use. This is especially true for mobile or ground-mounted vertical antennas. Avoid transmitting with more than 25 W in a VHF mobile installation unless it is possible to first measure the RF fields inside the vehicle. At the 1-kW level, both HF and VHF directional antennas should be at least 35 ft above inhabited areas. Avoid using indoor and attic-mounted antennas if at all possible. If open-wire feeders are used, ensure that it is not possible for people (or animals) to come into accidental contact with the feed line.

All parts of your dipole antenna should be as high and far away from people as possible. Directional, high-gain antennas should be mounted higher than any nearby buildings or other structures that people could have access to while you are transmitting. This will help ensure that you are not directing excessive amounts of RF energy toward people. Ground-mounted antennas must also be installed so no one can be exposed to RF radiation in excess of the MPE limits. You might even consider installing a protective fence around the base of a ground-mounted transmitting antenna. By keeping people a safe distance from the antenna you can ensure that no one will be exposed to excessive amounts of RF energy.

The best place to mount the antenna for a mobile installation is in the center of a metal roof. This is most practical for a VHF or UHF station, but may not be possible for an HF station because of the overall height of the vehicle and antenna. The roof will provide an excellent shield to prevent the driver and passengers from being exposed to excessive amounts of RF energy.

• Don't operate high-power amplifiers with the covers removed, especially at VHF/UHF.

When the metal covers are properly fastened in place, any RF that might radiate from the circuit will be contained inside the cabinet. The RF only leaves the cabinet through the coaxial cable connection to a properly connected feed line.

If you build RF equipment, such as a home made transmatch or even a transmitter or amplifier, be sure to construct a metal cabinet with secure covers. Aluminum or other metal conductive materials make good enclosures.

• In the UHF/SHF region, never look into the open end of an activated length of waveguide or microwave feed-horn antenna or point it toward anyone. (If you do, you may be exposing your eyes to more than the maximum permissible exposure level of RF radiation.) Never point a high-gain, narrow-beamwidth antenna (a paraboloid, for instance) toward people. Use caution in aiming an EME (moonbounce) array toward the horizon; EME arrays may deliver an effective radiated power of 250,000 W or more.

You should be especially careful with RF in the range of 1270 MHz because this is close to a resonant frequency for your eyes and other structures in your head and body. Take steps to ensure that the antenna is far from your eyes!

• With hand-held transceivers, keep the antenna away from your head and use the lowest power possible to maintain communications. Use a separate microphone and hold the rig as far away from you as possible. This will reduce your exposure to the RF energy.

• Don't work on antennas that have RF power applied.

You should also take precautions to ensure that no one can activate the transmitter while you are making repairs to your antenna or adjusting the feed line. One way to do this is to turn off the transmitter power supply and disconnect the antenna feed line. This also applies to work on a microwave feed horn or waveguide.

• Don't stand or sit close to a power supply or linear amplifier when the ac power is turned on. Stay at least 24 inches away from power transformers, electrical fans and other sources of high-level 60-Hz magnetic fields.

[Turn to Chapter 12 now and study questions G0D01 through G0D11 and questions G0E01, G0E04, G0E07 and G0E08. Review this section if any of those questions give you difficulty.]

FIELD STRENGTH MEASUREMENTS AND CALCULATIONS

The FCC maximum permissible exposure limits are given in terms of electric and magnetic field strengths and power density or plane-wave-equivalent power density. So how do you determine if the transmitted signal from your station is within these RF exposure limits? You must analyze, measure or otherwise determine your transmitted field strengths and power density. This means there are a number of ways you can perform the required routine RF radiation evaluation.

One way to do this is by making direct measurements of the electric and magnetic field strengths around your antenna while transmitting a signal. If you happen to have a calibrated field-strength meter with a calibrated field-strength sensor (antenna), you can make accurate measurements. Unfortunately, such calibrated meters are expensive and not normally found in an amateur's tool box. The relative field-strength meters many amateurs use are not accurate enough to make this type of measurement.

Even if you do have access to a laboratory-grade calibrated field-strength meter, you must be aware of factors that can upset your readings. Reflections from ground and nearby conductors (power lines, other antennas, house wiring, etc) can easily confuse field strength readings. For example, the measuring probe and the person making the measurement can interact with the antenna radiation if they are in the near-field zone. In addition, you must know the frequency response of the test equipment and probes, and use them only within the appropriate range. Even the orientation of the test probe with respect to the test antenna polarization is important.

Why should we be concerned with the separation between the source antenna and the field-strength meter, which has its own receiving antenna? One important reason is that if you place a receiving antenna very close to an antenna when you measure the field strength, *mutual coupling* between the two antennas may actually alter the radiation from the antenna you are trying to measure.

This sort of mutual coupling can occur in the region very close to the antenna under test. This region is called the *reactive* **near-field region of an antenna**. The term "reactive" refers to the fact that the mutual impedance between the transmitting and receiving antennas can be either capacitive or inductive in nature. The reactive near field is sometimes called the "induction field," meaning that the magnetic field usually is predominant over the electric field in this region. The antenna acts as though it were a rather large, lumped-constant inductor or capacitor, storing energy in the reactive near field rather than propagating it into space.

For simple wire antennas, the reactive near field is considered to be within about a half wavelength from an antenna's radiating center. For making field-strength measurements, we do not want to be too close to the antenna being measured.

The strength of the reactive near field decreases in a complicated fashion as you increase the distance from the antenna. Beyond the reactive near field, the antenna's radiated field is divided into two other regions: the *radiating near field* and the *radiating far field*. Nearly any metal object or other conductor that is located within the radiating near field can alter the radiation pattern of the antenna. Conductors such as telephone wiring or aluminum siding on a building that is located in the radiating near field will interact with the theoretical electric and magnetic fields to add or subtract intensity. This results in areas of varying field strength. Although you have measured the fields in the general area around your antenna and found that your station meets the MPE limits, there may still be "hot spots" or areas of higher field strengths within that region. In the near field of an antenna, the field strength varies in a way that depends on the type of antenna and other nearby objects as you move farther away from the antenna.

Because the boundary between the fields is rather "fuzzy," experts debate where one field begins and another leaves off, but the boundary between the radiating near and far fields for a full-sized dipole or Yagi antenna is generally accepted as:

$$D \approx \frac{2L^2}{\lambda}$$
(Equation 10-1)

where:

D = distance between the antenna and the boundary

L = largest dimension of the physical antenna, expressed in the same units of measurement as the wavelength

λ = wavelength of the RF energy

Remember, many specialized antennas do not follow the rule of thumb in Equation 10-1 exactly. In general, however, the wavelength of the energy and the physical size of the antenna are the factors that help determine the boundary between the

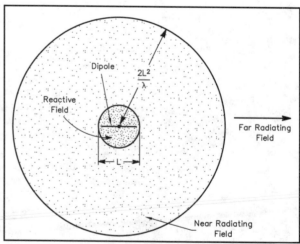

Figure 10-2 — This drawing illustrates the reactive near field, the radiating near field and the far field around a half wavelength dipole antenna.

near and far fields of an antenna. Figure 10-2 shows the three fields in front of a simple wire antenna.

The radiating **far field of the antenna** forms the traveling electromagnetic waves. Far-field radiation is distinguished by the fact that the power density is proportional to the inverse square of the distance. (That means if you double the distance from the antenna, the power density will be one fourth as strong.) The electric and magnetic fields are perpendicular to each other in the wave front, and are in time phase. The total energy is equally divided between the electric and magnetic fields. Beyond several wavelengths from the antenna, these are the only fields we need to consider. For accurate measurement of radiation patterns, we must place our measuring instruments at least several wavelengths away from the antenna under test.

In the far field there is a simple relationship between the electric (E) field and the magnetic (H) field of an electromagnetic wave. The strength of the E field divided by the strength of the H field is a constant 377 ohms, sometimes called the *impedance of free space.*

$$\frac{E}{H} = \text{Impedance of Free Space} = 377 \ \Omega \qquad\qquad \text{(Equation 10-2)}$$

where:
  E = electric field strength in volts per meter
  H = magnetic field strength in amperes per meter

This calculation is only valid in the far field of the antenna. In the near field the relationship is not this simple. This calculation may prove useful to you as you analyze your station for compliance with the FCC MPE limits. If you know the E or H field strength at some point in the far field then you can calculate the other value at that same point.

If you don't have the necessary measuring equipment, you can perform some calculations to determine the electric and magnetic field strengths from your station. This is normally done using computer programs, which take into account the gain and directivity of an antenna. There are a variety of programs available. The most reliable ones are based on the Numerical Electromagnetic Code (NEC) program that uses the Method of Moments analysis. (MININEC is a variation of the original program, shortened to run on personal computers.) While these are powerful analysis tools, you must be careful to accurately model the antenna and all conductors that might be within a few wavelengths of the antenna for reliable results.

If you measure or calculate the electric or magnetic field strength or power density at some point in the far field of your antenna, then you can calculate the field strengths or power density at other points in the far field. Rather than learning the extensive math involved with a complete calculation, though, let's just explore some simple relationships that you can use to make some quick estimates.

We will start by considering a sphere surrounding our antenna at some point in the far field of the antenna. All of the power radiated from our antenna must flow through that sphere. Next, imagine a second sphere with a radius of twice the first one. The same total power also flows through the second sphere. The second sphere has four times as much surface area as the first one, because its radius is double the first radius. See Figure 10-3. (The area of a sphere is calculated by multiplying the square of the radius times 4 pi: $A = 4 \pi R^2$.) We can use this relationship to write a simple equation:

$$\text{Power Density}_1 \times \left(\text{Distance}_1\right)^2 = \text{Power Density}_2 \times \left(\text{Distance}_2\right)^2 \quad \text{(Equation 10-3)}$$

If we know the power density at some distance and want to find the power density at a second distance we can simply solve this equation for Power Density$_2$.

$$\text{Power Density}_2 = \text{Power Density}_1 \times \frac{\left(\text{Distance}_1\right)^2}{\left(\text{Distance}_2\right)^2} \quad \text{(Equation 10-4)}$$

For example, suppose you calculate the free-space far-field power density of the signal from your 18-MHz Yagi antenna to be 10 mW/m^2 at a distance of 3 wavelengths. What will be the power density at a distance of 6 wavelengths?

$$\text{Power Density}_2 = \text{Power Density}_1 \times \frac{(\text{Distance}_1)^2}{(\text{Distance}_2)^2} = 10\frac{\text{mW}}{\text{m}^2} \times \frac{(3\lambda)^2}{(6\lambda)^2}$$

$$= 10\frac{\text{mW}}{\text{m}^2} \times \frac{9\lambda^2}{36\lambda^2} = 10\frac{\text{mW}}{\text{m}^2} \times \frac{1}{4} = 2.5\frac{\text{mW}}{\text{m}^2}$$

Equation 10-4 provides a simple mathematical formula that will help you make this type of calculation for any power density and distances in the far field of an antenna. You might also recognize that you can multiply by the ratio of the square of the distances. Use the method that makes more sense to you.

As another example, suppose you measure the free-space far-field power density of an antenna to be 9 mW / m^2 at a distance of 5 wavelengths. What will be the power density at a distance of 15 wavelengths? We can use Equation 10-4 again.

$$\text{Power Density}_2 = \text{Power Density}_1 \times \frac{(\text{Distance}_1)^2}{(\text{Distance}_2)^2} = 9\frac{\text{mW}}{\text{m}^2} \times \frac{(5\lambda)^2}{(15\lambda)^2}$$

$$= 9\frac{\text{mW}}{\text{m}^2} \times \frac{25\lambda^2}{225\lambda^2} = 9\frac{\text{mW}}{\text{m}^2} \times \frac{1}{9} = 1\frac{\text{mW}}{\text{m}^2}$$

You might also reach this answer by recognizing that the ratio of the distances squared is 9. Then you can divide by that value to get the new power density.

Power density is related to the square of the electric and magnetic field strengths. This means that the electric and magnetic field strengths will decrease linearly with distance. We can write another equation for field strength, then:

$$\text{Field Strength}_1 \times \text{Distance}_1 = \text{Field Strength}_2 \times \text{Distance}_2 \quad \text{(Equation 10-5)}$$

We can also solve this equation for Field Strength$_2$ and write a new equation.

$$\text{Field Strength}_2 = \text{Field Strength}_1 \times \frac{\text{Distance}_1}{\text{Distance}_2} \quad \text{(Equation 10-6)}$$

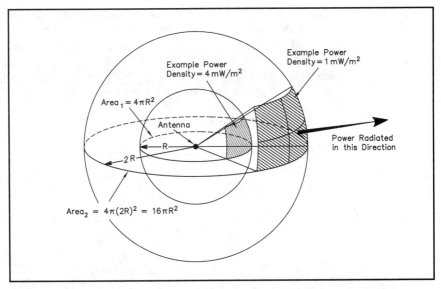

Figure 10-3 — This drawing illustrates that the power density of the RF energy radiated from an antenna decreases as the square of the distance. This is because the area of a sphere increases as the square of the radius (A = 4πR^2).

In this case you can simply multiply by the ratio of the distances.

For example, suppose you measure the electric field strength 5 wavelengths from a 10-MHz dipole antenna, and you get a reading of 1.0 millivolts per meter. What will the field strength be at a distance of 10 wavelengths?

$$\text{Field Strength}_2 = 1.0\,\frac{mV}{m} \times \frac{5\lambda}{10\lambda} = 1.0\,\frac{mV}{m} \times \frac{1}{2} = 0.50\,\frac{mV}{m}$$

As another example, suppose you measure the free-space far-field strength of a 28-MHz Yagi antenna to be 4.0 mV / m at a distance of 5 wavelengths from the antenna. What will the field strength be 20 wavelengths from the antenna?

$$\text{Field Strength}_2 = 4.0\,\frac{mV}{m} \times \frac{5\lambda}{20\lambda} = 4.0\,\frac{mV}{m} \times \frac{1}{4} = 1.0\,\frac{mV}{m}$$

As a final example of this type of calculation, let's suppose you calculate the free-space far-field electric field strength of a 1.8-MHz dipole antenna at a distance of 4 wavelengths from the antenna. If the field strength is 9 microvolts per meter, what will it be at a distance of 12 wavelengths from the antenna?

$$\text{Field Strength}_2 = 9.0\,\frac{\mu V}{m} \times \frac{4\lambda}{12\lambda} = 9.0\,\frac{\mu V}{m} \times \frac{1}{3} = 3.0\,\frac{\mu V}{m}$$

If you know a magnetic field strength you can also use Equation 10-6 to calculate a new field strength at some other distance.

[Congratulations! You have completed your study of the RF safety material for your General license exam. This also completes your study for all of the material on the exam, if you have followed the book from beginning to end. Before you are done, however, you have a few more questions to review. Turn to Chapter 12 now and study questions G0C01 through G0C06 and questions G0C08 and G0C09. If you have any difficulty with those questions, review this section.]

SETTING UP YOUR HF STATION

For many new General licensees, this will be your first venture onto the HF amateur bands. Now you'll have the opportunity to experience first-hand the excitement of contacting another amateur continents away. Or perhaps it is the lure of exchanging slow-scan television pictures or operating radioteletype that has enticed you to earn the General license. In any case, you probably have a million questions about selecting equipment, installing antennas and operating practices.

The ARRL publishes a library of technical and operating books to assist you in becoming an active Amateur Radio operator. We can't duplicate all that information here, but we collected some material for this chapter that we hope will start you on a successful path. What other books might you want in your library? The ultimate reference books are the "ARRL Big Three:" *The ARRL Handbook for Radio Amateurs*, *The ARRL Antenna Book*, and *The ARRL Operating Manual*. You may not want or need the detailed technical information these books contain right now, however. ARRL books like *The DXCC Companion*, *Your HF Digital Companion*, *Practical Packet Radio*, *Your Packet Companion*, and *Your Mobile Companion* contain operating guidelines to help you get started on specific modes or operating styles. *Your Ham Antenna Companion* contains a wealth of proven antenna-design information for simple antennas you can build with basic materials. *The ARRL Antenna Compendium* series contains many new and interesting tips and antenna projects you can build. *Understanding Basic Electronics* is written in an easy-to-understand style for electronics beginners and those who want to review their knowledge of basic electronics. You can purchase these and the many other ARRL books from your local Amateur Radio equipment dealer or directly from the American Radio Relay League, 225 Main Street, Newington, CT 06111-1494, Phone 860-594-0200. You can also order directly from our World Wide Web site at: **http://www.arrl.org/**

EQUIPMENT CHOICES FOR BEGINNERS

Our discussion of equipment here is limited. There is a more-detailed discussion of beginner's equipment needs in *Now You're Talking!*, published by the ARRL. In this chapter we will try to give you some basic information to help you set up your first HF station.

Beginners often call the ARRL Technical Department to ask which radio or antenna is best. In truth, the choice of a radio is very subjective; the best radio for you is determined by the space available for your station, your budget, your personal operating goals and inclinations.

Start by considering your needs. Make a list: How much room do you have for your station? What modes and bands would you like to operate? Do you want to invest the time and effort to learn about complicated features? From the list, you can derive requirements for your equipment. For example, if CW operation interests you, narrow filters are important. Blocking and intermodulation-distortion dynamic ranges are important for contesting or weak-signal work. DXers (those who pursue contacts with foreign countries) need convenient split-frequency operation (and the more frequency memories, the better).

No one can point to one best radio, or make the buying decision for you. With that warning out of the way, here are descriptions of some typical HF stations suitable for beginners. By all means, collect many such opinions from your ham friends before forming your own opinion and making a purchase.

For general HF operation, a basic modern transceiver offers the following qualities:

Modes — SSB and CW (10-m FM is a common option)

Frequency control
- stable VFO, PTO or frequency synthesizer,
- a digital frequency display
- easy split-frequency operation by means of dual VFOs, frequency memories or an external VFO
- RIT for small receiver-frequency offsets

Bandwidth
- 2 to 3-kHz crystal IF filter for SSB
- 250 to 600-Hz crystal IF filter for CW

Power Output — 100 W from broadband solid-state (transistor) finals

Recent Evolution of Amateur Radio Equipment

The power amplifier (PA) stages of modern transceivers all use transistors. The broadband designs eliminate the frequent adjustment and tuning required of older HF transceivers that used tube-type PAs. Digital circuits are prominent, as frequency synthesizers, multiple VFOs, switched-capacitor filters and microprocessor controllers appear in many radios. Some of the newer radios even include digital signal processing (DSP) circuitry! All these radios are suitable for packet radio, AMTOR and RTTY, which require fast transmit-receive switching and high transmitter duty cycles. Many radios can even be controlled by an external computer.

Selecting Older Radios

Many older radios hold some sentimental value, yet they may be nightmares under modern operating conditions. The frequency accuracy and stability of amateur equipment has increased steadily over the years. With this increased stability have come narrower receiver bandwidths that allow more stations to operate in less spectrum. While older radios may well perform their intended function today, they may not fit into modern Amateur Radio practices. To give some perspective, let's consider radios for HF operation.

As an example, a very inexpensive HF CW station might include a Heath DX-40 transmitter with a VF-1 VFO and an HR-10B receiver. This station may seem attractive, since it may have a price tag under $200. This gear is typical of inexpensive stations of the 1950s and '60s. Worldwide CW communication is possible with such a simple station, but operation would be limited: It does not cover the 30, 17 and 12-meter amateur bands. The transmitter does not operate SSB (voice). The VFO offers insufficient band spread and excessive drift by today's standards. Receiver bandwidth is about 12 kHz. In a crowded band you would hear five or six signals at once. Many enjoyable, if noncompetitive, contacts could be made with the station, but $500 or less would likely buy a transceiver that covers all HF bands with CW and SSB (possibly FM, too) capabilities and a receiver bandwidth of 500 to 2000 Hz.

In general, Amateur Radio equipment has improved so much in the last two decades that only enthusiasts with a special interest should consider buying equipment made before the early 1980s. Hence, most operators will be happier with an HF radio made since 1985 or so.

There are some notable exceptions to the time line, and chief among those are radios made by Collins Radio and R. L. Drake Company. The Collins Radio permeability-tuned oscillators and filters are legendary. Collins radios such as the "S-line" are not as easy to operate as the average modern transceiver, but they were top performers in their day, and are still quite useful today.

A Drake T4XC or an R4C may appear at a bargain price. Even though the transmitter uses sweep tubes, it merits consideration. Drake produced stable VFOs with a permeability tuned oscillator and quality radios.

EQUIPMENT FEATURES

The array of features available on amateur equipment can be bewildering. Here are brief explanations of some common features and their usefulness.

Frequency Tuning and Display

Of all the controls on a rig, you use the frequency control most often. Choose a dial mechanism you are comfortable reading and tuning. Make sure the knob

Ten-Tec's Scout is a good basic radio with simple-to-use controls. Each band uses a separate plug-in module. This helps minimize operating controls and reduces cost.

operates smoothly. Avoid radios that feel sloppy and slip or skip.

Two different types of tuning-dial mechanisms are available on ham transceivers and separate transmitter/receiver combinations: *digital* and *analog*. Most manufacturers now use digital displays. These are generally quite accurate and easier to read than analog dials.

Analog circular dials are usually marked at 1-kHz intervals. Some circular dials tune "backwards": clockwise motion decreases frequency rather than increasing it. Also, some circular dials have different frequency indicators for different modes; that can be confusing.

You may hear of a "slide-rule" analog dial: a rectangular display with a moving pointer that indicates frequency on one or more scales. Slide-rule dials are common on shortwave-broadcast receivers, but they are not precise enough for most amateur operation.

Other Receive Features

Sensitivity is the ability of a receiver to detect weak signals. *Selectivity* is the ability of a receiver to separate two closely spaced signals. This determines how well you can receive one signal that is very close to another. Selectivity is generally more important than sensitivity. The ability to isolate the signal you are receiving from all the others nearby directly affects how much you will enjoy your time on the air.

Some receivers have a *crystal calibrator*, sometimes called a marker generator. It produces a signal every 25, 50 or 100 kHz. You can use the calibrator to make sure the dial or display is accurate.

Noise blankers are most useful for filtering ignition noise produced by cars and trucks. Some noise blankers can help reduce power-line noise as well. A few of the newer radios offer adjustable or multiple noise blankers to combat various types of electrical impulse noise.

Some radios allow you to select between several IF filters, such as a narrow or wide SSB filter or a narrow or wide CW filter. This can be a helpful interference-fighting feature, and can also prove useful when you want a narrow filter for RTTY operation with the radio set in the upper or lower sideband position.

Generally, the better radios pack in more interference-fighting features, such as the ability to adjust the tuning of the IF passband. Such features add cost to the radio, so you have to make some compromises. Extra money spent on receive features is often worthwhile, however.

Transmit Features

Speech processing increases the average power of a single-sideband signal. This can be done in the audio stages or the RF stages. RF processing is better. Used properly, a speech processor can greatly improve the readability of a signal. Almost all SSB transmitters and transceivers built since 1980 include a speech processor. On some rigs, there is no adjustment for the speech processor: just an on/off control. Other gear has one or more variable controls to set the speech processing level.

Some radios also include a *speech monitor*. This feature allows you to listen to a sample of the transmitted audio. You will probably have to use headphones so the monitored audio doesn't get back into the microphone. It can be helpful to monitor your transmitted signal as you adjust the speech processor, for example. A speech monitor is helpful so you can listen to the transmitted signal when you are operating radioteletype or slow-scan TV, too.

A *voice-operated transmit (VOX)* circuit puts a transceiver into the transmit mode automatically when you speak into the microphone, then back to receive when

The ICOM IC-706MkII is another good example of a trend toward simple-to-use transceivers.

The Kenwood TS-570D is a marvel of modern miniaturization. The rig includes a general-coverage receiver, a 100-W transmitter with built-in electronic keyer and even digital signal processing (DSP) circuitry. All this fits in a package the size of a large shoebox.

you stop talking. There are usually three VOX controls: *gain*, *delay* and *anti-VOX*. Gain sets the circuit sensitivity and determines how loud a sound must be before it turns on the circuit. Delay determines how long the transmitter stays on after you stop talking. The Anti-VOX setting prevents received audio from tripping the switch circuit. These controls are only adjusted occasionally, so they are often located on the back, top or bottom of a transceiver.

Synthesized transceivers offer almost unlimited frequency flexibility. Many transceivers with phase-locked loop (PLL) frequency synthesizers use digital memory to allow you to select one of two variable-frequency oscillators (VFOs). For added convenience, synthesized transceivers often have *memories* to store your favorite frequencies and offer automatic *scanning* up and down a band, or among memory channels.

Many radios now have a built-in electronic *keyer* for CW operation. Even if your radio includes this feature, you may want an external keyer, such as a memory keyer that allows you to store several messages that can be transmitted with a simple button press. Keyers that use relays with floating (ungrounded) contacts in the output circuit are more flexible than those with transistor output stages because transmitter key-jack voltage polarity is unimportant with a relay. But relay contacts can stick, and the trend is to use transistorized output stages in modern keyers. If you use an electronic keyer with a transistor switch in the output circuit, transmitter keying polarity and voltage must be considered.

Modern transistorized rigs may use either *positive* or *negative* polarity at the key jack. Some transistorized rigs require that the keying voltage go to 0 V; others need only a TTL false level (0.8 V maximum) to key properly.

Before you connect a keyer to any rig, check the key-jack voltage and polarity. Check the equipment manuals, and make sure the keyer will work with the rig.

There are ways to change a keyer output circuit if needed. (You can use a transistor or optoisolator, for instance). See *The ARRL Handbook* for more information about keyers and transmitter keying.

A Perspective on Performance Measurements

Receivers

Comparing the performance of one radio to another is difficult at best. The features of one may outweigh those of a second, even though its performance is lower under some conditions. Although the final decision on which radio to buy is usually based on personal preference, there are ways to compare receiver performance characteristics. The most important parameters are noise floor, intermodulation distortion and blocking (gain compression).

The *noise floor* determines the minimum discernible signal (MDS) that the operator can hear. A signal at the MDS level increases the receiver audio output by 3 dB over the background noise. (The specific tests performed on equipment reviewed at the ARRL Lab are described under "Measuring Receiver Performance" in *The ARRL Handbook*.)

Intermodulation distortion (IMD) is the production of spurious responses that results from the mixing of desired and undesired signals in a receiver. IMD occurs in any receiver when signals of sufficient magnitude are present. ARRL Product Reviews in our membership journal, *QST*, present IMD performance as the IMD dynamic range (IMD DR). IMD DR is the difference, in dB, between the noise floor and the strength of two equal incoming signals that produce a third-order product 3 dB above the noise floor.

The Yaesu FT-1000MP is an example of a modern full-featured transceiver. Numerous knobs, dials and buttons greet the user with many operating options. Many advanced digital signal processing (DSP) features are included. There are even two receivers with their own tuning knobs built in.

Blocking dynamic range (Blocking DR) is the difference, in dB, between the noise floor and a signal that causes 1 dB of gain compression in the receiver. It indicates the signal level, above the noise floor, that begins to cause desensitization.

What do these measurements mean? When the IMD DR is exceeded, false signals begin to appear along with the desired signal. When the Blocking DR is exceeded, the receiver begins losing its ability to amplify weak signals. Typically, the IMD DR is 20 dB or more below the Blocking DR, so false signals appear well before sensitivity is significantly decreased.

Phase noise has been a hot topic in recent years. It is low-level noise resulting from phase differences between the local oscillator (LO) output and a perfect sine wave of the same frequency. It effectively widens the LO signal and produces false signals similar to IMD effects. A discussion of phase noise is beyond the scope of this book. The technical side of the problem is fully treated in J. Grebenkemper's "Phase Noise and its Effects on Amateur Communications" in March and April 1988 *QST*.

A receiver should provide the signal we are trying to copy at a particular moment, and no others. If the station is near sources of strong signals, both IMD DR and Blocking DR are important. If it is far from other transmitters, MDS may be the most significant factor. When circumstances lie between those two extremes, other features may drive the decision.

Transmitters

ARRL Product Review transmitter test procedures check for spurious radiation in the forms of harmonics and IMD. The limits for both problems are set by the FCC, and graphics of the spectral test results appear with each review.

BUYING USED EQUIPMENT

There are many different sources of used ham gear. You can buy gear from equipment retailers and local hams. You may see what you want listed in the pages of ham magazines (see the *QST* Ham Ads) or used-equipment flyers. Other sources are auctions, flea markets, hamfests and even garage sales.

ARRL Product Reviews in *QST* are an excellent source of information about equipment you may wish to purchase. Extensive laboratory measurements and on-the-air tests are made and results reported. The ARRL Technical Information Service can tell you when the review of a particular radio was published. (Call 860-594-0200, write to ARRL Headquarters, 225 Main Street, Newington, CT 06111 or by e-mail to tis@arrl.org) You can purchase back issues or photocopies of the articles for radios in which you are interested. *The ARRL Radio Buyer's Sourcebook* — Volumes 1 and 2 are currently available — is a collection of Product Reviews that provide a wealth of comparative information.

Local retailers are usually safe sources for used equipment. Many dealers route used equipment through their service shop before selling it. This ensures that the gear is working properly. Some dealers even allow you to operate the equipment before you buy it. This is the best way to determine a rig's capabilities and condition. Dealers usually offer a warranty (30 days is typical). Ask about the warranty *before* you buy.

Individual sellers usually offer no guarantees. Ask to see the unit in operation. You might even wish to take along a more knowledgeable ham who can help you make the decision. A local ham can be a good source of information on used equipment.

Mail-order purchases from individuals require simple precautions: Try to be sure that you'll have the right to return the equipment if you don't like what you receive. Shipment by truck freight with the right of inspection permits you to examine the package contents before you accept delivery. If you don't like what you receive, simply refuse delivery. You may be asked to pay by bank check or money order, rather than personal check.

Auctions, hamfests and flea markets are common sources of used equipment. A careful buyer can get excellent equipment there, but you should study a little before you shop. What are the capabilities of the equipment, its current market value, cost of repairs and availability of repair parts? If you don't know these things, ask at your local club. Maybe someone more knowledgeable would be willing to go along with you.

Keep an eye on the classified sections of radio magazines. Know the going prices for radios that interest you, and never pay a high price without a demonstration. Try to buy equipment that was of high quality when it was new; it is more likely to serve you well when it is old.

When you are not able to test equipment before you buy it, a thorough visual inspection by an experienced eye will generally suffice if the price is right. You can usually tell a lot from the external appearance of equipment. If it looks physically abused, chances are it has been treated badly on the air as well.

When you find a good prospect, open the cabinet. Look for evidence of missing parts, fire or damage. Purchase modified equipment if you trust the seller, or if the modifications are well documented and can be easily removed. (Modifications are only as good as the skill of the person who installed them.) There is one other important point to keep in mind when you buy used equipment from any source. Be sure you get an owner's manual with the radio! Some hams may even have the service or shop manual. A shop manual can be a valuable addition, because it generally has more complete service procedures and troubleshooting guidelines.

If you are not getting at least an owner's manual with the radio, be cautious about making the purchase. Manuals for some pieces of equipment are available from the manufacturer. Several companies sell manuals for used or surplus equipment. See the advertising section of *QST*.

STATION LOCATION

Give some thought to station location. Hams put their equipment in many places. Some use the basement or attic, while others choose the den, kitchen, closet or a spare bedroom. Some hams with limited space build their station into a small closet. A fold-out shelf and folding chair form the operating position!

Where you put your station depends on the room you have available and on your personal tastes. There are, however, several things to keep in mind while searching for the best place. The photos show several ways amateur stations can be arranged.

If space permits, you can arrange all your equipment on a desk or table top.

Many operators prefer to stack some equipment on a shelf unit to save table space.

An armoire makes a good hiding place for your equipment. When the doors are closed it is just another piece of furniture in the room. The drawers provide convenient storage places for log books, headphones and other accessories.

One often-overlooked requirement for a good station location is adequate electrical service. Eventually you will have several pieces of station equipment and accessories, many of which will require power to operate. Be sure at least one, and preferably several, electrical outlets are located near your operating position. Be sure the outlets provide the proper voltage and current for your rig. The power supplies for most modern radios require only a few amperes at 120 V. You may run into problems, however, if your shack is on the same circuit as the air conditioner or washing machine. The total current drawn at any one time must not exceed rated limits. Someday you'll probably upgrade and may want to purchase a linear amplifier. If so, you should have a 240-V line in the shack, or the capability to get one.

Another must for your station is a good ground connection. A good ground not only reduces the possibility of electrical shock but also improves the performance of your station. By connecting all of your equipment to ground, you will help to avoid stray RF current in the shack. Stray RF can cause equipment to malfunction. A good ground can also help reduce the possibility of interference. The wire connecting your station to an earth ground should be as short as possible.

Basement and first-floor locations generally make it easier to provide a good ground connection for your station. You can also find a way to put your ham shack on the second or third floor or even on the top floor of a high-rise apartment, for that matter.

Your radio station will require a feed line of some sort to connect the antenna to the radio. So you will need a convenient means of getting the feed line into the shack. There are many ways of doing this, but one of the easiest and most effective requires only a window. Many hams simply replace the glass pane in a nearby window with a clear acrylic panel. The panel can be drilled to accept as many feed lines as needed. Special threaded "feedthrough" connectors make the job easy. If you decide to relocate your station, the glass pane can be replaced. This will restore the window to its original condition.

A simpler, more temporary approach is to pass the feed lines through the open window and close it gently. Do this carefully, because crushed coaxial cable will give you nothing but trouble. Be sure to secure the window with a block of wood or some other "locking" device. Your new equipment, seen through an open window, may tempt an unwanted visitor!

Another important requirement for your station is comfort. The space should be large enough so you can spread out as needed. Operating from a telephone booth isn't much fun! Because you will probably be spending some time in your shack (an understatement!), be sure it will be warm in the winter and cool in the summer. It should also be as dry as possible. High humidity can cause such equipment problems as high-voltage arcing and switch-contact failure.

If your station is in an area often used by other family members, be sure they know what they shouldn't touch. You should have some means of ensuring that no "unauthorized" person can use your equipment. One way to do this is to install a key-operated on-off switch in the equipment power line. When the switch is turned off and you have the key in your pocket, you will be sure that no one can misuse your station.

If you don't have room to dedicate to your Amateur Radio station, you might consider using simple, lightweight equipment. This station can be set up on a table for an operating session, and stored away when not in use.

You will eventually want to operate late at night to snag the "rare ones" on 80 and 40 meters. Although a Morse code or voice contact is music to your ears, it may not endear you to a sleeping family. Putting your station in a bedroom shared with others may not be the best idea. You can keep the "music" to yourself, however, by using a good pair of headphones when operating your station.

ARRANGING YOUR EQUIPMENT

Before you set everything up and hook up the cables, think about where you want each piece of equipment. While there is no one best layout for a ham station, some general rules do apply. Of course, the location you've chosen for your station may limit your choices a bit. For example, if you're going to put the station in the basement, you may have a lot of space. If you'll be using a corner of the bedroom or den, however, you may have to keep the equipment in a small area.

Generally, the piece of gear that requires the most adjustment is the transceiver (or receiver if you have one). Make sure you can conveniently reach its controls, and keep in mind which hand you're going to use to make the adjustments. It doesn't make much sense to put the transceiver on the left side of the desk or table if you're going to adjust it with your right hand. Once you've found the best location for the transceiver, you can position the rest of your equipment around it.

If you'll be using Morse code, placement of the telegraph key is also very important. It must be easy to reach with the hand you send with, and placed so your arm will be supported when you're using it. Try to position it away from anything dangerous, such as sharp corners and edges, rough surfaces and electrical wires.

If you have room for a desk or table long enough to hold all your gear, you might prefer to keep everything on one surface. If you're pressed for space, however, a shelf built above the desk top is a good solution. Make certain the shelf is high enough to permit free air circulation above your transceiver. Leave at least 3 inches of space between the top of the tallest unit on the desktop and the bottom of your shelf. In building the shelf, keep in mind the weight of the equipment you're going to place on it. Try to restrict the shelf space to units you don't have to adjust very often such as the station clock, SWR meter and antenna rotator control box.

After you have a good idea of where you want everything, you can start connecting the cables. Often a dummy load or dummy antenna is also connected. Many hams use an antenna switch to select the dummy load or one of several antennas.

PRACTICAL ANTENNAS

Hams use many different kinds of antennas. There is no one best kind, so you will have to select an antenna type based on the available space, supports, cost and other factors. In this section we will give you some pointers on building and installing half-wavelength dipole antennas and quarter-wavelength vertical antennas for the HF bands.

The Half-Wave Dipole Antenna

Probably the most common amateur antenna is a wire cut to $1/2 \lambda$ at the operating frequency. The feed line attaches across an insulator at the center of the wire.

Table 11-1

Half-Wavelength Dipole Lengths for the Amateur HF Bands

Wavelength (m)	Frequency (MHz)	Length (ft)
160	1.8	260
	2.0	234
80	3.5	133.7
	4.0	117
40	7.0	66.9
	7.3	64.1
30	10.1	46.3
	10.15	46.1
20	14.0	33.4
	14.35	32.6
17	18.068	25.9
	18.168	25.8
15	21.0	22.3
	21.45	21.8
12	24.89	18.8
	24.99	18.7
10	28.0	16.7
	29.7	15.8

This is the half-wave dipole. We often refer to an antenna like this as a *dipole antenna*. (*Di* means two, so a dipole has two equal parts. A dipole could be a length other than $1/2$ λ.) The feed line connects to the center, so each side of a dipole is $1/4$-λ long.

You probably remember the equation to calculate the length of a half-wavelength dipole antenna.

$$\text{Length (in feet)} = \frac{468}{f \text{ (in MHz)}} \qquad \text{(Equation 11-1)}$$

The factor 468 in this equation takes into account antenna end effects, the slower velocity of the electromagnetic wave in wire than in free space and a few other factors. The result is a length that gives an approximate length for the antenna. You will probably have to adjust the final length, depending on the height of the antenna, nearby objects and other factors associated with your location. Notice that the frequency is given in megahertz and the antenna length is in feet for this equation. Table 11-1 lists calculated lengths for $1/2$-λ dipoles at each end of the HF bands. This table shows how the length varies over the band. You should calculate the length for the section of the band you plan to operate on most.

Figure 11-1A shows the construction of a basic $1/2$-λ dipole antenna. Parts B through D show enlarged views of how to attach the insulators. You can use just about any kind of copper or copper-clad steel wire for your dipole. Most hardware or electrical supply stores carry suitable wire. Ordinary house wire, or two-conductor small-appliance wire (called "zip cord") can work well. Avoid using zip cord on 40 and 80 meters, however.

House wire and stranded wire will stretch with time, so a heavy gauge copper-clad steel wire is best. This wire consists of a copper jacket over a steel core. Such construction provides the strength of steel combined with the excellent conducting properties of copper. You can sometimes find copper-clad steel wire at a radio store. This wire is used for electric fences to keep farm animals in their place, so another place to try is a farm supply store.

Remember, you want a good conductor for the antenna, but the wire must also be strong. The wire must support itself *and* the weight of the feed line connected at the center. Although you can make a dipole antenna from almost any size wire, 12 or 14 gauge is usually best.

Cut your dipole according to the dimension found by Equation 11-1, but leave a little extra length to wrap the ends around the insulators. You'll need a feed line to connect it to your transmitter. If you plan to use coaxial cable to feed your dipole, look for some with a heavy braided shield. If possible, get good quality cable that has at least 95% shielding. If you stick with name brand cable, you'll get a

Figure 11-1—Simple half-wave dipole antenna construction. B and C show how to connect the wire ends to various insulator types. D shows the feed-line connection at the center.

Figure 11-2—Preparing coaxial cable for connection to antenna wire.
A—Remove the outer insulation with a sharp knife or wire stripper. If you nick
the braid, start over. B—Push the braid in accordion fashion against the outer
jacket. C—Spread the shield strands at the point where the outer insulation
ends. D—Fish the center conductor through the opening in the braid. Now strip
the center conductor insulation back far enough to make the connection and tin
(flow solder onto) both center conductor and shield. Be careful not to use too
much solder, which will make the conductors inflexible. Also be careful not to
apply too much heat, or you will melt the insulation. A pair of pliers used as a
heat sink will help. The outer jacket removed in step A can be slipped over the
braid as an insulator, if necessary. Be sure to slide it onto the braid before
soldering the leads to the antenna wires.

Figure 11-3—Various commercially made antenna insulators.

good quality feed line. Figure 11-2 shows the steps required to prepare the cable end for attachment to the antenna wires at the center insulator.

The final items you'll need for your dipole are three insulators. You can purchase them from your local radio or hardware store. Figure 11-3 shows some common insulator types. You can also make your own insulators from plastic or Teflon blocks. See Figure 11-4. One insulator goes on each end and another holds the two wires together in the center. Figure 11-5 shows some examples of how the feed line can attach to the antenna wires at a center insulator.

Antenna Location

Once you have assembled your dipole, find a good place to put it. *Never* put your antenna under, or over the top of electrical power lines. If they ever come into contact with your antenna, you could be electrocuted. Avoid running your antenna parallel to power lines that come close to your station. Otherwise you may receive unwanted electrical noise. Sometimes power-line noise can cover up all but the strongest signals your receiver hears. You'll also want to avoid running your antenna too close to metal objects. These could be rain gutters, metal beams, metal siding, or even electrical wiring in the attic of your house. Metal objects tend to shield your antenna, reducing its capability.

The key to good dipole operation is height. How high? One wavelength above ground is good, and this ranges from about 35 feet on 10 meters to about 240 feet on 80 meters. Install the antenna as high as possible, to get it clear of buildings and trees. Of course very few people can get their antennas 240 feet in the air, so 40 to

Figure 11-4—Some ideas for homemade antenna insulators.

Figure 11-5—Some dipole center insulators have connectors for easy feeder removal. Others have a direct solder connection to the feed line.

60 feet is a good average height for an 80-meter dipole. Don't despair if you can get your antenna up only 20 feet or so, though. Low antennas can work well. Generally, the higher above ground and surrounding objects you can get your antenna, the greater the success you'll have. You'll find this to be true even if you can get only part of your antenna up high.

Normally you will support the dipole at both ends. The supports can be trees, buildings, poles or anything else high enough. Sometimes, however, there is just no way you can put your dipole high in the air at both ends. If you're faced with this problem, you have two reasonably good alternatives. You can support your dipole in the middle or at one end.

You can support the antenna in the middle, with both ends drooping toward the ground or with one end higher than the other in a sloping configuration. If you don't have the room to install a dipole in the standard form, don't be afraid to experiment a little. You can get away with bending the ends to fit your property, or even making a horizontal V-shaped antenna. Many hams have enjoyed countless hours of successful operating with antennas bent in a variety of shapes and angles.

Antenna Installation

After you've built your antenna and chosen its location, how do you get it up? There are many schools of thought on putting up antennas. Can you support at least one end of your antenna on a mast, tower, building or in an easily climbed tree? If so, you have solved some of your problems. Unfortunately, this is not always the case. Hams use several methods to get antenna support ropes into trees. Most methods involve a weight attached to a rope or line. You might be able to tie a rope around a rock and throw it over the intended support. This method works for low antennas. Even a major league pitcher, however, would have trouble getting an antenna much higher than 40 feet with this method.

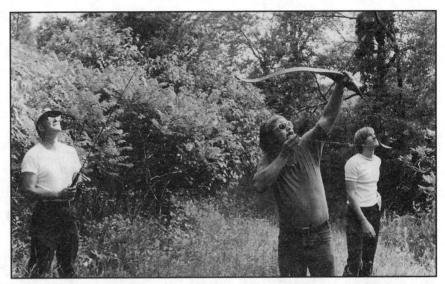

Figure 11-6—There are many ways to get an antenna support rope into a tree. These hams use a bow and arrow to shoot a lightweight fishing line over the desired branch. Then they attach the support rope to the fishing line and pull it up into the tree.

A better method is to use a bow and arrow, a fishing rod or even a slingshot to launch the weight and rope. See Figures 11-6 and 11-7. You'll find that strong, lightweight fishing line is the best line to attach to the weight. (Lead fishing weights are a good choice.) Regular rope is too heavy to shoot any great distance. When you have successfully cleared the supporting tree, remove the weight. Then tie the support rope to the fishing line and reel it in.

If your first attempt doesn't go over the limb you were hoping for, try again. Don't just reel in the line, however. Let the weight down to the ground first and take it off the line. Then you can reel the line in without getting the weight tangled in the branches.

You can put antenna supports in trees 120 feet and higher with this method. As with any type of marksmanship, make sure all is clear downrange before shooting. Your neighbors will not appreciate stray arrows, sinkers or rocks falling in their yards!

When your support ropes are in place, attach them to the ends of the dipole and haul it up. Pull the dipole reasonably tight, but not so tight that it is under a lot of strain. Tie the ends off so they are out of reach of passersby. Be sure to leave enough rope so you can let the dipole down temporarily if necessary.

Just one more step and your antenna installation is complete. After routing the coaxial cable to your station, cut it to length and install the proper connector for your rig. Usually this connector will be a PL-259, sometimes called a UHF connector. Figure 11-8 shows how to attach one of these fittings to RG-8 or RG-11 cable. Follow the step-by-step instructions exactly as illustrated and you should have no trouble. Be sure to place the coupling ring on

Figure 11-7—Another method for getting an antenna support into a tree. Small hose clamps attach a casting reel to the wrist bracket of a slingshot. Monofilament fishing line attached to a 1-ounce sinker is easily shot over almost any tree. Remove the sinker and rewind the line for repeated shots. When you find a suitable path through the tree, use the fishing line to pull a heavier line over the tree.

Figure 11-8—The PL-259 or UHF connector is almost universal for amateur HF work. It is also popular for equipment operating in the VHF range. Steps A through E illustrate how to install the connector properly. Despite its name, the UHF connector is rarely used on frequencies above 225 MHz.

the cable *before* you install the connector body! If you are using RG-58 or RG-59 cable, use an adapter to fit the cable to the connector. Figure 11-9 illustrates the steps for installing the connector with adapter. The PL-259 is standard on most rigs. If you require another kind of connector, consult your radio instruction manual or *The ARRL Handbook for Radio Amateurs* for installation information.

Tuning the Antenna

When you build an antenna, you cut it to the length given by an equation. This length is just a first approximation. Nearby trees, buildings or large metal objects and height above ground all affect the antenna resonant frequency. An SWR meter

1) Cut end of cable even. Remove vinyl jacket 3/4" — don't nick braid. Slide coupling ring and adapter on cable.

2) Fan braid slightly and fold back over cable.

3) Position adapter to dimension shown. Press braid down over body of adapter and trim to 3/8". Bare 5/8" of center conductor. Tin exposed center conductor.

4) Screw the plug assembly on adapter. Solder braid to shell through solder holes. Solder conductor to contact sleeve.

5) Screw coupling ring on assembly.

Figure 11-9—If you use RG-58 or RG-59 with a PL-259 connector, you should use an adapter, as shown here. Thanks to Amphenol Electronic Components, RF Division, Bunker Ramo Corp, for this information.

can help you determine if you should shorten or lengthen the antenna. The correct length provides the best impedance match for your transmitter.

The first step is to measure the SWR at the bottom, middle and top of the band. On 80 meters, for example, you would check the SWR at 3.626, 3.700 and 3.749 MHz. For operation in the phone portion of the band (usually called 75 meters) you should check at 3.851 MHz and 3.999 MHz. Notice that we selected test frequencies that stay inside the appropriate General frequency limits. (A friend with a higher license class can help you check the SWR over a wider frequency range.) Graph the readings, as shown in Figure 11-10. You could be lucky—no further antenna adjustments may be necessary, depending on your transmitter.

Many tube-type transmitters include an output tuning network. They will usually operate fine with an SWR of 3:1 or less. Most solid-state transmitters (using all transistors and integrated circuits) do not include such an output tuning network. These no-tune radios begin to shut down—the power output drops off — with an SWR much higher than 1.5:1. In any event, most hams like to prune their antennas for the lowest SWR they can get at the center of the band. With a full-size dipole 30 or 40 feet high, your SWR should be less than 2:1. If you can get the SWR down to 1.5:1, great! It's not worth the time and effort to do any better than that.

If the SWR is lower at the low-frequency end of the band, your antenna is probably too long. Making the antenna *shorter* will *increase* the resonant frequency. Disconnect the transmitter and try shortening your antenna at each end. The amount to trim off depends on two things. First is which band the antenna is operating on, and, second, how much you want to change the resonant frequency. Let's say the antenna is cut for the 80-meter band. You'll probably need to cut 8 or 10 inches off each end to move the resonant frequency 50 kHz. You may have to trim only an inch or less for small frequency changes on the 10-meter band. Measure the SWR again (remember to recheck the calibra-

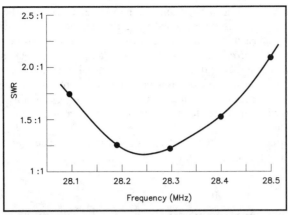

Figure 11-10—This graph shows how the SWR might vary across an amateur frequency band. The point of lowest SWR here is near the center of the band, so no further antenna-length adjustments are necessary.

tion). If the SWR went down, keep shortening the antenna until the SWR at the center of the band is less than 2:1.

If the SWR is lower at the high-frequency end of the band, your antenna was probably too short to begin with. If so, you must add more wire until the SWR is acceptable. Making the antenna *longer* will *decrease* the resonant frequency. Before you solder more wire on the antenna ends, try attaching a 12-inch wire on each end. Use alligator clips to attach a length of wire. You don't need to move the insulators yet. Clip a wire on each end and again measure the SWR. Chances are the antenna will now be too long. You will need to shorten it a little at a time until the SWR is below 2:1.

Once you know how much wire you need to add, cut two pieces and solder them to the ends of the antenna. When you add wire, be sure to make a sound mechanical connection before soldering. Remember that these joints must bear the weight of the antenna and the feed line. After you solder the wire, reinstall the insulators at the antenna ends, past the solder connections.

If the SWR is very high, you may have a problem that can't be cured by simple tuning. A very high SWR may mean that your feed line is open or shorted. Perhaps a connection isn't making good electrical contact. It could also be that your antenna is touching metal. A metal mast, the rain gutter on your house or some other conductor would add considerable length to the antenna. If the SWR is very high, check all connections and feed lines, and be sure the antenna clears surrounding objects.

Now you have enough information to construct, install and adjust your dipole antenna. You'll need a separate dipole antenna for each band you expect to operate on. Sometimes a 40-meter dipole will also work on 15 meters, though. Check the SWR on 15 meters—you may have a two-for-one dipole!

The Quarter-Wave Vertical Antenna

The quarter-wavelength vertical antenna is simple and popular. It requires only one support and can be very effective. On the HF bands (80 to 10 meters) it is often used for DX work. Vertical antennas send radio energy equally well in all compass directions. This is why we sometimes call them *nondirectional antennas* or *omnidirectional antennas*. They also tend to concentrate the signals toward the horizon. Vertical antennas do not generally radiate strong signals straight up, like horizontal dipoles do. Because they concentrate the signals toward the horizon, we say they have *gain* as compared to a dipole. Gain always refers to a comparison with another antenna. A dipole is one common comparison antenna for stating antenna gain.

Use Equation 11-2 to find $^1\!/_4$ λ for the radiator. The frequency is given in megahertz and the length is in feet in this equation.

$$\text{Length (in feet)} = \frac{234}{\text{f (in MHz)}}$$
(Equation 11-2)

Table 11-2 gives approximate lengths for the radiator and each ground radial of a $^1\!/_4$-λ vertical at each end of the HF bands.

As with $^1\!/_2$-λ dipoles, the resonant frequency of a $^1\!/_4$-λ vertical decreases as the length increases. Shorter antennas have higher resonant frequencies.

The $^1\!/_4$-λ vertical also has radials. For operation on 80 through 10 meters, the vertical may be at ground level, and the radials placed on the ground. The key to successful operation with a ground-mounted vertical antenna is a good radial system. The best radial system uses *many* ground radials. Lay them out like the spokes of a wheel, with the vertical at the center. Some hams have buried ground radial systems containing over 100 individual wires.

Ideally, these wires would be $^1\!/_4$ λ long or more at the lowest operating frequency. With such a system, earth or ground losses will be negligible. When the antenna is mounted at ground level, radial length is not very critical, however. Studies show that with fewer radials you can use shorter lengths, but with a corresponding loss in antenna efficiency.[1,2] Some of your transmitter power does

[1]J. O. Stanley, "Optimum Ground Systems for Vertical Antennas," *QST*, December 1976, pp 14-15.
[2]B. Edwards, "Radial Systems for Ground-Mounted Vertical Antennas," *QST*, June 1985, pp 28-30. This article is reproduced in *Vertical Antenna Classics*, available from the ARRL.

Table 11-2
Quarter-Wavelength Vertical Antenna Lengths for the Amateur HF Bands

Wavelength (m)	Frequency (MHz)	Length (ft)
160	1.8	130
	2.0	117
80	3.5	66.9
	4.0	58.5
40	7.0	33.4
	7.3	32.1
30	10.1	23.2
	10.15	23.1
20	14.0	16.7
	14.35	16.3
17	18.068	13.0
	18.168	12.9
15	21.0	11.1
	21.45	10.9
12	24.89	9.4
	24.99	9.4
10	28.0	8.4
	29.7	7.9

no more than warm the earth beneath your antenna. With 24 radials, there is no point in making them longer than about $^1/_8 \lambda$. With 16 radials, a length greater than 0.1 λ is unwarranted. Four radials should be considered an absolute minimum. Don't put the radials more than about an inch below the ground surface.

Compared with 120 radials of 0.4 λ, antenna efficiency with 24 radials is roughly 63%. For 16 radials, the efficiency is roughly 50%. So it pays to put in as many radials as you can.

If you place the vertical above ground, you reduce earth losses drastically. Here, the wires should be cut to $^1/_4 \lambda$ for the band you plan to use. Above ground, you need only a few radials—two to five. If you install a multiband vertical antenna above ground, use separate ground radials for each band you plan to use. These lengths are more critical than for a ground-mounted vertical. For elevated verticals, you should have a minimum of two radials for each band. You can mount a vertical on a pipe driven into the ground, on the chimney or on a tower.

The radials at the bottom of a vertical antenna mounted above ground form a surface that acts like the ground under the antenna. These antennas are sometimes called *ground-plane antennas.*

Once a vertical antenna is several feet above ground, there is little advantage in more height. (This assumes your antenna is above nearby obstructions.) For sky-wave signals, a height of 15 feet for the base is almost as good as 50. This isn't the case for a horizontal antenna, where height is important for working DX. Only if you can get the vertical up 2 or 3 wavelengths does the low-angle radiation begin to improve. Even then the improvement is only slight.

CONCLUSION

The information presented in this chapter is intended to help you begin assembling your Amateur Radio station. It won't answer every question you may have, however. A local ham or radio club can prove very helpful. In addition, the many books published by the American Radio Relay League provide a wealth of technical and operating assistance.

Perhaps the most important piece of advice we can leave you with is to experiment, and have fun.

GENERAL CLASS (ELEMENT 3B) QUESTION POOL—WITH ANSWERS

●N'T START HERE!

This chapter contains the complete question pool for the Element 3B exam. Element 3B is part of the General class Amateur Radio license exam. To earn a General class license, you must also pass the Element 2 (Novice) and Element 3A (Technician) written exams, in addition to the Element 1B 13-wpm Morse-code exam. You have credit for passing the Element 2 exam if you have a Novice license. You also have credit for the Element 3A exam if you hold a Technician or Technician Plus license. If you do not have a Novice, Technician or Technician Plus license you will have to pass those written exams. In that case, you should be studying a copy of the ARRL publication *Now You're Talking!*

Before you read the questions and answers printed in this chapter, be sure to read the text in the previous chapters. Use these questions as review exercises, when the text tells you to study them. (Paper clips make excellent place markers to help you find your place in the text and the question pool as you study.) Don't try to memorize all the questions and answers.

The material in this book has been carefully written and presented to guide you step-by-step through the learning process. By understanding the electronics principles and Amateur Radio concepts as they are presented, your insight into our hobby and your appreciation for the privileges granted by an Amateur Radio license will be greatly enhanced.

This question pool, released by the Volunteer Examiner Coordinators' Question Pool Committee in December 1997, will be used on exams beginning July 1, 1998. The pool is scheduled to be used until June 30, 2002. Changes to FCC Rules and other factors may result in some questions being "locked out" or removed from the pool. It is also possible that the question pool will be revised earlier because of significant changes to FCC Rules or schedule revisions. Such changes will be announced in *QST* and other Amateur Radio publications.

How Many Questions?

The FCC specifies that an Element 3B exam must include 30 questions. Ten subelements make up each of the Novice, Technician and General class exam question pools. (The Advanced and Amateur Extra question pools consist of nine subelements.) The FCC also specifies the number of questions from each subelement that must appear on the exam. For example, there must be three questions from the Operating Procedures subelement and one question from the Circuit Components subelement. Table 12-1 summarizes the number of questions to be selected from each subelement on the General class (Element 3B) exam. These numbers are also included at the beginning of each subelement in the question pool.

Table 12-1

General Class Exam Content

Subelement	Topic	Number of Questions
G1	Commission's Rules	4
G2	Operating Procedures	3
G3	Radio-Wave Propagation	3
G4	Amateur Radio Practices	5
G5	Electrical Principles	2
G6	Circuit Components	1
G7	Practical Circuits	1
G8	Signals and Emissions	2
G9	Antennas and Feed Lines	4
G0	RF Safety Practices	5

The Volunteer Examiner Coordinators' Question Pool Committee has broken the subelements into smaller groups. Each subelement has the same number of groups as there are questions from that subelement on the exam. This means there are three groups for the Operating Procedures subelement and two groups for the Electrical Principles subelement. The Question Pool Committee suggests one question from each group be used on the exam. These groups are called out with a list of topics given in bold type in the question pool. They are labeled alphabetically within each subelement. The four groups in the Commission's Rules subelement are labeled G1A through G1D.

The question numbers used in the question pool relate to the syllabus or study guide printed at the end of the Introduction, before Chapter 1 of this book. The syllabus is an outline of topics covered by the exam. Each question number begins with a G to indicate the question is from the General question pool. Next is a number to indicate from which of the 10 subelements the question is taken. A letter following this number indicates the subelement group to which the question belongs. Each question number ends with a two-digit number to specify its position in the set. So question G2A01 is the first question in the A group of the second subelement. Question G9C08 is the eighth question in the C group of the ninth subelement.

This question pool contains more than 10 times the number of questions necessary to make up an exam. This ensures that the examiners have sufficient questions from which to choose when they make up an exam.

Who Picks the Questions?

The FCC allows Volunteer-Examiner teams to select the questions that will be used on amateur exams. If your test is coordinated by the ARRL/VEC, however, your test will be prepared by the VEC, or by using a computer program supplied by the VEC.

Question Pool Format

The rest of this chapter contains the entire Element 3B question pool. We have printed the answer key to these questions along the edge of the page. There is a line to indicate where you should fold the page to hide the answer key while you study. (Fold the edge of the page under rather than over the page, so you don't cover part of the questions on the page.) After making your best effort to answer the questions, you can look at the answers to check your understanding.

We have also included page references along with the answers. These page numbers indicate where in this book you will find the text discussion related to each question. If you have any problems with a question, refer to the page listed for that question. You may have to study beyond the listed page number to review all the related material. With the "Commission's Rules" questions of Subelement 1, we have also included references to the sections of Part 97 of the FCC Rules. Chapter 1 of this book includes the appropriate text of these rules, along with an explanation to help you answer the questions. Chapter 1 does *not* include a complete copy of Part 97, however. For the complete text of the FCC Rules governing Amateur Radio, we recommend a copy of *The FCC Rule Book*, published by the ARRL. That book includes the complete text for Part 97, along with text to explain all the rules.

Good luck with your studies.

Answer Key

Page numbers tell you where to look in this book for more information.

Subelement G1

Numbers in [square brackets] indicate sections in Part 97, the Amateur Radio Rules.

ELEMENT 3B (GENERAL CLASS) QUESTION POOL

As released by the Question Pool Committee, National Conference of Volunteer Examiner Coordinators
December 1, 1997

Subelement G1 — Commission's Rules

[4 Exam Questions — 4 Groups]

G1A General control operator frequency privileges; local control; repeater and harmful interference definitions; third-party communications

G1A01
(C)
[97.301d]
Page 1-3

G1A01
What are the frequency limits for General class operators in the 160-meter band (ITU Region 2)?
A. 1800 - 1900-kHz
B. 1900 - 2000-kHz
C. 1800 - 2000-kHz
D. 1825 - 2000-kHz

G1A02
(A)
[97.301d]
Page 1-3

G1A02
What are the frequency limits for General class operators in the 75/80-meter band (ITU Region 2)?
A. 3525 - 3750-kHz and 3850 - 4000-kHz
B. 3525 - 3775-kHz and 3875 - 4000-kHz
C. 3525 - 3750-kHz and 3875 - 4000-kHz
D. 3525 - 3775-kHz and 3850 - 4000-kHz

G1A03
(D)
[97.301d]
Page 1-3

G1A03
What are the frequency limits for General class operators in the 40-meter band (ITU Region 2)?
A. 7025 - 7175-kHz and 7200 - 7300-kHz
B. 7025 - 7175-kHz and 7225 - 7300-kHz
C. 7025 - 7150-kHz and 7200 - 7300-kHz
D. 7025 - 7150-kHz and 7225 - 7300-kHz

G1A04
(A)
[97.301d]
Page 1-3

G1A04
What are the frequency limits for General class operators in the 30-meter band?
A. 10100 - 10150-kHz
B. 10100 - 10175-kHz
C. 10125 - 10150-kHz
D. 10125 - 10175-kHz

G1A05

What are the frequency limits for General class operators in the 20-meter band?

A. 14025 - 14100-kHz and 14175 - 14350-kHz
B. 14025 - 14150-kHz and 14225 - 14350-kHz
C. 14025 - 14125-kHz and 14200 - 14350-kHz
D. 14025 - 14175-kHz and 14250 - 14350-kHz

G1A06

What are the frequency limits for General class operators in the 15-meter band?

A. 21025 - 21200-kHz and 21275 - 21450-kHz
B. 21025 - 21150-kHz and 21300 - 21450-kHz
C. 21025 - 21150-kHz and 21275 - 21450-kHz
D. 21025 - 21200-kHz and 21300 - 21450-kHz

G1A07

What are the frequency limits for General class operators in the 12-meter band?

A. 24890 - 24990-kHz
B. 24890 - 24975-kHz
C. 24900 - 24990-kHz
D. 24900 - 24975-kHz

G1A08

What are the frequency limits for General class operators in the 10-meter band?

A. 28000 - 29700-kHz
B. 28025 - 29700-kHz
C. 28100 - 29600-kHz
D. 28125 - 29600-kHz

G1A09

As a General class control operator at a Novice station, how must you identify the Novice station when transmitting on 7250-kHz?

A. With your call sign, followed by the word "controlling" and the Novice call sign
B. With the Novice call sign, followed by the slant bar "/" (or any suitable word) and your own call sign
C. With your call sign, followed by the slant bar "/" (or any suitable word) and the Novice call sign
D. A Novice station should not be operated on 7250-kHz, even with a General control operator

G1A05
(B)
[97.301d]
Page 1-3

G1A06
(D)
[97.301d]
Page 1-3

G1A07
(A)
[97.301d]
Page 1-3

G1A08
(A)
[97.301d]
Page 1-3

G1A09
(B)
[97.119e]
Page 1-4

G1A10
(D)
[97.205a]
Page 1-4

G1A10
Under what circumstances may a 10-meter repeater retransmit the 2-meter signal from a Technician class operator?
A. Under no circumstances
B. Only if the station on 10 meters is operating under a Special Temporary Authorization allowing such retransmission
C. Only during an FCC-declared general state of communications emergency
D. Only if the 10-meter control operator holds at least a General class license

G1A11
(A)
[97.3a37]
Page 1-4

G1A11
What kind of amateur station simultaneously retransmits the signals of other stations on a different channel?
A. Repeater station
B. Space station
C. Telecommand station
D. Relay station

G1A12
(B)
[97.3a22]
Page 1-4

G1A12
What name is given to a form of interference that seriously degrades, obstructs or repeatedly interrupts a radiocommunication service?
A. Intentional interference
B. Harmful interference
C. Adjacent interference
D. Disruptive interference

G1A13
(C)
[97.115,
97.117]
Page 1-5

G1A13
What types of messages may be transmitted by an amateur station to a foreign country for a third party?
A. Messages for which the amateur operator is paid
B. Messages facilitating the business affairs of any party
C. Messages of a technical nature or remarks of a personal character
D. No messages may be transmitted to foreign countries for third parties

G1B Antenna structure limitations; good engineering and good amateur practice; beacon operation; restricted operation; retransmitting radio signals

G1B01
(C)
[97.15a]
Page 1-10

G1B01
Up to what height above the ground may you install an antenna structure without needing FCC approval unless your station is in close proximity to an airport as defined in the FCC Rules?
A. 50 feet
B. 100 feet
C. 200 feet
D. 300 feet

G1B02
If the FCC Rules DO NOT specifically cover a situation, how must you operate your amateur station?
A. In accordance with general licensee operator principles
B. In accordance with good engineering and good amateur practice
C. In accordance with practices adopted by the Institute of Electrical and Electronics Engineers
D. In accordance with procedures set forth by the International Amateur Radio Union

G1B03
Which of the following types of stations may normally transmit only one-way communications?
A. Repeater station
B. Beacon station
C. HF station
D. VHF station

G1B04
Which of the following does NOT need to be true if an amateur station gathers news information for broadcast purposes?
A. The information is more quickly transmitted by Amateur Radio
B. The information must involve the immediate safety of life of individuals or the immediate protection of property
C. The information must be directly related to the event
D. The information cannot be transmitted by other means

G1B05
Under what limited circumstances may music be transmitted by an amateur station?
A. When it produces no dissonances or spurious emissions
B. When it is used to jam an illegal transmission
C. When it is transmitted on frequencies above 1215 MHz
D. When it is an incidental part of a space shuttle retransmission

G1B06
When may an amateur station in two-way communication transmit a message in a secret code in order to obscure the meaning of the communication?
A. When transmitting above 450 MHz
B. During contests
C. Never
D. During a declared communications emergency

G1B02
(B)
[97.101a]
Page 1-7

G1B03
(B)
[97.203g]
Page 1-10

G1B04
(A)
[97.113b]
Page1-10

G1B05
(D)
[97.113e]
Page 1-8

G1B06
(C)
[97.113a4]
Page 1-8

G1B07
(B)
[97.113a4]
Page 1-8

G1B07
What are the restrictions on the use of abbreviations or procedural signals in the amateur service?
A. There are no restrictions
B. They may be used if they do not obscure the meaning of a message
C. They are not permitted because they obscure the meaning of a message to FCC monitoring stations
D. Only "10-codes" are permitted

G1B08
(A)
[97.113a4]
Page 1-8

G1B08
When are codes or ciphers permitted in two-way domestic amateur communications?
A. Never, if intended to obscure meaning
B. During contests
C. During nationally declared emergencies
D. On frequencies above 2.3-GHz

G1B09
(A)
[97.113a4]
Page 1-8

G1B09
When are codes or ciphers permitted in two-way international amateur communications?
A. Never, if intended to obscure meaning
B. During contests
C. During internationally declared emergencies
D. On frequencies above 2.3-GHz

G1B10
(D)
[97.113a4,
97.113e]
Page 1-8

G1B10
Which of the following amateur transmissions is NOT prohibited by the FCC Rules?
A. The playing of music
B. The use of obscene or indecent words
C. False or deceptive messages or signals
D. Retransmission of space shuttle communications

G1B11
(C)
[97.113a4,
97.113e]
Page 1-8

G1B11
What should you do to keep your station from retransmitting music or signals from a non-amateur station?
A. Turn up the volume of your transceiver
B. Speak closer to the microphone to increase your signal strength
C. Turn down the volume of background audio
D. Adjust your transceiver noise blanker

G1C Transmitter power standards; type acceptance of external RF-power-amplifiers; standards for type acceptance of external RF-power amplifiers; HF data emission standards

G1C01
What is the maximum transmitting power an amateur station may use on 3690-kHz?
A. 200 watts PEP output
B. 1000 watts PEP output
C. 1500 watts PEP output
D. The minimum power necessary to carry out the desired communications with a maximum of 2000 watts PEP output

G1C01
(A)
[97.313c1]
Page 1-11

G1C02
What is the maximum transmitting power an amateur station may use on 7080-kHz?
A. 200 watts PEP output
B. 1000 watts PEP output
C. 1500 watts PEP output
D. 2000 watts PEP output

G1C02
(C)
[97.313a,b]
Page 1-11

G1C03
What is the maximum transmitting power an amateur station may use on 10.140 MHz?
A. 200 watts PEP output
B. 1000 watts PEP output
C. 1500 watts PEP output
D. 2000 watts PEP output

G1C03
(A)
[97.313c1]
Page 1-11

G1C04
What is the maximum transmitting power an amateur station may use on 21.150 MHz?
A. 200 watts PEP output
B. 1000 watts PEP output
C. 1500 watts PEP output
D. 2000 watts PEP output

G1C04
(A)
[97.313c1]
Page 1-11

G1C05
What is the maximum transmitting power an amateur station may use on 24.950 MHz?
A. 200 watts PEP output
B. 1000 watts PEP output
C. 1500 watts PEP output
D. 2000 watts PEP output

G1C05
(C)
[97.313a,b]
Page 1-11

G1C06
(D)
[97.315a]
Page 1-11

G1C06
External RF power amplifiers designed to operate below what frequency may require FCC type acceptance?
A. 28 MHz
B. 35 MHz
C. 50 MHz
D. 144 MHz

G1C07
(B)
[97.315a]
Page 1-11

G1C07
Without a grant of FCC type acceptance, how many external RF amplifiers of a given design capable of operation below 144 MHz may you build or modify in one calendar year?
A. None
B. 1
C. 5
D. 10

G1C08
(B)
[97.317a3]
Page 1-12

G1C08
Which of the following standards must be met if FCC type acceptance of an external RF amplifier is required?
A. The amplifier must not be able to amplify a 28-MHz signal to more than ten times the input power
B. The amplifier must not be capable of reaching its designed output power when driven with less than 50 watts
C. The amplifier must not be able to be operated for more than ten minutes without a time delay circuit
D. The amplifier must not be able to be modified by an amateur operator

G1C09
(D)
[97.317b,c]
Page 1-12

G1C09
Which of the following would NOT disqualify an external RF power amplifier from being granted FCC type acceptance?
A. The capability of being modified by the operator for use outside the amateur bands
B. The capability of achieving full output power when driven with less than 50 watts
C. The capability of achieving full output power on amateur frequencies between 24 and 35 MHz
D. The capability of being switched by the operator to all amateur frequencies below 24 MHz

G1C10
(A)
[97.305c, 97.307f3]
Page 2-7

G1C10
What is the maximum symbol rate permitted for packet emissions below 28 MHz?
A. 300 bauds
B. 1200 bauds
C. 19.6 kilobauds
D. 56 kilobauds

G1C11
What is the maximum symbol rate permitted for RTTY emissions below 28 MHz?
A. 56 kilobauds
B. 19.6 kilobauds
C. 1200 bauds
D. 300 bauds

G1C11
(D)
[97.305c, 97.307f3]
Page 2-7

G1D Examination element preparation; examination administration; temporary station identification

G1D01
What telegraphy examination elements may you prepare if you hold a General class license?
A. None
B. Element 1A only
C. Element 1B only
D. Elements 1A and 1B

G1D01
(B)
[97.507a2]
Page 1-14

G1D02
What written examination elements may you prepare if you hold a General class license?
A. None
B. Element 2 only
C. Elements 2 and 3A
D. Elements 2, 3A and 3B

G1D02
(C)
[97.507a2,3]
Page 1-14

G1D03
What license examinations may you administer if you hold a General class license?
A. None
B. Novice only
C. Novice, Technician and Technician Plus
D. Novice, Technician and General

G1D03
(C)
[97.509b3i]
Page 1-14

G1D04
What minimum examination elements must an applicant pass for a Novice license?
A. Element 2 only
B. Elements 1A and 2
C. Elements 2 and 3A
D. Elements 1A, 2 and 3A

G1D04
(B)
[97.501f]
Page 1-15

G1D05
What minimum examination elements must an applicant pass for a Technician license?
A. Element 2 only
B. Elements 1A and 2
C. Elements 2 and 3A
D. Elements 1A, 2 and 3A

G1D05
(C)
[97.501e]
Page 1-15

G1D06
(D)
[97.501d]
Page 1-15

G1D06
What minimum examination elements must an applicant pass for a Technician Plus license?
A. Element 2 only
B. Elements 1A and 2
C. Elements 2 and 3A
D. Elements 1A, 2 and 3A

G1D07
(A)
[97.509a,b]
Page 1-14

G1D07
What are the requirements for administering Novice examinations?
A. Three VEC-accredited General class or higher VEs must be present
B. Two VEC-accredited General class or higher VEs must be present
C. Two General class or higher VEs must be present, but only one need be VEC accredited
D. Any two General class or higher VEs must be present

G1D08
(D)
[97.509b3i]
Page 1-14

G1D08
When may you participate as an administering Volunteer Examiner (VE) for a Novice license examination?
A. Once you have notified the FCC that you want to give an examination
B. Once you have a Certificate of Successful Completion of Examination (CSCE) for General class
C. Once you have prepared telegraphy and written examinations for the Novice license, or obtained them from a qualified supplier
D. Once you have been granted your FCC General class or higher license and received your VEC accreditation

G1D09
(B)
[97.119f2]
Page 1-16

G1D09
If you are a Technician licensee with a Certificate of Successful Completion of Examination (CSCE) for General privileges, how do you identify your station when transmitting on 14.035 MHz?
A. You must give your call sign and the location of the VE examination where you obtained the CSCE
B. You must give your call sign, followed by the slant mark "/", followed by the identifier "AG"
C. You may not operate on 14.035 MHz until your new license arrives
D. No special form of identification is needed

G1D10
(C)
[97.119f2]
Page 1-16

G1D10
If you are a Technician licensee with a Certificate of Successful Completion of Examination (CSCE) for General privileges, how do you identify your station when transmitting phone emissions on 14.325 MHz?
A. No special form of identification is needed
B. You may not operate on 14.325 MHz until your new license arrives
C. You must give your call sign, followed by any suitable word that denotes the slant mark and the identifier "AG"
D. You must give your call sign and the location of the VE examination where you obtained the CSCE

G1D11
If you are a Technician licensee with a Certificate of Successful Completion of Examination (CSCE) for General privileges, when must you add the special identifier "AG" after your call sign?
A. Whenever you operate using your new frequency privileges
B. Whenever you operate
C. Whenever you operate using Technician frequency privileges
D. A special identifier is not required as long as your General class license application has been filed with the FCC

G1D11
(A)
[97.119f2]
Page 1-16

Subelement G2 — Operating Procedures

[3 Exam Questions — 3 Groups]

G2A Phone; RTTY; repeater; VOX and full break-in CW

Subelement
G2

G2A01
Which sideband is commonly used for 20-meter phone operation?
A. Upper
B. Lower
C. Amplitude compandored
D. Double

G2A01
(A)
Page 2-2

G2A02
Which sideband is commonly used on 3925-kHz for phone operation?
A. Upper
B. Lower
C. Amplitude compandored
D. Double

G2A02
(B)
Page 2-2

G2A03
In what segment of the 80-meter band do most RTTY transmissions take place?
A. 3580 - 3620-kHz
B. 3500 - 3525-kHz
C. 3700 - 3750-kHz
D. 3775 - 3825-kHz

G2A03
(A)
Page 2-5

G2A04
In what segment of the 20-meter band do most RTTY transmissions take place?
A. 14.000 - 14.050 MHz
B. 14.070 - 14.095 MHz
C. 14.150 - 14.225 MHz
D. 14.275 - 14.350 MHz

G2A04
(B)
Page 2-5

General Class (Element 3B) Question Pool—With Answers   12-13

G2A05
(C)
Page 2-4

G2A05
What is the Baudot code?
A. A 7-bit code, with start, stop and parity bits
B. A 7-bit code in which each character has four mark and three space bits
C. A 5-bit code, with additional start and stop bits
D. A 6-bit code, with additional start, stop and parity bits

G2A06
(A)
Page 2-6

G2A06
What is ASCII?
A. A 7-bit code, with additional start, stop and parity bits
B. A 7-bit code in which each character has four mark and three space bits
C. A 5-bit code, with additional start and stop bits
D. A 5-bit code in which each character has three mark and two space bits

G2A07
(B)
Page 2-4

G2A07
What is the most common frequency shift for RTTY emissions in the amateur HF bands?
A. 85 Hz
B. 170 Hz
C. 425 Hz
D. 850 Hz

G2A08
(B)
Page 2-6

G2A08
What are the two major AMTOR operating modes?
A. Mode AM and Mode TR
B. Mode A (ARQ) and Mode B (FEC)
C. Mode C (CRQ) and Mode D (DEC)
D. Mode SELCAL and Mode LISTEN

G2A09
(A)
Page 2-3

G2A09
What is the usual input/output frequency separation for a 10-meter station in repeater operation?
A. 100-kHz
B. 600-kHz
C. 1.6 MHz
D. 170 MHz

G2A10
(B)
Page 2-2

G2A10
What is the circuit called that causes a transmitter to automatically transmit when an operator speaks into its microphone?
A. VXO
B. VOX
C. VCO
D. VFO

G2A11
Which of the following describes full break-in telegraphy?
A. Breaking stations send the Morse code prosign BK
B. Automatic keyers are used to send Morse code instead of hand keys
C. An operator must activate a manual send/receive switch before and after every transmission
D. Incoming signals are received between transmitted key pulses

G2B Operating courtesy; antenna orientation and HF operations; including logging practices; ITU Regions

G2B01
If you are the net control station of a daily HF net, what should you do if the frequency on which you normally meet is in use just before the net begins?
A. Reduce your output power and start the net as usual
B. Increase your power output so that net participants will be able to hear you over the existing activity
C. Cancel the net for that day
D. Conduct the net on a frequency 3 to 5-kHz away from the regular net frequency

G2B02
If a net is about to begin on a frequency which you and another station are using, what should you do?
A. As a courtesy to the net, move to a different frequency
B. Increase your power output to ensure that all net participants can hear you
C. Transmit as long as possible on the frequency so that no other stations may use it
D. Turn off your radio

G2B03
If propagation changes during your contact and you notice increasing interference from other activity on the same frequency, what should you do?
A. Tell the interfering stations to change frequency, since you were there first
B. Report the interference to your local Amateur Auxiliary Coordinator
C. Turn on your amplifier to overcome the interference
D. Move your contact to another frequency

G2B04
When selecting a CW transmitting frequency, what minimum frequency separation from a contact in progress should you allow to minimize interference?
A. 5 to 50 Hz
B. 150 to 500 Hz
C. 1 to 3-kHz
D. 3 to 6-kHz

G2A11
(D)
Page 2-3

G2B01
(D)
Page 2-8

G2B02
(A)
Page 2-8

G2B03
(D)
Page 2-8

G2B04
(B)
Page 2-7

G2B05
(B)
Page 2-7

G2B05
When selecting a single-sideband phone transmitting frequency, what minimum frequency separation from a contact in progress should you allow (between suppressed carriers) to minimize interference?
A. 150 to 500 Hz
B. Approximately 3-kHz
C. Approximately 6-kHz
D. Approximately 10-kHz

G2B06
(B)
Page 2-7

G2B06
When selecting a RTTY transmitting frequency, what minimum frequency separation from a contact in progress should you allow (center to center) to minimize interference?
A. 60 Hz
B. 250 to 500 Hz
C. Approximately 3-kHz
D. Approximately 6-kHz

G2B07
(B)
Page 2-9

G2B07
What is an azimuthal map?
A. A map projection centered on the North Pole
B. A map projection centered on a particular location, used to determine the shortest path between points on the surface of the earth
C. A map that shows the angle at which an amateur satellite crosses the equator
D. A map that shows the number of degrees longitude that an amateur satellite appears to move westward at the equator with each orbit

G2B08
(A)
Page 2-9

G2B08
What is the most useful type of map to use when orienting a directional HF antenna toward a distant station?
A. Azimuthal
B. Mercator
C. Polar projection
D. Topographical

G2B09
(C)
Page 2-9

G2B09
A directional antenna pointed in the long-path direction to another station is generally oriented how many degrees from its short-path heading?
A. 45 degrees
B. 90 degrees
C. 180 degrees
D. 270 degrees

G2B10
What is a band plan?
A. A voluntary guideline beyond the divisions established by the FCC for using different operating modes within an amateur band
B. A guideline from the FCC for making amateur frequency band allocations
C. A plan of operating schedules within an amateur band published by the FCC
D. A plan devised by a club to best use a frequency band during a contest

G2B10
(A)
Page 2-5

G2B11
In which International Telecommunication Union Region is the continental United States?
A. Region 1
B. Region 2
C. Region 3
D. Region 4

G2B11
(B)
Page 1-2

G2C Emergencies; including drills; communications and amateur auxiliary to the FCC's Compliance and Information Bureau

G2C01
What means may an amateur station in distress use to attract attention, make known its condition and location, and obtain assistance?
A. Only Morse code signals sent on internationally recognized emergency channels
B. Any means of radiocommunication, but only on internationally recognized emergency channels
C. Any means of radiocommunication
D. Only those means of radiocommunication for which the station is licensed

G2C01
(C)
Page 2-11

G2C02
During a disaster in the US, when may an amateur station make transmissions necessary to meet essential communication needs and assist relief operations?
A. When normal communication systems are overloaded, damaged or disrupted
B. Only when the local RACES net is activated
C. Never; only official emergency stations may transmit in a disaster
D. When normal communication systems are working but are not convenient

G2C02
(A)
Page 2-11

G2C03
(A)
Page 2-11

G2C03
If a disaster disrupts normal communications in your area, what may the FCC do?
A. Declare a temporary state of communication emergency
B. Temporarily seize your equipment for use in disaster communications
C. Order all stations across the country to stop transmitting at once
D. Nothing until the President declares the area a disaster area

G2C04
(D)
Page 2-11

G2C04
If a disaster disrupts normal communications in an area, what would the FCC include in any notice of a temporary state of communication emergency?
A. Any additional test questions needed for the licensing of amateur emergency communications workers
B. A list of organizations authorized to temporarily seize your equipment for disaster communications
C. Any special conditions requiring the use of non-commercial power systems
D. Any special conditions and special rules to be observed by stations during the emergency

G2C05
(D)
Page 2-11

G2C05
During an emergency, what power output limitations must be observed by a station in distress?
A. 200 watts PEP
B. 1500 watts PEP
C. 1000 watts PEP during daylight hours, reduced to 200 watts PEP during the night
D. There are no limitations during an emergency

G2C06
(C)
Page 2-11

G2C06
During a disaster in the US, what frequencies may be used to obtain assistance?
A. Only frequencies in the 80-meter band
B. Only frequencies in the 40-meter band
C. Any frequency
D. Any United Nations approved frequency

G2C07
(B)
Page 2-10

G2C07
If you are communicating with another amateur station and hear a station in distress break in, what should you do?
A. Continue your communication because you were on frequency first
B. Acknowledge the station in distress and determine its location and what assistance may be needed
C. Change to a different frequency so the station in distress may have a clear channel to call for assistance
D. Immediately cease all transmissions because stations in distress have emergency rights to the frequency

G2C08
Why do stations in the Radio Amateur Civil Emergency Service (RACES) participate in training tests and drills?
A. To practice orderly and efficient operations for the civil defense organization they serve
B. To ensure that members attend monthly on-the-air meetings
C. To ensure that RACES members are able to conduct tests and drills
D. To acquaint members of RACES with other members they may meet in an emergency

G2C08
(A)
Page 2-11

G2C09
What type of messages may be transmitted to an amateur station in a foreign country?
A. Messages of any type
B. Messages that are not religious, political, or patriotic in nature
C. Messages of a technical nature or personal remarks of relative unimportance
D. Messages of any type, but only if the foreign country has a third-party communications agreement with the US

G2C09
(C)
Page 1-5

G2C10
What is the Amateur Auxiliary to the FCC's Compliance and Information Bureau?
A. Amateur volunteers who are formally enlisted to monitor the airwaves for rules violations
B. Amateur volunteers who conduct amateur licensing examinations
C. Amateur volunteers who conduct frequency coordination for amateur VHF repeaters
D. Amateur volunteers who use their station equipment to help civil defense organizations in times of emergency

G2C10
(A)
Page 2-14

G2C11
What are the objectives of the Amateur Auxiliary to the FCC's Compliance and Information Bureau?
A. To conduct efficient and orderly amateur licensing examinations
B. To encourage amateur self-regulation and compliance with the rules
C. To coordinate repeaters for efficient and orderly spectrum usage
D. To provide emergency and public safety communications

G2C11
(B)
Page 2-14

Subelement G3 — Radio Wave Propagation

[3 Exam Questions — 3 Groups]

G3A Ionospheric disturbances; sunspots and solar radiation

G3A01
What can be done at an amateur station to continue communications during a
sudden ionospheric disturbance?
A. Try a higher frequency
B. Try the other sideband
C. Try a different antenna polarization
D. Try a different frequency shift

G3A02
What effect does a sudden ionospheric disturbance have on the day-time
ionospheric propagation of HF radio waves?
A. It disrupts higher-latitude paths more than lower-latitude paths
B. It disrupts signals on lower frequencies more than those on higher
   frequencies
C. It disrupts communications via satellite more than direct communications
D. None, only areas on the night side of the earth are affected

G3A03
How long does it take the increased ultraviolet and X-ray radiation from solar
flares to affect radio-wave propagation on the earth?
A. The effect is almost instantaneous
B. 1.5 minutes
C. 8 minutes
D. 20 to 40 hours

G3A04
What is solar flux?
A. The density of the sun's magnetic field
B. The radio energy emitted by the sun
C. The number of sunspots on the side of the sun facing the earth
D. A measure of the tilt of the earth's ionosphere on the side toward the sun

G3A05
What is the solar-flux index?
A. A measure of solar activity that is taken annually
B. A measure of solar activity that compares daily readings with results from
   the last six months
C. Another name for the American sunspot number
D. A measure of solar activity that is taken at a specific frequency

G3A06

What is a geomagnetic disturbance?

A. A sudden drop in the solar-flux index
B. A shifting of the earth's magnetic pole
C. Ripples in the ionosphere
D. A dramatic change in the earth's magnetic field over a short period of time

G3A06
(D)
Page 3-10

G3A07

At which latitudes are propagation paths more sensitive to geomagnetic disturbances?

A. Those greater than 45 degrees latitude
B. Those between 5 and 45 degrees latitude
C. Those near the equator
D. All paths are affected equally

G3A07
(A)
Page 3-10

G3A08

What can be the effect of a major geomagnetic storm on radio-wave propagation?

A. Improved high-latitude HF propagation
B. Degraded high-latitude HF propagation
C. Improved ground-wave propagation
D. Improved chances of UHF ducting

G3A08
(B)
Page 3-10

G3A09

What phenomenon has the most effect on radio communication beyond ground-wave or line-of-sight ranges?

A. Solar activity
B. Lunar tidal effects
C. The F1 region of the ionosphere
D. The F2 region of the ionosphere

G3A09
(A)
Page 3-7

G3A10

Which two types of radiation from the sun influence propagation?

A. Subaudible-frequency and audio-frequency emissions
B. Electromagnetic and particle emissions
C. Polar-region and equatorial emissions
D. Infrared and gamma-ray emissions

G3A10
(B)
Page 3-10

G3A11

When sunspot numbers are high, what is the affect on radio communications?

A. High-frequency radio signals are absorbed
B. Frequencies above 300 MHz become usable for long-distance communication
C. Long-distance communication in the upper HF and lower VHF range is enhanced
D. High-frequency radio signals become weak and distorted

G3A11
(C)
Page 3-7

G3B01
(B)
Page 3-6

G3B01
If the maximum usable frequency (MUF) on the path from Minnesota to France is 24 MHz, which band should offer the best chance for a successful contact?
A. 10 meters
B. 15 meters
C. 20 meters
D. 40 meters

G3B02
(C)
Page 3-6

G3B02
If the maximum usable frequency (MUF) on the path from Ohio to Germany is 17 MHz, which band should offer the best chance for a successful contact?
A. 80 meters
B. 40 meters
C. 20 meters
D. 2 meters

G3B03
(C)
Page 3-7

G3B03
If the HF radio-wave propagation (skip) is generally good on the 24-MHz and 28-MHz bands for several days, when might you expect a similar condition to occur?
A. 7 days later
B. 14 days later
C. 28 days later
D. 90 days later

G3B04
(A)
Page 3-8

G3B04
What is one way to determine if the maximum usable frequency (MUF) is high enough to support 28-MHz propagation between your station and western Europe?
A. Listen for signals on the 10-meter beacon frequency
B. Listen for signals on the 20-meter beacon frequency
C. Listen for signals on the 39-meter broadcast frequency
D. Listen for WWVH time signals on 20 MHz

G3B05
(A)
Page 3-6

G3B05
What usually happens to radio waves with frequencies below the maximum usable frequency (MUF) when they are sent into the ionosphere?
A. They are bent back to the earth
B. They pass through the ionosphere
C. They are completely absorbed by the ionosphere
D. They are bent and trapped in the ionosphere to circle the Earth

G3B06
Where would you tune to hear beacons that would help you determine propagation conditions on the 20-meter band?
A. 28.2 MHz
B. 21.1 MHz
C. 14.1 MHz
D. 18.1 MHz

G3B07
During periods of low solar activity, which frequencies are the least reliable for long-distance communication?
A. Frequencies below 3.5 MHz
B. Frequencies near 3.5 MHz
C. Frequencies on or above 10 MHz
D. Frequencies above 20 MHz

G3B08
At what point in the solar cycle does the 20-meter band usually support worldwide propagation during daylight hours?
A. At the summer solstice
B. Only at the maximum point of the solar cycle
C. Only at the minimum point of the solar cycle
D. At any point in the solar cycle

G3B09
What is one characteristic of gray-line propagation?
A. It is very efficient
B. It improves local communications
C. It is very poor
D. It increases D-region absorption

G3B10
What is the maximum distance along the Earth's surface that is normally covered in one hop using the F2 region?
A. 180 miles
B. 1200 miles
C. 2500 miles
D. None; the F2 region does not support radio-wave propagation

G3B11
What is the maximum distance along the Earth's surface that is normally covered in one hop using the E region?
A. 180 miles
B. 1200 miles
C. 2500 miles
D. None of these choices is correct

G3B06
(C)
Page 3-8

G3B07
(D)
Page 3-7

G3B08
(D)
Page 3-7

G3B09
(A)
Page 3-13

G3B10
(C)
Page 3-4

G3B11
(B)
Page 3-4

G3C Height of ionospheric regions; critical angle and frequency; HF scatter

G3C01
(B)
Page 3-4

G3C01
What is the average height of maximum ionization of the E region?
A. 45 miles
B. 70 miles
C. 200 miles
D. 1200 miles

G3C02
(A)
Page 3-4

G3C02
When can the F2 region be expected to reach its maximum height at your location?
A. At noon during the summer
B. At midnight during the summer
C. At dusk in the spring and fall
D. At noon during the winter

G3C03
(C)
Page 3-4

G3C03
Why is the F2 region mainly responsible for the longest-distance radio-wave propagation?
A. Because it exists only at night
B. Because it is the lowest ionospheric region
C. Because it is the highest ionospheric region
D. Because it does not absorb radio waves as much as other ionospheric regions

G3C04
(D)
Page 3-5

G3C04
What is the "critical angle" as used in radio-wave propagation?
A. The lowest takeoff angle that will return a radio wave to the earth under specific ionospheric conditions
B. The compass direction of a distant station
C. The compass direction opposite that of a distant station
D. The highest takeoff angle that will return a radio wave to the earth under specific ionospheric conditions

G3C05
(C)
Page 3-2

G3C05
What is the main reason the 160-, 80- and 40-meter amateur bands tend to be useful only for short-distance communications during daylight hours?
A. Because of a lack of activity
B. Because of auroral propagation
C. Because of D-region absorption
D. Because of magnetic flux

G3C06
(B)
Page 3-11

G3C06
What is a characteristic of HF scatter signals?
A. High intelligibility
B. A wavering sound
C. Reversed modulation
D. Reversed sidebands

G3C07
What makes HF scatter signals often sound distorted?
A. Auroral activity and changes in the earth's magnetic field
B. Propagation through ground waves that absorb much of the signal
C. The state of the E-region at the point of refraction
D. Energy scattered into the skip zone through several radio-wave paths

G3C07
(D)
Page 3-11

G3C08
Why are HF scatter signals usually weak?
A. Only a small part of the signal energy is scattered into the skip zone
B. Auroral activity absorbs most of the signal energy
C. Propagation through ground waves absorbs most of the signal energy
D. The F region of the ionosphere absorbs most of the signal energy

G3C08
(A)
Page 3-11

G3C09
What type of radio-wave propagation allows a signal to be detected at a distance too far for ground-wave propagation but too near for normal sky-wave propagation?
A. Ground wave
B. Scatter
C. Sporadic-E skip
D. Short-path skip

G3C09
(B)
Page 3-12

G3C10
When does scatter propagation on the HF bands most often occur?
A. When the sunspot cycle is at a minimum and D-region absorption is high
B. At night
C. When the F1 and F2 regions are combined
D. When communicating on frequencies above the maximum usable frequency (MUF)

G3C10
(D)
Page 3-11

G3C11
What is one way the vertical incidence critical frequency measurement might be used?
A. It can be used to measure noise arriving vertically from outer space
B. It can be used to measure the vertical angle at which to set your beam antenna
C. It can be used to determine the size of coronal holes in the ionosphere
D. It can be used to determine the maximum usable frequency for long-distance communication at the time of measurement

G3C11
(D)
Page 3-6

Subelement G4 — Amateur Radio Practices

[5 Exam Questions — 5 Groups]

G4A Two-tone test; electronic TR switch; amplifier neutralization

G4A01
What kind of input signal is used to test the amplitude linearity of a single-sideband phone transmitter while viewing the output on an oscilloscope?
A. Normal speech
B. An audio-frequency sine wave
C. Two audio-frequency sine waves
D. An audio-frequency square wave

G4A02
When testing the amplitude linearity of a single-sideband transmitter, what kind of audio tones are fed into the microphone input and on what kind of instrument is the transmitter output observed?
A. Two harmonically related tones are fed in, and the output is observed on an oscilloscope
B. Two harmonically related tones are fed in, and the output is observed on a distortion analyzer
C. Two non harmonically related tones are fed in, and the output is observed on an oscilloscope
D. Two non harmonically related tones are fed in, and the output is observed on a distortion analyzer

G4A03
What audio frequencies are used in a two-tone test of the linearity of a single-sideband phone transmitter?
A. 20 Hz and 20-kHz tones must be used
B. 1200 Hz and 2400 Hz tones must be used
C. Any two audio tones may be used, but they must be within the transmitter audio passband, and must be harmonically related
D. Any two audio tones may be used, but they must be within the transmitter audio passband, and should not be harmonically related

G4A04
What measurement can be made of a single-sideband phone transmitter's amplifier by performing a two-tone test using an oscilloscope?
A. Its percent of frequency modulation
B. Its percent of carrier phase shift
C. Its frequency deviation
D. Its linearity

G4A05
At what point in an HF transceiver block diagram would an electronic TR switch normally appear?
A. Between the transmitter and low-pass filter
B. Between the low-pass filter and antenna
C. At the antenna feed point
D. At the power supply feed point

G4A06
Why is an electronic TR switch preferable to a mechanical one?
A. It allows greater receiver sensitivity
B. Its circuitry is simpler
C. It has a higher operating speed
D. It allows cleaner output signals

G4A07
As a power amplifier is tuned, what reading on its grid-current meter indicates the best neutralization?
A. A minimum change in grid current as the output circuit is changed
B. A maximum change in grid current as the output circuit is changed
C. Minimum grid current
D. Maximum grid current

G4A08
Why is neutralization necessary for some vacuum-tube amplifiers?
A. To reduce the limits of loaded Q
B. To reduce grid-to-cathode leakage
C. To cancel AC hum from the filament transformer
D. To cancel oscillation caused by the effects of interelectrode capacitance

G4A09
In a properly neutralized RF amplifier, what type of feedback is used?
A. 5%
B. 10%
C. Negative
D. Positive

G4A10
What does a neutralizing circuit do in an RF amplifier?
A. It controls differential gain
B. It cancels the effects of positive feedback
C. It eliminates AC hum from the power supply
D. It reduces incidental grid modulation

G4A11
What is the reason for neutralizing the final amplifier stage of a transmitter?
A. To limit the modulation index
B. To eliminate self oscillations
C. To cut off the final amplifier during standby periods
D. To keep the carrier on frequency

G4A05
(A)
Page 4-13

G4A06
(C)
Page 4-13

G4A07
(A)
Page 4-9

G4A08
(D)
Page 4-7

G4A09
(C)
Page 4-8

G4A10
(B)
Page 4-8

G4A11
(B)
Page 4-7

G4B Test equipment: oscilloscope; signal tracer; antenna noise bridge; monitoring oscilloscope; field-strength meters

G4B01
(D)
Page 4-2
G4B01
What item of test equipment contains horizontal- and vertical-channel amplifiers?
A. An ohmmeter
B. A signal generator
C. An ammeter
D. An oscilloscope

G4B02
(D)
Page 4-4
G4B02
What is a digital oscilloscope?
A. An oscilloscope used only for signal tracing in digital circuits
B. An oscilloscope used only for troubleshooting computers
C. An oscilloscope used only for troubleshooting switching power supply circuits
D. An oscilloscope designed around digital technology rather than analog technology

G4B03
(D)
Page 4-4
G4B03
How would a signal tracer normally be used?
A. To identify the source of radio transmissions
B. To make exact drawings of signal waveforms
C. To show standing wave patterns on open-wire feed-lines
D. To identify an inoperative stage in a receiver

G4B04
(B)
Page 4-4
G4B04
Why would you use a noise bridge?
A. To measure the noise figure of an antenna or other electrical circuit
B. To measure the impedance of an antenna or other electrical circuit
C. To cancel electrical noise picked up by an antenna
D. To tune out noise in a receiver

G4B05
(C)
Page 4-5
G4B05
How is a noise bridge normally used?
A. It is connected at an antenna's feed point and reads the antenna's noise figure
B. It is connected between a transmitter and an antenna and is tuned for minimum SWR
C. It is connected between a receiver and an antenna of unknown impedance and is tuned for minimum noise
D. It is connected between an antenna and ground and is tuned for minimum SWR

G4B06

What is the best instrument to use to check the signal quality of a CW or single-sideband phone transmitter?

A. A monitoring oscilloscope
B. A field-strength meter
C. A sidetone monitor
D. A signal tracer and an audio amplifier

G4B06
(A)
Page 4-3

G4B07

What signal source is connected to the vertical input of a monitoring oscilloscope when checking the quality of a transmitted signal?

A. The IF output of a monitoring receiver
B. The audio input of the transmitter
C. The RF signals of a nearby receiving antenna
D. The RF output of the transmitter

G4B07
(D)
Page 4-3

G4B08

What instrument can be used to determine the horizontal radiation pattern of an antenna?

A. A field-strength meter
B. A grid-dip meter
C. An oscilloscope
D. A signal tracer and an audio amplifier

G4B08
(A)
Page 4-5

G4B09

How is a field-strength meter normally used?

A. To determine the standing-wave ratio on a transmission line
B. To check the output modulation of a transmitter
C. To monitor relative RF output
D. To increase average transmitter output

G4B09
(C)
Page 4-5

G4B10

What simple instrument may be used to monitor relative RF output during antenna and transmitter adjustments?

A. A field-strength meter
B. An antenna noise bridge
C. A multimeter
D. A metronome

G4B10
(A)
Page 4-5

G4B11

By how many times must the power output of a transmitter be increased to raise the S-meter reading on a nearby receiver from S8 to S9?

A. Approximately 2 times
B. Approximately 3 times
C. Approximately 4 times
D. Approximately 5 times

G4B11
(C)
Page 4-12

G4C Audio rectification in consumer electronics; RF ground

G4C01
(B)
Page 4-15

G4C01
What devices would you install in home-entertainment systems to reduce or eliminate audio-frequency interference?
A. Bypass inductors
B. Bypass capacitors
C. Metal-oxide varistors
D. Bypass resistors

G4C02
(B)
Page 4-16

G4C02
What should be done if a properly operating amateur station is the cause of interference to a nearby telephone?
A. Make internal adjustments to the telephone equipment
B. Install RFI filters at the affected telephone
C. Stop transmitting whenever the telephone is in use
D. Ground and shield the local telephone distribution amplifier

G4C03
(C)
Page 4-15

G4C03
What sound is heard from a public-address system if audio rectification of a nearby single-sideband phone transmission occurs?
A. A steady hum whenever the transmitter's carrier is on the air
B. On-and-off humming or clicking
C. Distorted speech from the transmitter's signals
D. Clearly audible speech from the transmitter's signals

G4C04
(A)
Page 4-15

G4C04
What sound is heard from a public-address system if audio rectification of a nearby CW transmission occurs?
A. On-and-off humming or clicking
B. Audible, possibly distorted speech
C. Muffled, severely distorted speech
D. A steady whistling

G4C05
(C)
Page 4-15

G4C05
How can you minimize the possibility of audio rectification of your transmitter's signals?
A. By using a solid-state transmitter
B. By using CW emission only
C. By ensuring that all station equipment is properly grounded
D. By installing bypass capacitors on all power supply rectifiers

G4C06
If your third-floor amateur station has a ground wire running 33 feet down to a ground rod, why might you get an RF burn if you touch the front panel of your HF transceiver?
A. Because the ground rod is not making good contact with moist earth
B. Because the transceiver's heat-sensing circuit is not working to start the cooling fan
C. Because of a bad antenna connection, allowing the RF energy to take an easier path out of the transceiver through you
D. Because the ground wire is a resonant length on several HF bands and acts more like an antenna than an RF ground connection

G4C06
(D)
Page 4-17

G4C07
Which of the following is NOT an important reason to have a good station ground?
A. To reduce the cost of operating a station
B. To reduce electrical noise
C. To reduce interference
D. To reduce the possibility of electric shock

G4C07
(A)
Page 4-17

G4C08
What is one good way to avoid stray RF energy in your amateur station?
A. Keep the station's ground wire as short as possible
B. Use a beryllium ground wire for best conductivity
C. Drive the ground rod at least 14 feet into the ground
D. Make a couple of loops in the ground wire where it connects to your station

G4C08
(A)
Page 4-17

G4C09
Which of the following statements about station grounding is NOT true?
A. Braid from RG-213 coaxial cable makes a good conductor to tie station equipment together into a station ground
B. Only transceivers and power amplifiers need to be tied into a station ground
C. According to the National Electrical Code, there should be only one grounding system in a building
D. The minimum length for a good ground rod is 8 feet

G4C09
(B)
Page 4-17

G4C10
Which of the following statements about station grounding is true?
A. The chassis of each piece of station equipment should be tied together with high-impedance conductors
B. If the chassis of all station equipment is connected with a good conductor, there is no need to tie them to an earth ground
C. RF hot spots can occur in a station located above the ground floor if the equipment is grounded by a long ground wire
D. A ground loop is an effective way to ground station equipment

G4C10
(C)
Page 4-17

G4C11
Which of the following is NOT covered in the National Electrical
Code?
A. Minimum conductor sizes for different lengths of amateur
   antennas
B. The size and composition of grounding conductors
C. Electrical safety inside the ham shack
D. The RF exposure limits of the human body

G4D   Speech processors; PEP calculations; wire sizes and fuses

G4D01
What is the reason for using a properly adjusted speech processor
with a single-sideband phone transmitter?
A. It reduces average transmitter power requirements
B. It reduces unwanted noise pickup from the microphone
C. It improves voice-frequency fidelity
D. It improves signal intelligibility at the receiver

G4D02
If a single-sideband phone transmitter is 100% modulated, what will a
speech processor do to the transmitter's power?
A. It will increase the output PEP
B. It will add nothing to the output PEP
C. It will decrease the peak power output
D. It will decrease the average power output

G4D03
How is the output PEP of a transmitter calculated if an oscilloscope is
used to measure the transmitter's peak load voltage across a resistive
load?
A. PEP = [(Vp)(Vp)] / (RL)
B. PEP = [(0.707 PEV)(0.707 PEV)] / RL
C. PEP = (Vp)(Vp)(RL)
D. PEP = [(1.414 PEV)(1.414 PEV)] / RL

G4D04
What is the output PEP from a transmitter if an oscilloscope measures
200 volts peak-to-peak across a 50-ohm resistor connected to the
transmitter output?
A. 100 watts
B. 200 watts
C. 400 watts
D. 1000 watts

G4D05
What is the output PEP from a transmitter if an oscilloscope measures 500 volts peak-to-peak across a 50-ohm resistor connected to the transmitter output?
A. 500 watts
B. 625 watts
C. 1250 watts
D. 2500 watts

G4D05
(B)
Page 4-11

G4D06
What is the output PEP of an unmodulated carrier transmitter if an average-reading wattmeter connected to the transmitter output indicates 1060 watts?
A. 530 watts
B. 1060 watts
C. 1500 watts
D. 2120 watts

G4D06
(B)
Page 4-11

G4D07
Which wires in a four-conductor line cord should be attached to fuses in a 240-VAC primary (single phase) power supply?
A. Only the "hot" (black and red) wires
B. Only the "neutral" (white) wire
C. Only the ground (bare) wire
D. All wires

G4D07
(A)
Page 4-19

G4D08
What size wire is normally used on a 15-ampere, 120-VAC household lighting circuit?
A. AWG number 14
B. AWG number 16
C. AWG number 18
D. AWG number 22

G4D08
(A)
Page 4-21

G4D09
What size wire is normally used on a 20-ampere, 120-VAC household appliance circuit?
A. AWG number 20
B. AWG number 16
C. AWG number 14
D. AWG number 12

G4D09
(D)
Page 4-21

G4D10
What maximum size fuse or circuit breaker should be used in a household appliance circuit using AWG number 12 wiring?
A. 100 amperes
B. 60 amperes
C. 30 amperes
D. 20 amperes

G4D10
(D)
Page 4-21

G4D11
(A)
Page 4-21

G4D11
What maximum size fuse or circuit breaker should be used in a household appliance circuit using AWG number 14 wiring?
A. 15 amperes
B. 20 amperes
C. 30 amperes
D. 60 amperes

G4E Common connectors used in amateur stations: types; when to use; fastening methods; precautions when using; HF mobile radio installations; emergency power systems; generators; battery storage devices and charging sources including solar; wind generation

G4E01
(D)
Page 4-24

G4E01
Which of the following connectors is NOT designed for RF transmission lines?
A. PL-259
B. Type N
C. BNC
D. DB-25

G4E02
(D)
Page 4-20

G4E02
When installing a power plug on a line cord, which of the following should you do?
A. Twist the wire strands neatly and fasten them so they don't cause a short circuit
B. Observe the correct wire color conventions for plug terminals
C. Use proper grounding techniques
D. All of these choices

G4E03
(A)
Page 4-23

G4E03
Which of the following power connections would be the best for a 100-watt HF mobile installation?
A. A direct, fused connection to the battery using heavy gauge wire
B. A connection to the fuse-protected accessory terminal strip or distribution panel
C. A connection to the cigarette lighter
D. A direct connection to the alternator or generator

G4E04
(D)
Page 4-23

G4E04
Why is it best NOT to draw the DC power for a 100-watt HF transceiver from an automobile's cigarette lighter socket?
A. The socket is not wired with an RF-shielded power cable
B. The DC polarity of the socket is reversed from the polarity of modern HF transceivers
C. The power from the socket is never adequately filtered for HF transceiver operation
D. The socket's wiring may not be adequate for the current being drawn by the transceiver

G4E05
Which of the following most limits the effectiveness of an HF mobile transceiver operating in the 75-meter band?
A. The vehicle's electrical system wiring
B. The wire gauge of the DC power line to the transceiver
C. The HF mobile antenna system
D. The rating of the vehicle's alternator or generator

G4E05
(C)
Page 4-23

G4E06
Which of the following is true of both a permanent or temporary emergency generator installation?
A. The generator should be located in a well ventilated area
B. The installation should be grounded
C. Extra fuel supplies, especially gasoline, should not be stored in an inhabited area
D. All of these choices

G4E06
(D)
Page 4-22

G4E07
Which of the following is true of a lead-acid storage battery as it is being charged?
A. It tends to cool off
B. It gives off explosive oxygen gas
C. It gives off explosive hydrogen gas
D. It takes in oxygen from the surrounding air

G4E07
(C)
Page 4-22

G4E08
What is the name of the process by which sunlight is directly changed into electricity?
A. Photovoltaic conversion
B. Photosensitive conduction
C. Photosynthesis
D. Photocoupling

G4E08
(A)
Page 4-22

G4E09
What is the approximate open-circuit voltage from a modern, well illuminated photovoltaic cell?
A. 0.02 VDC
B. 0.2 VDC
C. 1.38 VDC
D. 0.5 VDC

G4E09
(D)
Page 4-22

G4E10
What determines the proper size solar panel to use in a solar-powered battery-charging circuit?
A. The panel's voltage rating and maximum output current
B. The amount of voltage available per square inch of panel
C. The panel's open-circuit current
D. The panel's short-circuit voltage

G4E10
(A)
Page 4-23

G4E11
(C)
Page 4-23

G4E11
What is the biggest disadvantage to using wind power as the primary source of power for an emergency station?
A. The conversion efficiency from mechanical energy to electrical energy is less than 2 percent
B. The voltage and current ratings of such systems are not compatible with amateur equipment
C. A large electrical storage system is needed to supply power when the wind is not blowing
D. All of these choices are correct

Subelement
G5

Subelement G5 — Electrical Principles

[2 Exam Questions — 2 Groups]

G5A Impedance; including matching; resistance; including ohm; reactance; inductance; capacitance and metric divisions of these values

G5A01
(C)
Page 5-16

G5A01
What is impedance?
A. The electric charge stored by a capacitor
B. The opposition to the flow of AC in a circuit containing only capacitance
C. The opposition to the flow of AC in a circuit
D. The force of repulsion between one electric field and another with the same charge

G5A02
(B)
Page 5-14

G5A02
What is reactance?
A. Opposition to DC caused by resistors
B. Opposition to AC caused by inductors and capacitors
C. A property of ideal resistors in AC circuits
D. A large spark produced at switch contacts when an inductor is de-energized

G5A03
(D)
Page 5-15

G5A03
In an inductor, what causes opposition to the flow of AC?
A. Resistance
B. Reluctance
C. Admittance
D. Reactance

G5A04
(C)
Page 5-14

G5A04
In a capacitor, what causes opposition to the flow of AC?
A. Resistance
B. Reluctance
C. Reactance
D. Admittance

G5A05

How does a coil react to AC?

A. As the frequency of the applied AC increases, the reactance decreases

B. As the amplitude of the applied AC increases, the reactance increases

C. As the amplitude of the applied AC increases, the reactance decreases

D. As the frequency of the applied AC increases, the reactance increases

G5A05
(D)
Page 5-15

G5A06

How does a capacitor react to AC?

A. As the frequency of the applied AC increases, the reactance decreases

B. As the frequency of the applied AC increases, the reactance increases

C. As the amplitude of the applied AC increases, the reactance increases

D. As the amplitude of the applied AC increases, the reactance decreases

G5A06
(A)
Page 5-14

G5A07

When will a power source deliver maximum output to the load?

A. When the impedance of the load is equal to the impedance of the source

B. When the load resistance is infinite

C. When the power-supply fuse rating equals the primary winding current

D. When air wound transformers are used instead of iron-core transformers

G5A07
(A)
Page 5-17

G5A08

What happens when the impedance of an electrical load is equal to the internal impedance of the power source?

A. The source delivers minimum power to the load

B. The electrical load is shorted

C. No current can flow through the circuit

D. The source delivers maximum power to the load

G5A08
(D)
Page 5-17

G5A09

Why is impedance matching important?

A. So the source can deliver maximum power to the load

B. So the load will draw minimum power from the source

C. To ensure that there is less resistance than reactance in the circuit

D. To ensure that the resistance and reactance in the circuit are equal

G5A09
(A)
Page 5-17

G5A10
What unit is used to measure reactance?
A. Mho
B. Ohm
C. Ampere
D. Siemens

G5A11
What unit is used to measure impedance?
A. Volt
B. Ohm
C. Ampere
D. Watt

G5B Decibel; Ohm's Law; current and voltage dividers; electrical power calculations and series and parallel components; transformers (either voltage or impedance); sine wave root-mean-square (RMS) value

G5B01
A two-times increase in power results in a change of how many dB?
A. 1 dB higher
B. 3 dB higher
C. 6 dB higher
D. 12 dB higher

G5B02
In a parallel circuit with a voltage source and several branch resistors, how is the total current related to the current in the branch resistors?
A. It equals the average of the branch current through each resistor
B. It equals the sum of the branch current through each resistor
C. It decreases as more parallel resistors are added to the circuit
D. It is the sum of each resistor's voltage drop multiplied by the total number of resistors

G5B03
How many watts of electrical power are used if 400 VDC is supplied to an 800-ohm load?
A. 0.5 watts
B. 200 watts
C. 400 watts
D. 320,000 watts

G5B04
How many watts of electrical power are used by a 12-VDC light bulb that draws 0.2 amperes?
A. 60 watts
B. 24 watts
C. 6 watts
D. 2.4 watts

G5B05
How many watts are being dissipated when 7.0 milliamperes flow through 1.25 kilohms?
A. Approximately 61 milliwatts
B. Approximately 39 milliwatts
C. Approximately 11 milliwatts
D. Approximately 9 milliwatts

G5B05
(A)
Page 5-8

G5B06
What is the voltage across a 500-turn secondary winding in a transformer if the 2250-turn primary is connected to 120 VAC?
A. 2370 volts
B. 540 volts
C. 26.7 volts
D. 5.9 volts

G5B06
(C)
Page 5-18

G5B07
What is the turns ratio of a transformer to match an audio amplifier having a 600-ohm output impedance to a speaker having a 4-ohm impedance?
A. 12.2 to 1
B. 24.4 to 1
C. 150 to 1
D. 300 to 1

G5B07
(A)
Page 5-19

G5B08
What is the impedance of a speaker that requires a transformer with a turns ratio of 24 to 1 to match an audio amplifier having an output impedance of 2000 ohms?
A. 576 ohms
B. 83.3 ohms
C. 7.0 ohms
D. 3.5 ohms

G5B08
(D)
Page 5-20

G5B09
A DC voltage equal to what value of an applied sine-wave AC voltage would produce the same amount of heat over time in a resistive element?
A. The peak-to-peak value
B. The RMS value
C. The average value
D. The peak value

G5B09
(B)
Page 5-13

G5B10
What is the peak-to-peak voltage of a sine wave that has an RMS voltage of 120 volts?
A. 84.8 volts
B. 169.7 volts
C. 204.8 volts
D. 339.4 volts

G5B10
(D)
Page 5-13

G5B11
A sine wave of 17 volts peak is equivalent to how many volts RMS?
A. 8.5 volts
B. 12 volts
C. 24 volts
D. 34 volts

Subelement G6 — Circuit Components

[1 Exam Question — 1 Group]

G6A Resistors; capacitors; inductors; rectifiers and transistors; etc.

G6A01
If a carbon resistor's temperature is increased, what will happen to the resistance?
A. It will increase by 20% for every 10 degrees centigrade
B. It will stay the same
C. It will change depending on the resistor's temperature coefficient rating
D. It will become time dependent

G6A02
What type of capacitor is often used in power-supply circuits to filter the rectified AC?
A. Disc ceramic
B. Vacuum variable
C. Mica
D. Electrolytic

G6A03
What function does a capacitor serve if it is used in a power-supply circuit to filter transient voltage spikes across the transformer's secondary winding?
A. Clipper capacitor
B. Trimmer capacitor
C. Feedback capacitor
D. Suppressor capacitor

G6A04
Where is the source of energy connected in a transformer?
A. To the secondary winding
B. To the primary winding
C. To the core
D. To the plates

G6A05
If no load is attached to the secondary winding of a transformer, what is current in the primary winding called?
A. Magnetizing current
B. Direct current
C. Excitation current
D. Stabilizing current

G6A06
What is the peak-inverse-voltage rating of a power-supply rectifier?
A. The maximum transient voltage the rectifier will handle in the conducting direction
B. 1.4 times the AC frequency
C. The maximum voltage the rectifier will handle in the non-conducting direction
D. 2.8 times the AC frequency

G6A07
What are the two major ratings that must not be exceeded for silicon-diode rectifiers used in power-supply circuits?
A. Peak inverse voltage; average forward current
B. Average power; average voltage
C. Capacitive reactance; avalanche voltage
D. Peak load impedance; peak voltage

G6A08
What is the output waveform of an unfiltered full-wave rectifier connected to a resistive load?
A. A series of pulses at twice the frequency of the AC input
B. A series of pulses at the same frequency as the AC input
C. A sine wave at half the frequency of the AC input
D. A steady DC voltage

G6A09
A half-wave rectifier conducts during how many degrees of each cycle?
A. 90 degrees
B. 180 degrees
C. 270 degrees
D. 360 degrees

G6A10
A full-wave rectifier conducts during how many degrees of each cycle?
A. 90 degrees
B. 180 degrees
C. 270 degrees
D. 360 degrees

G6A05
(A)
Page 6-8

G6A06
(C)
Page 6-11

G6A07
(A)
Page 6-11

G6A08
(A)
Page 7-6

G6A09
(B)
Page 7-2

G6A10
(D)
Page 7-2

G6A11
When two or more diodes are connected in parallel to increase the current-handling capacity of a power supply, what is the purpose of the resistor connected in series with each diode?
A. The resistors ensure that one diode doesn't take most of the current
B. The resistors ensure the thermal stability of the power supply
C. The resistors regulate the power supply output voltage
D. The resistors act as swamping resistors in the circuit

Subelement G7 — Practical Circuits

[1 Exam Question — 1 Group]

G7A Power supplies and filters; single-sideband transmitters and receivers

G7A01
What safety feature does a power-supply bleeder resistor provide?
A. It improves voltage regulation
B. It discharges the filter capacitors
C. It removes shock hazards from the induction coils
D. It eliminates ground-loop current

G7A02
Where is a power-supply bleeder resistor connected?
A. Across the filter capacitor
B. Across the power-supply input
C. Between the transformer primary and secondary windings
D. Across the inductor in the output filter

G7A03
What components are used in a power-supply filter network?
A. Diodes
B. Transformers and transistors
C. Quartz crystals
D. Capacitors and inductors

G7A04
What should be the minimum peak-inverse-voltage rating of the rectifier in a full-wave power supply?
A. One-quarter the normal output voltage of the power supply
B. Half the normal output voltage of the power supply
C. Equal to the normal output voltage of the power supply
D. Double the normal peak output voltage of the power supply

G7A05
What should be the minimum peak-inverse-voltage rating of the rectifier in a half-wave power supply?
A. One-quarter to one-half the normal peak output voltage of the power supply
B. Half the normal output voltage of the power supply
C. Equal to the normal output voltage of the power supply
D. One to two times the normal peak output voltage of the power supply

G7A05
(D)
Page 7-5

G7A06
What should be the impedance of a low-pass filter as compared to the impedance of the transmission line into which it is inserted?
A. Substantially higher
B. About the same
C. Substantially lower
D. Twice the transmission line impedance

G7A06
(B)
Page 7-8

G7A07
In a typical single-sideband phone transmitter, what circuit processes signals from the balanced modulator and sends signals to the mixer?
A. Carrier oscillator
B. Filter
C. IF amplifier
D. RF amplifier

G7A07
(B)
Page 7-10

G7A08
In a single-sideband phone transmitter, what circuit processes signals from the carrier oscillator and the speech amplifier and sends signals to the filter?
A. Mixer
B. Detector
C. IF amplifier
D. Balanced modulator

G7A08
(D)
Page 7-10

G7A09
In a single-sideband phone superheterodyne receiver, what circuit processes signals from the RF amplifier and the local oscillator and sends signals to the IF filter?
A. Balanced modulator
B. IF amplifier
C. Mixer
D. Detector

G7A09
(C)
Page 7-11

G7A10
In a single-sideband phone superheterodyne receiver, what circuit processes signals from the IF amplifier and the BFO and sends signals to the AF amplifier?
A. RF oscillator
B. IF filter
C. Balanced modulator
D. Detector

G7A10
(D)
Page 7-12

G7A11
In a single-sideband phone superheterodyne receiver, what circuit processes signals from the IF filter and sends signals to the detector?
A. RF oscillator
B. IF amplifier
C. Mixer
D. BFO

Subelement G8 — Signals And Emissions

[2 Exam Questions — 2 Groups]

G8A Signal information; AM; FM; single and double sideband and carrier; bandwidth; modulation envelope; deviation; overmodulation

G8A01
What type of modulation system changes the amplitude of an RF wave for the purpose of conveying information?
A. Frequency modulation
B. Phase modulation
C. Amplitude-rectification modulation
D. Amplitude modulation

G8A02
What type of modulation system changes the phase of an RF wave for the purpose of conveying information?
A. Pulse modulation
B. Phase modulation
C. Phase-rectification modulation
D. Amplitude modulation

G8A03
What type of modulation system changes the frequency of an RF wave for the purpose of conveying information?
A. Phase-rectification modulation
B. Frequency-rectification modulation
C. Amplitude modulation
D. Frequency modulation

G8A04
What emission is produced by a reactance modulator connected to an RF power amplifier?
A. Multiplex modulation
B. Phase modulation
C. Amplitude modulation
D. Pulse modulation

G8A05
In what emission type does the instantaneous amplitude (envelope) of the RF signal vary in accordance with the modulating audio?
A. Frequency shift keying
B. Pulse modulation
C. Frequency modulation
D. Amplitude modulation

G8A05
(D)
Page 8-2

G8A06
How much should the carrier be suppressed below peak output power in a properly designed single-sideband (SSB) transmitter?
A. No more than 20 dB
B. No more than 30 dB
C. At least 40 dB
D. At least 60 dB

G8A06
(C)
Page 8-5

G8A07
What is one advantage of carrier suppression in a double-sideband phone transmission?
A. Only half the bandwidth is required for the same information content
B. Greater modulation percentage is obtainable with lower distortion
C. More power can be put into the sidebands
D. Simpler equipment can be used to receive a double-sideband suppressed-carrier signal

G8A07
(C)
Page 8-5

G8A08
Which popular phone emission uses the narrowest frequency bandwidth?
A. Single-sideband
B. Double-sideband
C. Phase-modulated
D. Frequency-modulated

G8A08
(A)
Page 8-5

G8A09
What happens to the signal of an overmodulated single-sideband or double-sideband phone transmitter?
A. It becomes louder with no other effects
B. It occupies less bandwidth with poor high-frequency response
C. It has higher fidelity and improved signal-to-noise ratio
D. It becomes distorted and occupies more bandwidth

G8A09
(D)
Page 8-5

G8A10
How should the microphone gain control be adjusted on a single-sideband phone transmitter?
A. For full deflection of the ALC meter on modulation peaks
B. For slight movement of the ALC meter on modulation peaks
C. For 100% frequency deviation on modulation peaks
D. For a dip in plate current

G8A10
(B)
Page 8-6

G8A11
(C)
Page 8-6

G8A11
What is meant by flattopping in a single-sideband phone transmission?
A. Signal distortion caused by insufficient collector current
B. The transmitter's automatic level control is properly adjusted
C. Signal distortion caused by excessive drive
D. The transmitter's carrier is properly suppressed

G8B Frequency mixing; multiplication; bandwidths; HF data communications

G8B01
(A)
Page 8-8

G8B01
What receiver stage combines a 14.25-MHz input signal with a 13.795-MHz oscillator signal to produce a 455-kHz intermediate frequency (IF) signal?
A. Mixer
B. BFO
C. VFO
D. Multiplier

G8B02
(B)
Page 8-8

G8B02
If a receiver mixes a 13.800-MHz VFO with a 14.255-MHz received signal to produce a 455-kHz intermediate frequency (IF) signal, what type of interference will a 13.345-MHz signal produce in the receiver?
A. Local oscillator
B. Image response
C. Mixer interference
D. Intermediate interference

G8B03
(A)
Page 8-8

G8B03
What stage in a transmitter would change a 5.3-MHz input signal to 14.3 MHz?
A. A mixer
B. A beat frequency oscillator
C. A frequency multiplier
D. A linear translator

G8B04
(D)
Page 8-13

G8B04
What is the name of the stage in a VHF FM transmitter that selects a harmonic of an HF signal to reach the desired operating frequency?
A. Mixer
B. Reactance modulator
C. Preemphasis network
D. Multiplier

G8B05
(C)
Page 8-15

G8B05
Why isn't frequency modulated (FM) phone used below 29.5 MHz?
A. The transmitter efficiency for this mode is low
B. Harmonics could not be attenuated to practical levels
C. The bandwidth would exceed FCC limits
D. The frequency stability would not be adequate

G8B06

What is the total bandwidth of an FM-phone transmission having a 5-kHz deviation and a 3-kHz modulating frequency?

A. 3 kHz
B. 5 kHz
C. 8 kHz
D. 16 kHz

G8B06 (D) Page 8-15

G8B07

What is the frequency deviation for a 12.21-MHz reactance-modulated oscillator in a 5-kHz deviation, 146.52-MHz FM-phone transmitter?

A. 41.67 Hz
B. 416.7 Hz
C. 5 kHz
D. 12 kHz

G8B07 (B) Page 8-14

G8B08

How is frequency shift related to keying speed in an FSK signal?

A. The frequency shift in hertz must be at least four times the keying speed in WPM
B. The frequency shift must not exceed 15 Hz per WPM of keying speed
C. Greater keying speeds require greater frequency shifts
D. Greater keying speeds require smaller frequency shifts

G8B08 (C) Page 8-16

G8B09

What do RTTY, Morse code, AMTOR and packet communications have in common?

A. They are multipath communications
B. They are digital communications
C. They are analog communications
D. They are only for emergency communications

G8B09 (B) Page 8-15

G8B10

What is the duty cycle required of a transmitter when sending Mode B (FEC) AMTOR?

A. 50%
B. 75%
C. 100%
D. 125%

G8B10 (C) Page 8-17

G8B11

In what segment of the 20-meter band are most AMTOR operations found?

A. At the bottom of the slow-scan TV segment, near 14.230 MHz
B. At the top of the SSB phone segment, near 14.325 MHz
C. In the middle of the CW segment, near 14.100 MHz
D. At the bottom of the RTTY segment, near 14.075 MHz

G8B11 (D) Page 8-17

Subelement G9 — Antennas And Feed-Lines

[4 Exam Questions — 4 Groups]

G9A Yagi antennas — physical dimensions; impedance matching; radiation patterns; directivity and major lobes

G9A01
(A)
Page 9-13

G9A01
How can the SWR bandwidth of a parasitic beam antenna be increased?
A. Use larger diameter elements
B. Use closer element spacing
C. Use traps on the elements
D. Use tapered-diameter elements

G9A02
(B)
Page 9-10

G9A02
Approximately how long is the driven element of a Yagi antenna for 14.0 MHz?
A. 17 feet
B. 33 feet
C. 35 feet
D. 66 feet

G9A03
(B)
Page 9-10

G9A03
Approximately how long is the director element of a Yagi antenna for 21.1 MHz?
A. 42 feet
B. 21 feet
C. 17 feet
D. 10.5 feet

G9A04
(C)
Page 9-11

G9A04
Approximately how long is the reflector element of a Yagi antenna for 28.1 MHz?
A. 8.75 feet
B. 16.6 feet
C. 17.5 feet
D. 35 feet

G9A05
(B)
Page 9-10

G9A05
Which statement about a three-element Yagi antenna is true?
A. The reflector is normally the shortest parasitic element
B. The director is normally the shortest parasitic element
C. The driven element is the longest parasitic element
D. Low feed-point impedance increases bandwidth

G9A06
What is one effect of increasing the boom length and adding directors to a Yagi antenna?
A. Gain increases
B. SWR increases
C. Weight decreases
D. Wind load decreases

G9A06
(A)
Page 9-11

G9A07
Why is a Yagi antenna often used for radio communications on the 20-meter band?
A. It provides excellent omnidirectional coverage in the horizontal plane
B. It is smaller, less expensive and easier to erect than a dipole or vertical antenna
C. It helps reduce interference from other stations off to the side or behind
D. It provides the highest possible angle of radiation for the HF bands

G9A07
(C)
Page 9-11

G9A08
What does "antenna front-to-back ratio" mean in reference to a Yagi antenna?
A. The number of directors versus the number of reflectors
B. The relative position of the driven element with respect to the reflectors and directors
C. The power radiated in the major radiation lobe compared to the power radiated in exactly the opposite direction
D. The power radiated in the major radiation lobe compared to the power radiated 90 degrees away from that direction

G9A08
(C)
Page 9-12

G9A09
What is the "main lobe" of a Yagi antenna radiation pattern?
A. The direction of least radiation from the antenna
B. The point of maximum current in a radiating antenna element
C. The direction of maximum radiated field strength from the antenna
D. The maximum voltage standing wave point on a radiating element

G9A09
(C)
Page 9-11

G9A10
What is a good way to get maximum performance from a Yagi antenna?
A. Optimize the lengths and spacing of the elements
B. Use RG-58 feed-line
C. Use a reactance bridge to measure the antenna performance from each direction around the antenna
D. Avoid using towers higher than 30 feet above the ground

G9A10
(A)
Page 9-13

G9A11
(D)
Page 9-13

G9A11
Which of the following is NOT a Yagi antenna design variable that should be considered to optimize the forward gain, front-to-rear gain ratio and SWR bandwidth?
A. The physical length of the boom
B. The number of elements on the boom
C. The spacing of each element along the boom
D. The polarization of the antenna elements

G9B Loop antennas — physical dimensions; impedance matching; radiation patterns; directivity and major lobes

G9B01
(B)
Page 9-14

G9B01
Approximately how long is each side of a cubical-quad antenna driven element for 21.4 MHz?
A. 1.17 feet
B. 11.7 feet
C. 47 feet
D. 469 feet

G9B02
(A)
Page 9-14

G9B02
Approximately how long is each side of a cubical-quad antenna driven element for 14.3 MHz?
A. 17.6 feet
B. 23.4 feet
C. 70.3 feet
D. 175 feet

G9B03
(B)
Page 9-14

G9B03
Approximately how long is each side of a cubical-quad antenna reflector element for 29.6 MHz?
A. 8.23 feet
B. 8.7 feet
C. 9.7 feet
D. 34.8 feet

G9B04
(B)
Page 9-16

G9B04
Approximately how long is each leg of a symmetrical delta-loop antenna driven element for 28.7 MHz?
A. 8.75 feet
B. 11.7 feet
C. 23.4 feet
D. 35 feet

G9B05
(C)
Page 9-16

G9B05
Approximately how long is each leg of a symmetrical delta-loop antenna driven element for 24.9 MHz?
A. 10.99 feet
B. 12.95 feet
C. 13.45 feet
D. 40.36 feet

G9B06
Approximately how long is each leg of a symmetrical delta-loop antenna reflector element for 14.1 MHz?
A. 18.26 feet
B. 23.76 feet
C. 24.35 feet
D. 73.05 feet

G9B06
(C)
Page 9-16

G9B07
Which statement about two-element delta loops and quad antennas is true?
A. They compare favorably with a three-element Yagi
B. They perform poorly above HF
C. They perform very well only at HF
D. They are effective only when constructed using insulated wire

G9B07
(A)
Page 9-17

G9B08
Compared to a dipole antenna, what are the directional radiation characteristics of a cubical-quad antenna?
A. The quad has more directivity in the horizontal plane but less directivity in the vertical plane
B. The quad has less directivity in the horizontal plane but more directivity in the vertical plane
C. The quad has more directivity in both horizontal and vertical planes
D. The quad has less directivity in both horizontal and vertical planes

G9B08
(C)
Page 9-17

G9B09
Moving the feed point of a multielement quad antenna from a side parallel to the ground to a side perpendicular to the ground will have what effect?
A. It will significantly increase the antenna feed-point impedance
B. It will significantly decrease the antenna feed-point impedance
C. It will change the antenna polarization from vertical to horizontal
D. It will change the antenna polarization from horizontal to vertical

G9B09
(D)
Page 9-15

G9B10
What does the term "antenna front-to-back ratio" mean in reference to a delta-loop antenna?
A. The number of directors versus the number of reflectors
B. The relative position of the driven element with respect to the reflectors and directors
C. The power radiated in the major radiation lobe compared to the power radiated in exactly the opposite direction
D. The power radiated in the major radiation lobe compared to the power radiated 90 degrees away from that direction

G9B10
(C)
Page 9-17

G9B11
(C)
Page 9-17

G9B11
What is the "main lobe" of a delta-loop antenna radiation pattern?
A. The direction of least radiation from an antenna
B. The point of maximum current in a radiating antenna element
C. The direction of maximum radiated field strength from the antenna
D. The maximum voltage standing wave point on a radiating element

G9C Random wire antennas — physical dimensions; impedance matching; radiation patterns; directivity and major lobes; feed point impedance of $1/2$-wavelength dipole and $1/4$-wavelength vertical antennas

G9C01
(A)
Page 9-3

G9C01
What type of multiband transmitting antenna does NOT require a feed-line?
A. A random-wire antenna
B. A triband Yagi antenna
C. A delta-loop antenna
D. A Beverage antenna

G9C02
(D)
Page 9-3

G9C02
What is one advantage of using a random-wire antenna?
A. It is more efficient than any other kind of antenna
B. It will keep RF energy out of your station
C. It doesn't need an impedance matching network
D. It is a multiband antenna

G9C03
(B)
Page 9-3

G9C03
What is one disadvantage of a random-wire antenna?
A. It must be longer than 1 wavelength
B. You may experience RF feedback in your station
C. It usually produces vertically polarized radiation
D. You must use an inverted-T matching network for multiband operation

G9C04
(D)
Page 9-5

G9C04
What is an advantage of downward sloping radials on a ground-plane antenna?
A. It lowers the radiation angle
B. It brings the feed-point impedance closer to 300 ohms
C. It increases the radiation angle
D. It brings the feed-point impedance closer to 50 ohms

G9C05
(B)
Page 9-5

G9C05
What happens to the feed-point impedance of a ground-plane antenna when its radials are changed from horizontal to downward-sloping?
A. It decreases
B. It increases
C. It stays the same
D. It approaches zero

G9C06
What is the low-angle radiation pattern of an ideal half-wavelength dipole HF antenna installed a half-wavelength high, parallel to the earth?
A. It is a figure-eight at right angles to the antenna
B. It is a figure-eight off both ends of the antenna
C. It is a circle (equal radiation in all directions)
D. It is two smaller lobes on one side of the antenna, and one larger lobe on the other side

G9C06
(A)
Page 9-6

G9C07
How does antenna height affect the horizontal (azimuthal) radiation pattern of a horizontal dipole HF antenna?
A. If the antenna is too high, the pattern becomes unpredictable
B. If the antenna is less than one-half wavelength high, the azimuthal pattern is almost omnidirectional
C. Antenna height has no effect on the pattern
D. If the antenna is less than one-half wavelength high, radiation off the ends of the wire is eliminated

G9C07
(B)
Page 9-6

G9C08
If the horizontal radiation pattern of an antenna shows a major lobe at 0 degrees and a minor lobe at 180 degrees, how would you describe the radiation pattern of this antenna?
A. Most of the signal would be radiated towards 180 degrees and a smaller amount would be radiated towards 0 degrees
B. Almost no signal would be radiated towards 0 degrees and a small amount would be radiated towards 180 degrees
C. Almost all the signal would be radiated equally towards 0 degrees and 180 degrees
D. Most of the signal would be radiated towards 0 degrees and a smaller amount would be radiated towards 180 degrees

G9C08
(D)
Page 9-12

G9C09
If a slightly shorter parasitic element is placed 0.1 wavelength away and parallel to an HF dipole antenna mounted above ground, what effect will this have on the antenna's radiation pattern?
A. The radiation pattern will not be affected
B. A major lobe will develop in the horizontal plane, parallel to the two elements
C. A major lobe will develop in the vertical plane, away from the ground
D. A major lobe will develop in the horizontal plane, toward the parasitic element

G9C09
(D)
Page 9-8

G9C10
(B)
Page 9-8

G9C10
If a slightly longer parasitic element is placed 0.1 wavelength away and parallel to an HF dipole antenna mounted above ground, what effect will this have on the antenna's radiation pattern?
A. The radiation pattern will not be affected
B. A major lobe will develop in the horizontal plane, away from the parasitic element, toward the dipole
C. A major lobe will develop in the vertical plane, away from the ground
D. A major lobe will develop in the horizontal plane, parallel to the two elements

G9C11
(B)
Page 9-3

G9C11
Where should the radial wires of a ground-mounted vertical antenna system be placed?
A. As high as possible above the ground
B. On the surface or buried a few inches below the ground
C. Parallel to the antenna element
D. At the top of the antenna

G9D Popular antenna feed-lines — characteristic impedance and impedance matching; SWR calculations

G9D01
(A)
Page 9-18

G9D01
Which of the following factors help determine the characteristic impedance of a parallel-conductor antenna feed-line?
A. The distance between the centers of the conductors and the radius of the conductors
B. The distance between the centers of the conductors and the length of the line
C. The radius of the conductors and the frequency of the signal
D. The frequency of the signal and the length of the line

G9D02
(B)
Page 9-19

G9D02
What is the typical characteristic impedance of coaxial cables used for antenna feed-lines at amateur stations?
A. 25 and 30 ohms
B. 50 and 75 ohms
C. 80 and 100 ohms
D. 500 and 750 ohms

G9D03
(D)
Page 9-18

G9D03
What is the characteristic impedance of flat-ribbon TV-type twin-lead?
A. 50 ohms
B. 75 ohms
C. 100 ohms
D. 300 ohms

G9D04
What is the typical cause of power being reflected back down an antenna feed-line?
A. Operating an antenna at its resonant frequency
B. Using more transmitter power than the antenna can handle
C. A difference between feed line impedance and antenna feed-point impedance
D. Feeding the antenna with unbalanced feed-line

G9D05
What must be done to prevent standing waves of voltage and current on an antenna feed-line?
A. The antenna feed point must be at DC ground potential
B. The feed line must be cut to an odd number of electrical quarter-wavelengths long
C. The feed line must be cut to an even number of physical half-wavelengths long
D. The antenna feed-point impedance must be matched to the characteristic impedance of the feed-line

G9D06
If a center-fed dipole antenna is fed by parallel-conductor feed-line, how would an inductively coupled matching network be used in the antenna system?
A. It would not normally be used with parallel-conductor feed-lines
B. It would be used to increase the SWR to an acceptable level
C. It would be used to match the unbalanced transmitter output to the balanced parallel-conductor feed-line
D. It would be used at the antenna feed point to tune out the radiation resistance

G9D07
If a 160-meter signal and a 2-meter signal pass through the same coaxial cable, how will the attenuation of the two signals compare?
A. It will be greater at 2 meters
B. It will be less at 2 meters
C. It will be the same at both frequencies
D. It will depend on the emission type in use

G9D08
In what values are RF feed line losses usually expressed?
A. Bels/1000 ft
B. dB/1000 ft
C. Bels/100 ft
D. dB/100 ft

G9D04
(C)
Page 9-20

G9D05
(D)
Page 9-20

G9D06
(C)
Page 9-21

G9D07
(A)
Page 9-18

G9D08
(D)
Page 9-17

G9D09
(A)
Page 9-21

G9D09
What standing-wave-ratio will result from the connection of a 50-ohm feed line to a resonant antenna having a 200-ohm feed-point impedance?
A. 4:1
B. 1:4
C. 2:1
D. 1:2

G9D10
(D)
Page 9-21

G9D10
What standing-wave-ratio will result from the connection of a 50-ohm feed line to a resonant antenna having a 10-ohm feed-point impedance?
A. 2:1
B. 50:1
C. 1:5
D. 5:1

G9D11
(D)
Page 9-21

G9D11
What standing-wave-ratio will result from the connection of a 50-ohm feed line to a resonant antenna having a 50-ohm feed-point impedance?
A. 2:1
B. 50:50
C. 0:0
D. 1:1

Subelement
G0

Subelement G0 — RF Safety

[5 Exam Questions — 5 Groups]

G0A RF safety principles

G0A01
(A)
Page 10-2

G0A01
Depending on the wavelength of the signal, the energy density of the RF field, and other factors, in what way can RF energy affect body tissue?
A. It heats body tissue
B. It causes radiation poisoning
C. It causes the blood count to reach a dangerously low level
D. It cools body tissue

G0A02
(B)
Page 10-4

G0A02
Which property is NOT important in estimating RF energy's effect on body tissue?
A. Its duty cycle
B. Its critical angle
C. Its power density
D. Its frequency

G0A03
Which of the following has the most direct effect on the exposure level of RF radiation?
A. The maximum usable frequency of the ionosphere
B. The frequency (or wavelength) of the energy
C. The environment near the transmitter
D. The distance from the antenna

G0A04
What unit of measurement best describes the biological effects of RF fields at frequencies used by amateur operators?
A. Electric field strength (V/m)
B. Magnetic field strength (A/m)
C. Specific absorption rate (W/kg)
D. Power density (W/cm^2)

G0A05
RF radiation in which of the following frequency ranges has the most effect on the human eyes?
A. The 3.5-MHz range
B. The 2-MHz range
C. The 50-MHz range
D. The 1270-MHz range

G0A06
What does the term "athermal effects" of RF radiation mean?
A. Biological effects from RF energy other than heating
B. Chemical effects from RF energy on minerals and liquids
C. A change in the phase of a signal resulting from the heating of an antenna
D. Biological effects from RF energy in excess of the maximum permissible exposure level

G0A07
At what frequencies does the human body absorb RF energy at a maximum rate?
A. The high-frequency (3-30-MHz) range
B. The very-high-frequency (30-300-MHz) range
C. The ultra-high-frequency (300-MHz to 3-GHz) range
D. The super-high-frequency (3-GHz to 30-GHz) range

G0A08
What does "time averaging" mean when it applies to RF radiation exposure?
A. The average time of day when the exposure occurs
B. The average time it takes RF radiation to have any long term effect on the body
C. The total time of the exposure, e.g. 6 minutes or 30 minutes
D. The total RF exposure averaged over a certain time

G0A03
(B)
Page 10-3

G0A04
(C)
Page 10-3

G0A05
(D)
Page 10-3

G0A06
(A)
Page 10-4

G0A07
(B)
Page 10-6

G0A08
(D)
Page 10-7

G0A09
(D)
Page 10-11

G0A09
What guideline is used to determine whether or not a routine RF evaluation must be performed for an amateur station?
A. If the transmitter's PEP is 50 watts or more, an evaluation must always be performed
B. If the RF radiation from the antenna system falls within a controlled environment, an evaluation must be performed
C. If the RF radiation from the antenna system falls within an uncontrolled environment, an evaluation must be performed
D. If the transmitter's PEP and frequency are within certain limits given in Part 97, an evaluation must be performed

G0A10
(A)
Page 10-10

G0A10
If you perform a routine RF evaluation on your station and determine that its RF fields exceed the FCC's exposure limits in human-accessible areas, what are you required to do?
A. Take action to prevent human exposure to the excessive RF fields
B. File an Environmental Impact Statement (EIS-97) with the FCC
C. Secure written permission from your neighbors to operate above the controlled MPE limits
D. Nothing; simply keep the evaluation in your station records

G0A11
(C)
Page 10-13

G0A11
At a site with multiple transmitters operating at the same time, how is each transmitter included in the RF exposure site evaluation?
A. Only the RF field of the most powerful transmitter need be considered
B. The RF fields of all transmitters are multiplied together
C. Transmitters that produce more than 5% of the maximum permissible power density exposure limit for that transmitter must be included
D. Only the RF fields from any transmitters operating with high duty-cycle modes (greater than 50%) need to be considered

G0B RF safety rules and guidelines

G0B01
(C)
Page 10-8

G0B01
What are the FCC's RF-safety rules designed to control?
A. The maximum RF radiated electric field strength
B. The maximum RF radiated magnetic field strength
C. The maximum permissible human exposure to all RF radiated fields
D. The maximum RF radiated power density

G0B02
At a site with multiple transmitters, who must ensure that all FCC RF-safety regulations are met?
A. All licensees contributing more than 5% of the maximum permissible power density exposure for that transmitter are equally responsible
B. Only the licensee of the station producing the strongest RF field is responsible
C. All of the stations at the site are equally responsible, regardless of any station's contribution to the total RF field
D. Only the licensees of stations which are producing an RF field exceeding the maximum permissible exposure limit are responsible

G0B02
(A)
Page 10-13

G0B03
What effect does duty cycle have when evaluating RF exposure?
A. Low duty-cycle emissions permit greater short-term exposure levels
B. High duty-cycle emissions permit greater short-term exposure levels
C. The duty cycle is not considered when evaluating RF exposure
D. Any duty cycle may be used as long as it is less than 100 percent

G0B03
(A)
Page 10-3

G0B04
What is the threshold power used to determine if an RF environmental evaluation is required when the operation takes place in the 15-meter band?
A. 50 watts PEP
B. 100 watts PEP
C. 225 watts PEP
D. 500 watts PEP

G0B04
(B)
Page 10-11

G0B05
Why do the power levels used to determine if an RF environmental evaluation is required vary with frequency?
A. Because amateur operators may use a variety of power levels
B. Because Maximum Permissible Exposure (MPE) limits are frequency dependent
C. Because provision must be made for signal loss due to propagation
D. All of these choices are correct

G0B05
(B)
Page 10-12

G0B06
What is the threshold power used to determine if an RF environmental evaluation is required when the operation takes place in the 10-meter band?
A. 50 watts PEP
B. 100 watts PEP
C. 225 watts PEP
D. 500 watts PEP

G0B06
(A)
Page 10-11

G0B07
(D)
Page 10-11

G0B07
What is the threshold power used to determine if an RF environmental evaluation is required for transmissions in the amateur bands with frequencies less than 10 MHz?
A. 50 watts PEP
B. 100 watts PEP
C. 225 watts PEP
D. 500 watts PEP

G0B08
(D)
Page 10-11

G0B08
What amateur frequency bands have the lowest power limits above which an RF environmental evaluation is required?
A. All bands between 17 and 30 meters
B. All bands between 10 and 15 meters
C. All bands between 40 and 160 meters
D. All bands between 1.25 and 10 meters

G0B09
(C)
Page 10-11

G0B09
What is the threshold power used to determine if an RF safety evaluation is required when the operation takes place in the 20-meter band?
A. 50 watts PEP
B. 100 watts PEP
C. 225 watts PEP
D. 500 watts PEP

G0B10
(B)
Page 10-12

G0B10
Under what conditions would an RF environmental evaluation be required for an amateur repeater station where the transmitting antenna is NOT mounted on a building?
A. The repeater transmitter is activated for more than 6 minutes without 30 seconds pauses
B. The height above ground to the lowest point of the antenna is less than 10 m and the radiated power from the antenna exceeds 500 W ERP
C. The height above ground to the lowest point of the antenna is less than 2 m and the radiated power from the antenna exceeds 500 W ERP
D. When the radiated power from the antenna exceeds 50 W ERP

G0B11
Under what conditions would an RF environmental evaluation be required for an amateur repeater station where the transmitting antenna is mounted on a building?
A. The repeater transmitter is activated for more than 6 minutes without 30 seconds pauses
B. The height above ground to the lowest point of the antenna is less than 10 m and the radiated power from the antenna exceeds 50 W ERP
C. The height above ground to the lowest point of the antenna is less than 2 m and the radiated power from the antenna exceeds 50 W ERP
D. The radiated power from the antenna exceeds 500 W ERP

G0B11
(D)
Page 10-12

G0C Routine station evaluation and measurements (FCC Part 97 refers to RF radiation evaluation)

G0C01
If the free-space far-field strength of a 10-MHz dipole antenna measures 1.0 millivolts per meter at a distance of 5 wavelengths, what will the field strength measure at a distance of 10 wavelengths?
A. 0.10 millivolts per meter
B. 0.25 millivolts per meter
C. 0.50 millivolts per meter
D. 1.0 millivolts per meter

G0C01
(C)
Page 10-21

G0C02
If the free-space far-field strength of a 28-MHz Yagi antenna measures 4.0 millivolts per meter at a distance of 5 wavelengths, what will the field strength measure at a distance of 20 wavelengths?
A. 2.0 millivolts per meter
B. 1.0 millivolts per meter
C. 0.50 millivolts per meter
D. 0.25 millivolts per meter

G0C02
(B)
Page 10-21

G0C03
If the free-space far-field strength of a 1.8-MHz dipole antenna measures 9 microvolts per meter at a distance of 4 wavelengths, what will the field strength measure at a distance of 12 wavelengths?
A. 3 microvolts per meter
B. 3.6 microvolts per meter
C. 4.8 microvolts per meter
D. 10 microvolts per meter

G0C03
(A)
Page 10-21

G0C04
(D)
Page 10-20

G0C04
If the free-space far-field power density of a 18-MHz Yagi antenna measures 10 milliwatts per square meter at a distance of 3 wavelengths, what will it measure at a distance of 6 wavelengths?
A. 11 milliwatts per square meter
B. 5.0 milliwatts per square meter
C. 3.3 milliwatts per square meter
D. 2.5 milliwatts per square meter

G0C05
(B)
Page 10-20

G0C05
If the free-space far-field power density of an antenna measures 9 milliwatts per square meter at a distance of 5 wavelengths, what will the field strength measure at a distance of 15 wavelengths?
A. 3 milliwatts per square meter
B. 1 milliwatt per square meter
C. 0.9 milliwatt per square meter
D. 0.09 milliwatt per square meter

G0C06
(A)
Page 10-18

G0C06
What factors determine the location of the boundary between the near and far fields of an antenna?
A. Wavelength of the signal and physical size of the antenna
B. Antenna height and element material
C. Boom length and element material
D. Transmitter power and antenna gain

G0C07
(D)
Page 10-13

G0C07
Which of the following steps might an amateur operator take to ensure compliance with the RF safety regulations?
A. Post a copy of FCC Part 97 in the station
B. Post a copy of OET Bulletin 65 in the station
C. Nothing; amateur compliance is voluntary
D. Perform a routine RF exposure evaluation

G0C08
(C)
Page 10-19

G0C08
In the free-space far field, what is the relationship between the electric field (E field) and magnetic field (H field)?
A. The electric field strength is equal to the square of the magnetic field strength
B. The electric field strength is equal to the cube of the magnetic field strength
C. The electric and magnetic field strength has a fixed impedance relationship of 377 ohms
D. The electric field strength times the magnetic field strength equals 377 ohms

G0C09
What type of instrument can be used to accurately measure an RF field?
A. A receiver with an S meter
B. A calibrated field-strength meter with a calibrated antenna
C. A betascope with a dummy antenna calibrated at 50 ohms
D. An oscilloscope with a high-stability crystal marker generator

G0C10
If your station complies with the RF safety rules and you reduce its power output from 500 to 40 watts, how would the RF safety rules apply to your operations?
A. You would need to reevaluate your station for compliance with the RF safety rules because the power output changed
B. You would need to reevaluate your station for compliance with the RF safety rules because the transmitting parameters changed
C. You would not need to perform an RF safety evaluation, but your station would still need to be in compliance with the RF safety rules
D. The RF safety rules would no longer apply to your station because it would be operating with less than 50 watts of power

G0C11
If your station complies with the RF safety rules and you reduce its power output from 1000 to 500 watts, how would the RF safety rules apply to your operations?
A. You would need to reevaluate your station for compliance with the RF safety rules because the power output changed
B. You would need to reevaluate your station for compliance with the RF safety rules because the transmitting parameters changed
C. You would need to perform an RF safety evaluation to ensure your station would still be in compliance with the RF safety rules
D. Since your station was in compliance with RF safety rules at a higher power output, you need to do nothing more

G0D Practical RF-safety applications

G0D01
Considering RF safety, what precaution should you take if you install an indoor transmitting antenna?
A. Locate the antenna close to your operating position to minimize feed line losses
B. Position the antenna along the edge of a wall where it meets the floor or ceiling to reduce parasitic radiation
C. Locate the antenna as far away as possible from living spaces that will be occupied while you are operating
D. Position the antenna parallel to electrical power wires to take advantage of parasitic effects

G0C09
(B)
Page 10-17

G0C10
(C)
Page 10-14

G0C11
(D)
Page 10-14

G0D01
(C)
Page 10-15

G0D02
(A)
Page 10-17

G0D02
Considering RF safety, what precaution should you take whenever you make adjustments to the feed line of a directional antenna system?
A. Be sure no one can activate the transmitter
B. Disconnect the antenna-positioning mechanism
C. Point the antenna away from the sun so it doesn't concentrate solar energy on you
D. Be sure you and the antenna structure are properly grounded

G0D03
(A)
Page 10-15

G0D03
What is the best reason to place a protective fence around the base of a ground-mounted transmitting antenna?
A. To reduce the possibility of persons being exposed to levels of RF in excess of the maximum permissible exposure (MPE) limits
B. To reduce the possibility of animals damaging the antenna
C. To reduce the possibility of persons vandalizing expensive equipment
D. To improve the antenna's grounding system and thereby reduce the possibility of lightning damage

G0D04
(B)
Page 10-15

G0D04
What RF-safety precautions should you take before beginning repairs on an antenna?
A. Be sure you and the antenna structure are grounded
B. Be sure to turn off the transmitter and disconnect the feed-line
C. Inform your neighbors so they are aware of your intentions
D. Turn off the main power switch in your house

G0D05
(D)
Page 10-15

G0D05
What precaution should be taken when installing a ground-mounted antenna?
A. It should not be installed higher than you can reach
B. It should not be installed in a wet area
C. It should be painted so people or animals do not accidentally run into it
D. It should be installed so no one can be exposed to RF radiation in excess of the maximum permissible exposure (MPE) limits

G0D06
(B)
Page 10-16

G0D06
What precaution should you take before beginning repairs on a microwave feed horn or waveguide?
A. Wear tight-fitting clothes and gloves to protect your body and hands from sharp edges
B. Be sure the transmitter is turned off and the power source is disconnected
C. Wait until the weather is dry and sunny
D. Be sure propagation conditions are not favorable for troposphere ducting

G0D07

Why should directional high-gain antennas be mounted higher than nearby structures?

A. To eliminate inversion of the major and minor lobes
B. So they will not damage nearby structures with RF energy
C. So they will receive more sky waves and fewer ground waves
D. So they will not direct excessive amounts of RF energy toward people in nearby structures

G0D08

For best RF safety, where should the ends and center of a dipole antenna be located?

A. Near or over moist ground so RF energy will be radiated away from the ground
B. As close to the transmitter as possible so RF energy will be concentrated near the transmitter
C. As far away as possible to minimize RF exposure to people near the antenna
D. Close to the ground so simple adjustments can be easily made without climbing a ladder

G0D09

What should you do to reduce RF radiation exposure when operating at 1270 MHz?

A. Make sure that an RF leakage filter is installed at the antenna feed point
B. Keep the antenna away from your eyes when RF is applied
C. Make sure the standing wave ratio is low before you conduct a test
D. Never use a shielded horizontally polarized antenna

G0D10

For best RF safety for driver and passengers, where should the antenna of a mobile VHF transceiver be mounted?

A. On the right side of a metal rear bumper
B. On the left side of a metal rear bumper
C. In the center of a metal roof
D. On the top-center of the rear window glass

G0D11

Considering RF safety, which of the following is the best reason to mount the antenna of a mobile VHF transceiver in the center of a metal roof?

A. The roof will greatly shield the driver and passengers from RF radiation
B. The antenna will be out of the driver's line of sight
C. The center of a metal roof is the sturdiest mounting place for an antenna
D. The wind resistance of the antenna will be centered between the wheels and not drag on one side or the other

G0D07
(D)
Page 10-16

G0D08
(C)
Page 10-16

G0D09
(B)
Page 10-16

G0D10
(C)
Page 10-16

G0D11
(A)
Page 10-16

G0E RF-safety solutions

G0E01
(B)
Page 10-15

G0E01
If you receive minor burns every time you touch your microphone while you are transmitting, which of the following statements is true?
A. You need to use a low-impedance microphone
B. You and others in your station may be exposed to more than the maximum permissible level of RF radiation
C. You need to use a surge suppressor on your station transmitter
D. All of these choices are correct

G0E02
(D)
Page 10-14

G0E02
If measurements indicate that individuals in your station are exposed to more than the maximum permissible level of radiation, which of the following corrective measures would be effective?
A. Ensure proper grounding of the equipment
B. Ensure that all equipment covers are tightly fastened
C. Use the minimum amount of transmitting power necessary
D. All of these choices are correct

G0E03
(B)
Page 10-14

G0E03
If calculations show that you and your family may be receiving more than the maximum permissible RF radiation exposure from your 20-meter indoor dipole, which of the following steps might be appropriate?
A. Use RTTY instead of CW or SSB voice emissions
B. Move the antenna to a safe outdoor environment
C. Use an antenna-matching network to reduce your transmitted SWR
D. All of these choices are correct

G0E04
(D)
Page 10-15

G0E04
Considering RF exposure, which of the following steps should you take when installing an antenna?
A. Install the antenna as high and far away from populated areas as possible
B. If the antenna is a gain antenna, point it away from populated areas
C. Minimize feed line radiation into populated areas
D. All of these choices are correct

G0E05
(D)
Page 10-14

G0E05
What might you do if an RF radiation evaluation shows that your neighbors may be receiving more than the maximum RF radiation exposure limit from your Yagi antenna when it is pointed at their house?
A. Change from horizontal polarization to vertical polarization
B. Change from horizontal polarization to circular polarization
C. Use an antenna with a higher front to rear ratio
D. Take precautions to ensure you can't point your antenna at their house

G0E06
What might you do if an RF radiation evaluation shows that your neighbors may be receiving more than the maximum RF radiation exposure limit from your quad antenna when it is pointed at their house?
A. Reduce your transmitter power to a level that reduces their exposure to a value below the maximum permissible exposure (MPE) limit
B. Change from horizontal polarization to vertical polarization
C. Use an antenna with a higher front to side ratio
D. Use an antenna with a sharper radiation lobe

G0E07
Why does a dummy antenna provide an RF safe environment for transmitter adjusting?
A. The dummy antenna carries the RF energy far away from the station before releasing it
B. The RF energy is contained in a halo around the outside of the dummy antenna
C. The RF energy is not radiated from a dummy antenna, but is converted to heat
D. The dummy antenna provides a perfect match to the antenna feed impedance

G0E08
From an RF radiation exposure point of view, which of the following materials would be the best to use for your homemade transmatch enclosure?
A. Aluminum
B. Bakelite
C. Transparent acrylic plastic
D. Any nonconductive material

G0E09
From an RF radiation exposure point of view, what is the advantage to using a high-gain, narrow-beamwidth antenna for your VHF station?
A. High-gain antennas absorb stray radiation
B. The RF radiation can be better focused in a direction away from populated areas
C. Narrow-beamwidth antennas eliminate exposure in areas directly under the antenna
D. All of these choices are correct

G0E06
(A)
Page 10-14

G0E07
(C)
Page 10-15

G0E08
(A)
Page 10-16

G0E09
(B)
Page 10-14

G0E10
(C)
Page 10-15

G0E10
From an RF radiation exposure point of view, what is the disadvantage in using a high-gain, narrow-beamwidth antenna for your VHF station?
A. High-gain antennas must be fed with coaxial cable feed-line, which radiates stray RF energy
B. The RF radiation can be better focused in a direction away from populated areas
C. Individuals in the main beam of the radiation pattern will receive a greater exposure than when a low-gain antenna is used
D. All of these choices are correct

G0E11
(B)
Page 10-15

G0E11
If your station is located in a residential area, which of the following would best help you reduce the RF exposure to your neighbors from your amateur station?
A. Use RTTY instead of CW or SSB voice emissions
B. Install your antenna as high as possible to maximize the distance to nearby people
C. Use top-quality coaxial cable to reduce RF losses in the feed-line
D. Use an antenna matching network to reduce your transmitted SWR

Schematic Symbols Used in Circuit Diagrams

US Customary—Metric Conversion Factors

International System of Units (SI)—Metric Prefixes

Prefix	Symbol		Multiplication Factor
exa	E	10^{18} =	1 000 000 000 000 000 000
peta	P	10^{15} =	1 000 000 000 000 000
tera	T	10^{12} =	1 000 000 000 000
giga	G	10^{9} =	1 000 000 000
mega	M	10^{6} =	1 000 000
kilo	k	10^{3} =	1 000
hecto	h	10^{2} =	100
deca	da	10^{1} =	10
(unit)		10^{0} =	1
deci	d	10^{-1} =	0.1
centi	c	10^{-2} =	0.01
milli	m	10^{-3} =	0.001
micro	μ	10^{-6} =	0.000001
nano	n	10^{-9} =	0.000000001
pico	p	10^{-12} =	0.000000000001
femto	f	10^{-15} =	0.000000000000001
atto	a	10^{-18} =	0.000000000000000001

Linear
1 metre (m) = 100 centimetres (cm) = 1000 millimetres (mm)

Area
$1 \text{ m}^2 = 1 \times 10^4 \text{ cm}^2 = 1 \times 10^6 \text{ mm}^2$

Volume
$1 \text{ m}^3 = 1 \times 10^6 \text{ cm}^3 = 1 \times 10^9 \text{ mm}^3$
$1 \text{ litre (l)} = 1000 \text{ cm}^3 = 1 \times 10^6 \text{ mm}^3$

Mass
1 kilogram (kg) = 1 000 grams (g)
 (Approximately the mass of 1 litre of water)
1 metric ton (or tonne) = 1 000 kg

US Customary Units

Linear Units
12 inches (in) = 1 foot (ft)
36 inches = 3 feet = 1 yard (yd)
1 rod = 5½ yards = 16½ feet
1 statute mile = 1 760 yards = 5 280 feet
1 nautical mile = 6 076.11549 feet

Area
$1 \text{ ft}^2 = 144 \text{ in}^2$
$1 \text{ yd}^2 = 9 \text{ ft}^2 = 1\ 296 \text{ in}^2$
$1 \text{ rod}^2 = 30\frac{1}{4} \text{ yd}^2$
$1 \text{ acre} = 4840 \text{ yd}^2 = 43\ 560 \text{ ft}^2$
$1 \text{ acre} = 160 \text{ rod}^2$
$1 \text{ mile}^2 = 640 \text{ acres}$

Volume
$1 \text{ ft}^3 = 1\ 728 \text{ in}^3$
$1 \text{ yd}^3 = 27 \text{ ft}^3$

Liquid Volume Measure
$1 \text{ fluid ounce (fl oz)} = 8 \text{ fluidrams} = 1.804 \text{ in}^3$
1 pint (pt) = 16 fl oz
$1 \text{ quart (qt)} = 2 \text{ pt} = 32 \text{ fl oz} = 57\frac{3}{4} \text{ in}^3$
$1 \text{ gallon (gal)} = 4 \text{ qt} = 231 \text{ in}^3$
1 barrel = 31½ gal

Dry Volume Measure
$1 \text{ quart (qt)} = 2 \text{ pints (pt)} = 67.2 \text{ in}^3$
1 peck = 8 qt
$1 \text{ bushel} = 4 \text{ pecks} = 2\ 150.42 \text{ in}^3$

Avoirdupois Weight
1 dram (dr) = 27.343 grains (gr) or (gr a)
1 ounce (oz) = 437.5 gr
1 pound (lb) = 16 oz = 7 000 gr
1 short ton = 2 000 lb, 1 long ton = 2 240 lb

Troy Weight
1 grain troy (gr t) = 1 grain avoirdupois
1 pennyweight (dwt) or (pwt) = 24 gr t
1 ounce troy (oz t) = 480 grains
1 lb t = 12 oz t = 5 760 grains

Apothecaries' Weight
1 grain apothecaries' (gr ap) = 1 gr t = 1 gr a
1 dram ap (dr ap) = 60 gr
1 oz ap = 1 oz t = 8 dr ap = 480 fr
1 lb ap = 1 lb t = 12 oz ap = 5 760 gr

	Conversion				Conversion	
Metric Unit =	Factor ×	US Unit		Metric Unit =	Factor ×	US Unit

(Length)

Metric Unit	Factor	US Unit
mm	25.4	inch
cm	2.54	inch
cm	30.48	foot
m	0.3048	foot
m	0.9144	yard
km	1.609	mile
km	1.852	nautical mile

(Area)

Metric Unit	Factor	US Unit
mm^2	645.16	inch^2
cm^2	6.4516	in^2
cm^2	929.03	ft^2
m^2	0.0929	ft^2
cm^2	8361.3	yd^2
m^2	0.83613	yd^2
m^2	4047	acre
km^2	2.59	mi^2

(Mass) (Avoirdupois Weight)

Metric Unit	Factor	US Unit
grams	0.0648	grains
g	28.349	oz
g	453.59	lb
kg	0.45359	lb
tonne	0.907	short ton
tonne	1.016	long ton

(Volume)

Metric Unit	Factor	US Unit
mm^3	16387.064	in^3
cm^3	16.387	in^3
m^3	0.028316	ft^3
m^3	0.764555	yd^3
ml	16.387	in^3
ml	29.57	fl oz
ml	473	pint
ml	946.333	quart
l	28.32	ft^3
l	0.9463	quart
l	3.785	gallon
l	1.101	dry quart
l	8.809	peck
l	35.238	bushel

(Mass) (Troy Weight)

Metric Unit	Factor	US Unit
g	31.103	oz t
g	373.248	lb t

(Mass) (Apothecaries' Weight)

Metric Unit	Factor	US Unit
g	3.387	dr ap
g	31.103	oz ap
g	373.248	lb ap

Standard Resistance Values

Numbers in **bold** type are ± 10% values. Others are 5% values.

Ohms

1.0	3.6	**12**	43	**150**	510	**1800**	6200	**22000**	75000
1.1	**3.9**	13	**47**	160	**560**	2000	**6800**	24000	**82000**
1.2	4.3	**15**	51	**180**	620	**2200**	7500	**27000**	91000
1.3	**4.7**	16	**56**	200	**680**	2400	**8200**	30000	**100000**
1.5	5.1	**18**	62	**220**	750	**2700**	9100	**33000**	110000
1.6	**5.6**	20	**68**	240	**820**	3000	**10000**	36000	**120000**
1.8	6.2	**22**	75	**270**	910	**3300**	11000	**39000**	130000
2.0	**6.8**	24	**82**	300	**1000**	3600	**12000**	43000	**150000**
2.2	7.5	**27**	91	**330**	1100	**3900**	13000	**47000**	160000
2.4	**8.2**	30	**100**	360	**1200**	4300	**15000**	51000	**180000**
2.7	9.1	**33**	110	**390**	1300	**4700**	16000	**56000**	200000
3.0	**10.0**	36	**120**	430	**1500**	5100	**18000**	62000	**220000**
3.3	11.0	**39**	130	**470**	1600	**5600**	20000	**68000**	

Megohms

0.24	**0.62**	1.6	4.3	11.0
0.27	**0.68**	**1.8**	**4.7**	**12.0**
0.30	0.75	2.0	5.1	13.0
0.33	**0.82**	2.2	**5.6**	**15.0**
0.36	0.91	2.4	6.2	16.0
0.39	**1.0**	**2.7**	**6.8**	**18.0**
0.43	1.1	3.0	7.5	20.0
0.47	**1.2**	**3.3**	**8.2**	**22.0**
0.51	1.3	3.6	9.1	
0.56	**1.5**	**3.9**	**10.0**	

Resistor Color Code

Color	Sig. Figure	Decimal Multiplier	Tolerance (%)	Color	Sig. Figure	Decimal Multiplier	Tolerance (%)
Black	0	1		Violet	7	10,000,000	
Brown	1	10		Gray	8	100,000,000	
Red	2	100		White	9	1,000,000,000	
Orange	3	1,000		Gold	—	0.1	5
Yellow	4	10,000		Silver	—	0.01	10
Green	5	100,000		No color	—		20
Blue	6	1,000,000					

Standard Values for 1000-V Disc-Ceramic Capacitors

pF	pF	pF	pF
3.3	39	250	1000
5	47	270	1200
6	50	300	1500
6.8	51	330	1800
8	56	360	2000
10	68	390	2500
12	75	400	2700
15	82	470	3000
18	100	500	3300
20	120	510	3900
22	130	560	4700
24	150	600	5000
25	180	680	5600
27	200	750	6800
30	220	820	8200
33	240	910	10000

Common Values for Small Electrolytic Capacitors

μF	V*	μF	V*
33	6.3	10	35
33	10	22	35
100	10	33	35
220	10	47	35
330	10	100	35
470	10	220	35
10	16	330	35
22	16	470	35
33	16	1000	35
47	16	1	50
100	16	2.2	50
220	16	3.3	50
470	16	4.7	50
1000	16	10	50
2200	16	33	50
4.7	25	47	50
22	25	100	50
33	25	220	50
47	25	330	50
100	25	470	50
220	25	10	63
330	25	22	63
470	25	47	63
1000	25	1	100
2200	25	10	100
4.7	35	33	100

*Working voltage

Nomograph of SWR versus forward and reflected power for levels up to 20 watts. Dashed line shows an SWR of 1.5:1 for 10 W forward and 0.4 W reflected.

Nomograph of SWR versus forward and reflected power for levels up to 2000 watts. Dashed line shows an SWR of 2:1 for 90 W forward and 10 W reflected.

Fractions of an Inch with Metric Equivalents

Fractions Of An Inch		Decimals Of An Inch	Millimeters	Fractions Of An Inch		Decimals Of An Inch	Millimeters
	1/64	0.0156	0.397		33/64	0.5156	13.097
1/32		0.0313	0.794	17/32		0.5313	13.494
	3/64	0.0469	1.191		35/64	0.5469	13.891
1/16		0.0625	1.588	9/16		0.5625	14.288
	5/64	0.0781	1.984		37/64	0.5781	14.684
3/32		0.0938	2.381	19/32		0.5938	15.081
	7/64	0.1094	2.778		39/64	0.6094	15.478
1/8		0.1250	3.175	5/8		0.6250	15.875
	9/64	0.1406	3.572		41/64	0.6406	16.272
5/32		0.1563	3.969	21/32		0.6563	16.669
	11/64	0.1719	4.366		43/64	0.6719	17.066
3/16		0.1875	4.763	11/16		0.6875	17.463
	13/64	0.2031	5.159		45/64	0.7031	17.859
7/32		0.2188	5.556	23/32		0.7188	18.256
	15/64	0.2344	5.953		47/64	0.7344	18.653
1/4		0.2500	6.350	3/4		0.7500	19.050
	17/64	0.2656	6.747		49/64	0.7656	19.447
9/32		0.2813	7.144	25/32		0.7813	19.844
	19/64	0.2969	7.541		51/64	0.7969	20.241
5/16		0.3125	7.938	13/16		0.8125	20.638
	21/64	0.3281	8.334		53/64	0.8281	21.034
11/32		0.3438	8.731	27/32		0.8438	21.431
	23/64	0.3594	9.128		55/64	0.8594	21.828
3/8		0.3750	9.525	7/8		0.8750	22.225
	25/64	0.3906	9.922		57/64	0.8906	22.622
13/32		0.4063	10.319	29/32		0.9063	23.019
	27/64	0.4219	10.716		59/64	0.9219	23.416
7/16		0.4375	11.113	15/16		0.9375	23.813
	29/64	0.4531	11.509		61/64	0.9531	24.209
15/32		0.4688	11.906	31/32		0.9688	24.606
	31/64	0.4844	12.303		63/64	0.9844	25.003
1/2		0.5000	12.700	1		1.0000	25.400

EQUATIONS USED IN THIS BOOK

$$P = I \times E \tag{Equation 4-1}$$

$$I = \frac{E}{R} \tag{Equation 4-2}$$

$$P = \frac{E}{R} \times E = \frac{E^2}{R} \tag{Equation 4-3}$$

$$PEP = \frac{[(0.707\,PEV)(0.707\,PEV)]}{R_L} \tag{Equation 4-4}$$

$$\text{Peak Envelope Voltage} = \frac{\text{Peak} - \text{to} - \text{Peak Voltage}}{2} \tag{Equation 4-5}$$

$$E = I \times R \tag{Equation 5-1}$$

$$I = \frac{E}{R} \tag{Equation 5-2}$$

$$R = \frac{E}{I} \tag{Equation 5-3}$$

$$I_1 + I_2 + I_3 + \ldots = I_T \tag{Equation 5-4}$$

$$P = I \times E \tag{Equation 5-5}$$

$$I = \frac{P}{E} \tag{Equation 5-6}$$

$$E = \frac{P}{I} \qquad \text{(Equation 5-7)}$$

$$dB = 10 \times \log_{10}\left(\frac{P_2}{P_1}\right) \qquad \text{(Equation 5-8)}$$

$$V_{PEAK} = V_{RMS} \times \sqrt{2} = V_{RMS} \times 1.414 \qquad \text{(Equation 5-9)}$$

$$V_{RMS} = \frac{V_{PEAK}}{\sqrt{2}} = V_{PEAK} \times 0.707 \qquad \text{(Equation 5-10)}$$

$$X_C = \frac{1}{2\pi f C} \qquad \text{(Equation 5-11)}$$

$$X_L = 2\pi f L \qquad \text{(Equation 5-12)}$$

$$E_S = \frac{N_S}{N_P} \times E_P \qquad \text{(Equation 5-13)}$$

$$Z_P = Z_S \left(\frac{N_P}{N_S}\right)^2 \qquad \text{(Equation 5-14)}$$

$$\frac{N_P}{N_S} = \sqrt{\frac{Z_P}{Z_S}} \qquad \text{(Equation 5-15)}$$

$$Z_P \times \left(\frac{N_S}{N_P}\right)^2 = Z_S \qquad \text{(Equation 5-16)}$$

$$P = I \times E \qquad \text{(Equation 6-1)}$$

$$\text{Multiplication factor} = \frac{\text{Transmitter output frequency}}{\text{Oscillator frequency}} \qquad \text{(Equation 8-1)}$$

$$\text{Oscillator deviation} \times \text{Multiplication factor} = \text{Transmitter deviation} \qquad \text{(Equation 8-2)}$$

$$Bw = 2 \times (D + M) \qquad \text{(Equation 8-3)}$$

$$\text{(Yagi) } L_{DRIVEN} \text{ (in ft) } = \frac{468}{f(MHz)} \qquad \text{(Equation 9-1)}$$

$$\text{(Yagi) } L_{DIRECTOR} = L_{DRIVEN} \times 0.95 \qquad \text{(Equation 9-2)}$$

$$\text{(Yagi) } L_{REFLECTOR} = L_{DRIVEN} \times 1.05 \qquad \text{(Equation 9-3)}$$

$$\text{(Quad) Driven Element Length (in ft)} = \frac{1005}{f(\text{in MHz})} \qquad \text{(Equation 9-4)}$$

$$\text{(Quad) Director Element Length (in ft)} = \frac{975}{f(\text{in MHz})} \qquad \text{(Equation 9-5)}$$

$$\text{(Quad) Reflector Element Length (in ft)} = \frac{1030}{f(\text{in MHz})} \qquad \text{(Equation 9-6)}$$

$$SWR = \frac{E_{MAX}}{E_{MIN}} \qquad \text{(Equation 9-7)}$$

$$SWR = \frac{Z_0}{R} \text{ or } SWR = \frac{R}{Z_0} \qquad \text{(Equation 9-8)}$$

$$D \approx \frac{2L^2}{\lambda} \qquad \text{(Equation 10-1)}$$

$$\frac{E}{H} = \text{Impedance of Free Space} = 377 \, \Omega \qquad \text{(Equation 10-2)}$$

$$\text{Power Density}_1 \times (\text{Distance}_1)^2 = \text{Power Density}_2 \times (\text{Distance}_2)^2 \qquad \text{(Equation 10-3)}$$

$$\text{Power Density}_2 = \text{Power Density}_1 \times \frac{(\text{Distance}_1)^2}{(\text{Distance}_2)^2} \qquad \text{(Equation 10-4)}$$

$$\text{Field Strength}_1 \times \text{Distance}_1 = \text{Field Strength}_2 \times \text{Distance}_2 \qquad \text{(Equation 10-5)}$$

$$\text{Field Strength}_2 = \text{Field Strength}_1 \times \frac{\text{Distance}_1}{\text{Distance}_2} \qquad \text{(Equation 10-6)}$$

GLOSSARY OF KEY WORDS

Alternating current (ac) — Electric current that flows first in one direction in a wire and then in the other direction. The applied voltage is changing polarity as the current direction changes. This direction reversal continues at a rate that depends on the frequency of the ac.

Amateur Auxiliary — A voluntary organization, administered by the ARRL. The primary objectives are to foster amateur self-regulation and compliance with the rules.

Amateur Teleprinting Over Radio (AMTOR) — AMTOR provides error-correcting capabilities. See **Automatic Repeat Request** and **Forward Error Correction**.

American National Standard Code for Information Interchange (ASCII) — A seven-bit digital code used in computer and radioteleprinter applications.

Amplitude modulation (AM) — A method of combining an information signal and an RF carrier wave in which the amplitude of the RF envelope (carrier and sidebands) is varied in relation to the information signal strength.

Athermal effects of RF radiation — Biological effects of RF radiation not directly related to heating effects in exposed body tissue. While research is ongoing, no conclusive evidence has been found to demonstrate that such fields cause serious health effects at low-level energy exposure.

Audio rectification — Interference to electronic devices caused by a strong RF field that is rectified and amplified in the device.

Audio-frequency shift keying (AFSK) — A method of transmitting radioteletype information by switching between two audio tones fed into an FM transmitter microphone input. This is the RTTY mode most often used on VHF and UHF.

Automatic Repeat Request (ARQ) — One of two AMTOR communications modes. In ARQ, also called Mode A, the two stations are constantly confirming each other's transmissions. If information is lost, it is repeated until the receiving station confirms reception.

Azimuthal-equidistant projection map — A map made with its center at one geographic location and the rest of the continents projected from that point. Also called a great-circle map, this map is the most useful type for determining where to point a directional antenna to communicate with a specific location.

Balanced line — Feed line with two conductors having equal but opposite voltages, with neither conductor at ground potential.

Balanced modulator — A mixer circuit used in a single-sideband suppressed-carrier transmitter to combine a voice signal and the RF carrier-oscillator signal. The balanced modulator isolates the input signals from each other and the output, so that only the sum and the difference of the two input signals reach the output. The original carrier-oscillator signal or the pure audio signal do not reach the output. A modulated RF signal contains some information to be transmitted.

Balun — A transformer used between a *bal*anced and an *un*balanced system, such as for feeding a balanced antenna with an unbalanced feed line.

Band plan — An agreement for operating within a certain portion of the radio spectrum. Band plans set aside certain frequencies for each different mode of amateur operation, such as CW, SSB, RTTY, SSTV, FM, repeaters and simplex.

Band-pass filter — A circuit that allows signals to go through it only if they are within a certain range of frequencies, and attenuates signals above and below this range.

Bandwidth — The frequency range (measured in hertz) over· which a signal is stronger than some specified amount below the peak signal level. For example, if a certain signal is at least half as strong as the peak power level over a range of +3 kHz, the signal has a 3-dB bandwidth of 6 kHz.

Baudot — A five-bit digital code used in teleprinter application.

Beacon — An amateur station transmitting communications for the purposes of observing propagation and reception or other related experimental activities.

Beacon station — An amateur station transmitting communications for the purposes of observation of propagation and reception or other related experimental activities. [§97.3(a)(9)]

Bleeder resistor — A large-value resistor connected to the filter capacitor in a power supply to discharge the filter capacitors when the supply is switched off.

Broadcasting — Transmissions intended to be received by the general public, either direct or relayed. [§97.3(a)(10)] Broadcasting is prohibited on Amateur Radio.

Capacitor — An electronic component composed of two or more conductive plates separated by an insulating material. A capacitor stores energy in an electric field.

Cathode-ray tube (CRT) — A vacuum tube with a phosphor coating on the inside of the face. CRTs are used in oscilloscopes and as the "picture tube" in television receivers.

Coaxial cable — Feed line with a central conductor surrounded by plastic, foam or gaseous insulation, which in turn is covered by a shielding conductor and the entire cable is covered with vinyl insulation.

Coil — A conductor wound into a series of loops. (Also see **inductor**.)

Critical angle — If radio waves leave an antenna at an angle greater than the critical angle for that frequency they will pass through the ionosphere instead of returning to Earth.

Critical frequency — The highest frequency at which a vertically incident radio wave will return from the ionosphere. Above the critical frequency radio signals pass through the ionosphere instead of returning to the Earth.

Cubical quad antenna — A full-wavelength loop antenna built with its elements in the shape of squares.

Current — A flow of electrons in an electric circuit.

D region — The lowest region of the ionosphere. The D region contributes very little to short-wave radio propagation, acting mainly to absorb energy from radio waves below about 7.5 MHz during daylight.

Decibel (dB) — The smallest change in sound level that can be detected by the human ear. Power gains and losses are also expressed in decibels.

Delta loop antenna — A full-wavelength loop antenna built with its elements in the shape of equilateral triangles.

Detector — A mixer circuit used to recover the information signal from a modulated RF signal.

Deviation ratio — The ratio between the maximum change in RF-carrier frequency and the highest modulating frequency used in an FM transmitter.

Direct current (dc) — Electric current that flows in one direction only.

Directional antenna — An antenna that concentrates more of the transmitted energy in a particular direction. A directional antenna must be turned to provide the best signal coverage in various directions. Such antennas also receive signals better from the direction they are pointed. Also called a beam antenna.

Director — A parasitic element in "front" of the driven element in a multielement antenna.

Driven element — The element connected directly to the feed line in a multielement antenna.

Duty cycle — The ratio between the actual RMS value of an RF signal and the RMS value of a continuous signal having the same PEP value, expressed as a percentage. A duty cycle of 100% corresponds to a continuous carrier, such as a test signal.

E region — The second lowest ionospheric region, the E region exists only during the day, and under certain conditions may refract radio waves enough to return them to Earth.

Effective voltage — The value of a dc voltage that will heat a resistive component to the same temperature as the ac voltage that is being measured.

Electric field strength — This is the field resulting from the electric charge distribution present on a radiating element. Electric field strength is expressed in volts per meter (V / m).

Electromotive force (EMF) — The force or pressure that pushes a current through a circuit.

Emergency communications — Communications involving the immediate safety of human life and immediate protection of property when normal communication systems are not available.

Emission types — Any signals from a transmitter. Phone, data and CW are emission types.

F region — The highest ionospheric region, the F region refracts radio waves and returns them to Earth. The height of the F region varies greatly depending on the time of day, season of the year and amount of sunspot activity. During the day this region often splits into two regions, called the F1 and F2 regions.

Far field of an antenna — That region of the electromagnetic field surrounding an antenna where the field strength as a function of angle (the antenna pattern) is essentially independent of the distance from the antenna. In this region (also called the free-space region), the field has a predominantly plane-wave character. That is, locally uniform distributions of electric field strength and magnetic field strength are in a plane perpendicular to the direction of propagation.

Feed line — The wire or cable used to connect an antenna to the transmitter and receiver. (Also called *transmission line*.)

Field-strength meter — A simple test instrument used to show the presence of RF energy and the relative strength of the RF field.

Filter — A circuit that will allow some signals to pass through it but will greatly reduce the strength of others. In a power-supply circuit, a filter smoothes the ac ripple.

Flattopping — A distorted audio signal produced by an SSB transmitter with the microphone gain set too high. The peaks of the voice waveform are cut off in the transmitter because of overmodulation. Also called *clipping*.

Forward Error Correction (FEC) — One of two AMTOR communications modes. In the FEC mode, each character is sent twice. The receiving station checks for errors in the mark/space ratio. If an error is detected, a space is printed to show that an incorrect character was received. Also called Mode B.

Frequency deviation — The amount the carrier frequency in an FM transmitter changes as it is modulated.

Frequency modulation (FM) — The process of varying the frequency of an RF carrier in response to the instantaneous changes in an audible signal.

Frequency privileges — The specific band segments assigned to holders of each particular license . General operators have frequency privileges on the amateur high-frequency bands.

Frequency separation — The difference between a repeater input frequency (the frequency the repeater receives on) and the output frequency (the frequency it transmits on). Repeaters on the 10-meter band normally use a frequency separation of 100 kHz. (Also called **offset**.)

Frequency-shift keying (FSK) — A method of transmitting radioteletype information by switching an RF carrier between two separate frequencies. This is the RTTY mode most often used on HF.

Front-to-back ratio — The energy radiated from the front of a directive antenna divided by the energy radiated from the back of the antenna.

Full break-in (QSK) — With QSK, an amateur can hear signals between code characters. This allows another amateur to break into the communication without waiting for the transmitting station to finish.

Full-wave bridge rectifier — A full-wave rectifier circuit that uses four diodes and does not require a center-tapped transformer.

Full-wave rectifier — A circuit basically composed of two half-wave rectifiers. The full wave rectifier allows the full ac waveform to pass through; one half of the cycle is reversed in polarity. This circuit requires a center-tapped transformer.

Gain — An increase in the effective power radiated by an antenna in a certain desired direction, or an increase in received signal strength from a certain direction. This is at the expense of power radiated in, or signal strength received from, other directions.

Geomagnetic disturbance — A dramatic change in the Earth's magnetic field that occurs over a short time.

Gray line — A band around the Earth that separates daylight from darkness. It is a transition region between day and night.

Great-circle path — Either one of two direct paths between two points on the surface of the Earth. One of the great-circle paths is the shortest distance between those two points. Great-circle paths can be visualized if you think of a globe with a rubber band stretched around it, connecting the two points.

Ground-plane antenna — A vertical antenna built with a central radiating element one-quarter-wavelength long and several radials extending horizontally from the base. The radials are slightly longer than one-quarter wave, and may droop toward the ground.

Half-wave rectifier — A circuit that allows only half of the applied ac waveform to pass through it.

Half-wavelength dipole antenna — A fundamental antenna one-half wavelength long at the desired operating frequency, and connected to the feed line at the center. This is a popular amateur antenna.

Harmful interference — Interference that seriously degrades, obstructs or repeatedly interrupts a radiocommunication service operating in accordance with the Radio Regulations. [§97.3(a)(22)]

High-pass filter — A filter that allows signals above the cutoff frequency to pass through, and attenuates signals below the cutoff frequency.

Horizontally polarized wave — An electromagnetic wave with its electric lines of force parallel to the ground.

Image response — A form of interference to received signals that is produced when a mixer responds to a signal frequency equal to the LO – the IF when the desired signal frequency is equal to the LO + the IF. Also when the mixer responds to a signal frequency equal to the LO + IF when the desired signal frequency is the LO – IF.

Impedance — A term used to describe a combination of reactance and resistance in a circuit.

Inductor — An electrical component usually composed of a coil of wire wound on a central core. An inductor stores energy in a magnetic field.

International Telecommunication Union (ITU) — The international organization with responsibility for dividing the range of communications frequencies between the various services for the entire world.

Ionosphere — A region in the atmosphere about 30 to 260 miles above the Earth. The ionosphere is made up of charged particles, or ions.

Junction diode — An electronic component formed by placing a layer of N-type semiconductor material next to a layer of P-type material. Diodes allow current to flow in one direction only.

Local oscillator (LO) — A receiver circuit that generates a stable, pure signal used to mix with the received RF to produce a signal at the receiver intermediate frequency (IF).

Long-path communication — Communication made by pointing beam antennas in the directions indicated by the longer **great-circle path** between the stations. To work each other by long-path, an amateur in Hawaii would point his antenna west and an amateur in Florida would aim east.

Low-pass filter — A filter that allows signals below the cutoff frequency to pass through and attenuates signals above the cutoff frequency.

Magnetic field strength — This is the field resulting from the currents on a radiating element. Magnetic field strength is expressed in amperes per meter (A / m).

Magnetizing current — A small current that flows in a transformer primary winding, even with no load connected to the secondary.

Main lobe — The direction of maximum radiated field strength from an antenna. (Also called *major lobe*.)

Maximum average forward current — The highest average forward current that can flow through a diode for a given junction temperature.

Maximum Permissible Exposure (MPE) limits — The electric field strength, magnetic field strength and plane-wave equivalent power density associated with a radiated electromagnetic wave to which a person may be exposed without harmful effect, and with an acceptable safety factor.

Maximum usable frequency (MUF) — The highest frequency that allows a radio wave to reach a desired destination.

Mixer — A circuit that takes two or more input signals, and produces an output that includes the sum and difference of those signal frequencies.

Modulation — The process of varying some characteristic (amplitude, frequency or phase) of an RF carrier for the purpose of conveying information.

Modulation Index — The ratio between the maximum carrier frequency deviation and the audio modulating frequency at a given instant in an FM transmitter.

Monitor oscilloscope — A test instrument connected to an amateur transmitter and used to observe the shape of the transmitted-signal waveform.

Near field of an antenna — That region of the electromagnetic field immediately surrounding an antenna where the reactive field dominates and where the field strength as a function of angle (the antenna pattern) depends upon the distance from the antenna. It is a region in which the electric and magnetic fields do not have a substantial plane-wave character, but vary considerably from point to point.

Negative feedback — The process in which a portion of the amplifier output is returned to the input, 180° out of phase with the input signal.

Net — A group of amateurs who meet at regular times on a specific frequency to share common interests.

Neutralization — Feeding part of the output signal from an amplifier back to the input so it arrives out of phase with the input. This negative feedback neutralizes the effect of positive feedback caused by coupling between the input and output circuits in the amplifier.

Noise bridge — A test instrument used to determine the impedance of an antenna system.

Offset — The difference between a repeater's input and output frequencies. On 10 meters, for example, the repeater transmit offset is usually 100 kHz higher than the receive frequency. (Also called **frequency separation**.)

Ohm — The basic unit of resistance, reactance and impedance.

Ohm's Law — A basic law of electronics, it gives a relationship between voltage, resistance and current ($E = IR$).

One-way communications — Radio signals not directed to a specific amateur station, or for which no reply is expected. The FCC Rules provide for limited types of one-way communications on the amateur bands. [§97.111(b)]

Oscilloscope — An electronic test instrument used to observe waveforms and voltages on a cathode-ray tube.

Parallel-conductor feed line — Feed line constructed of two wires held a constant distance apart; either encased in plastic or constructed with insulating spacers placed at intervals along the line.

Parasitic element — Part of a directive antenna that derives energy from mutual coupling with the driven element. Parasitic elements are not connected directly to the feed line.

Peak envelope power (PEP) — The average power of the RF cycle having the greatest amplitude. (This occurs during a modulation peak.)

Peak-inverse-voltage (PIV) — The maximum voltage a diode can withstand when it is reverse biased (not conducting).

Phase — The time interval between one event and another in a regularly recurring cycle.

Phase modulation — Varying the phase of an RF carrier in response to the instantaneous changes in an audio signal.

Photovoltaic cell – A wafer of semiconductor material that produces electricity when light shines on it. Sometimes called a *solar cell*, each cell produces about $1/2$ volt when fully illuminated. Cells are connected in series to increase the voltage. The size or surface area of the cell determines the maximum current that the cell can supply. An array of cells forms a *solar panel* that can be used to charge a lead-acid storage battery.

Photovoltaic conversion — The process by which a semiconductor PN junction changes sunlight directly into electricity.

Polarization — The orientation of the electric lines of force in a radio wave, with respect to the surface of the Earth.

Power — The rate at which energy is consumed. In an electric circuit, power is found by multiplying the voltage applied to the circuit by the current through the circuit.

Power density — A measure of the power flow through a unit area normal (perpendicular) to the direction of propagation. It is usually expressed in watts per square meter (W / m^2)

Power supply — A device used to convert the available voltage and current source (often the 120-V ac household supply) to a form that is required for a specific circuit requirement. This will often be a higher or lower dc voltage.

Primary winding — The coil in a transformer that is connected to the energy source.

Propagation — The means by which radio waves travel from one place to another.

Pulsating dc — The output from a rectifier before it is filtered. The polarity of a pulsating dc source does not change, but the amplitude of the voltage changes with time.

Quarter-wavelength vertical antenna — An antenna constructed of a quarter-wavelength-long radiating element placed perpendicular to the Earth. (See **Ground-plane antenna**.)

Radio Amateur Civil Emergency Service (RACES) — Part of the amateur service that provides radio communications only for civil defense purposes.

Radio-Frequency Interference (RFI) — Interference to an electronic device (radio, TV, stereo) caused by RF energy from an amateur transmitter or other source.

Random-length wire antenna — A multiband antenna consisting of any convenient length of wire, connected directly to a transmitter or impedance-matching network without the use of feed line.

Reactance — The opposition to current that a capacitor or inductor creates in an ac circuit.

Reactance modulator — An electronic circuit whose capacitance or inductance changes in response to an audio input signal.

Rectifier — An electronic component that allows current to pass through it in only one direction.

Reflector — A parasitic element placed "behind" the driven element in a directive antenna.

Refract — To bend. Electromagnetic energy is refracted when it passes through a boundary between different types of material. Light is refracted as it travels from air into water or from water into air.

Repeater — An amateur station that automatically retransmits the signals of other amateur stations. [§97.3(a)(37)]

Resistance — The ability to oppose an electric current.

Resistor — Any material that opposes a current in an electrical circuit. An electronic component specifically designed to oppose current.

RF envelope — The shape of an RF signal as viewed on an oscilloscope.

Ripple — The amount of change between the maximum voltage and the minimum voltage in a pulsating dc waveform.

Root-mean-square (RMS) voltage — Another name for effective voltage. The term refers to the method of calculating the value.

Routine RF evaluation — A procedure required of some Amateur Radio stations, to determine that the station meets the maximum permissible exposure (MPE) limits established by FCC Rules.

S meter — A meter in a receiver that shows the relative strength of a received signal.

Scatter — Several factors may cause some energy from a radio signal to follow a path other than the idealized "straight line" shown on diagrams like Figure 3-1. Scattering can take place from Earth's ionospheric and atmospheric layers as well as objects in the wave path.

Secondary winding — The coil in a transformer that is connected to the load.

Short-path communication — Communication made by pointing beam antennas in the direction indicated by the shorter **great-circle path**.

Sideband — The sum or difference frequencies generated when an RF carrier is mixed with an audio signal.

Signal tracer — A test instrument that shows the presence of RF or AF energy in a circuit. The signal tracer is used to trace the flow of a signal through a multistage circuit.

Single sideband (SSB) — The type of voice (phone) operation used most often on the amateur high-frequency (HF) bands. One sideband and the carrier are removed from a double-sideband amplitude modulated (AM) signal, leaving only a single sideband to convey the voice information.

Single-sideband, suppressed-carrier signal — A radio signal in which only one of the two sidebands generated by amplitude modulation is transmitted. The other sideband and the RF carrier signal are removed before the signal is transmitted.

Single-sideband, suppressed-carrier, amplitude modulation (SSB) — A technique used to transmit voice information in which the amplitude of the RF carrier is modulated by the audio input, and the carrier and one sideband are suppressed.

Sky waves — Radio waves that travel from an antenna upward to the ionosphere, where they either pass through the ionosphere into space or are refracted back to Earth.

Solar flare — A large eruption of energy and solar material from the surface of the sun.

Solar flux — Radio energy coming from the sun.

Solar flux index — A measure of solar activity. The solar flux is a measure of the radio noise on 2800 MHz.

Specific absorption rate (SAR) — A measure of the rate at which RF energy is absorbed in body tissue. SAR is expressed in units of watts per kilogram (W / kg). The SAR depends on the frequency of the energy, the power density of the RF field that strikes the body and factors such as the polarization of the wave.

Speech processor — A device used to increase the average power contained in a speech waveform. Proper use of a speech processor can greatly improve the readability of a voice signal.

Splatter — Interference to adjacent signals caused by overmodulation of a transmitter.

Standing-wave ratio (SWR) — The ratio of maximum voltage to minimum voltage along a feed line. Also the ratio of antenna impedance to feed line impedance when the antenna is a purely resistive load.

Sudden Ionospheric Disturbance (SID) — A blackout of HF sky-wave communications that occurs after a solar flare.

Sunspots — Dark blotches that appear on the surface of the sun.

Superheterodyne receiver — A receiver that converts RF signals to an intermediate frequency before detecting them (converting the signals to audio).

Suppressor capacitor — A capacitor (often ceramic) connected across the transformer primary or secondary winding in a power supply. These capacitors are intended to suppress any transient voltage spikes, preventing them from getting through the power supply.

Temperature coefficient — A number used to show whether a component will increase or decrease in value as it gets warm.

Thermal effects of RF radiation — Body tissue changes that are directly related to heat production when RF energy is absorbed. For example, in extreme cases at high levels of SAR, hyperthermia and tissue damage can occur. It has been demonstrated that in extreme cases, RF-induced heating in the eyes of laboratory animals can result in cataract formation.

Third-party communication — A message from the control operator (first party) of an amateur station to another amateur station (second party) on behalf of another person (third party). [§97.3(a)(44)]

Time averaging — Transmitter power is averaged over times of 6 minutes for controlled RF environments or 30 minutes for uncontrolled RF environments for power density calculations to determine exposure levels.

Transformer — Mutually coupled coils used to change the voltage level of an ac power source to one more suitable for a particular circuit.

Transmit-receive (TR) switch — A mechanical switch relay or electronic circuit used to switch an antenna between a receiver and transmitter in an amateur station.

Two-tone test — Problems in a sideband transmitter can be detected by feeding two audio tones into the microphone input of the transmitter and observing the output on an oscilloscope.

Unbalanced line — Feed line with one conductor at ground potential, such as coaxial cable.

Varactor diode — A component whose capacitance varies as the reverse bias voltage is changed.

Vertically polarized wave — A radio wave that has its electric lines of force perpendicular to the surface of the Earth.

Voice-Operated Transmit (VOX) — Circuitry that activates the transmitter when the operator speaks into the microphone.

Voltage — The EMF or pressure that causes electrons to move through an electric circuit.

Yagi antenna — A directive antenna made with a half-wavelength driven element, and two or more parasitic elements arranged in the same horizontal plane.

ABOUT THE AMERICAN RADIO RELAY LEAGUE

The seed for Amateur Radio was planted in the 1890s, when Guglielmo Marconi began his experiments in wireless telegraphy. Soon he was joined by dozens, then hundreds, of others who were enthusiastic about sending and receiving messages through the air — some with a commercial interest, but others solely out of a love for this new communications medium. The United States government began licensing Amateur Radio operators in 1912.

By 1914, there were thousands of Amateur Radio operators — hams — in the United States. Hiram Percy Maxim, a leading Hartford, Connecticut, inventor and industrialist saw the need for an organization to band together this fledgling group of radio experimenters. In May 1914 he founded the American Radio Relay League (ARRL) to meet that need.

Today, with more than 170,000 members, ARRL is the largest organization of radio amateurs in the United States. The League is a not-for-profit organization that:

- promotes interest in Amateur Radio communications and experimentation
- represents US radio amateurs in legislative matters, and
- maintains fraternalism and a high standard of conduct among Amateur Radio operators.

At League headquarters in the Hartford suburb of Newington, the staff helps serve the needs of members. ARRL is also International Secretariat for the International Amateur Radio Union, which is made up of similar societies in more than 150 countries around the world.

ARRL publishes the monthly journal *QST*, as well as newsletters and many publications covering all aspects of Amateur Radio. Its headquarters station, W1AW, transmits Morse code practice sessions and bulletins of interest to radio amateurs. The League also coordinates an extensive field organization, which provides technical and other support for radio amateurs as well as communications for public-service activities. In addition, ARRL represents US amateurs with the Federal Communications Commission and other government agencies in the US and abroad.

Membership in ARRL means much more than receiving *QST* each month. In addition to the services already described, ARRL offers membership services on a personal level, such as the ARRL Volunteer Examiner Coordinator Program and a QSL bureau.

Full ARRL membership (available only to licensed radio amateurs in the US) gives you a voice in how the affairs of the organization are governed. League policy is set by a Board of Directors (one from each of 15 Divisions). Each year, half of the ARRL Board of Directors stands for election by the Full Members they represent. The day-to-day operation of ARRL HQ is managed by an Executive Vice President and a Chief Financial Officer.

No matter what aspect of Amateur Radio attracts you, ARRL membership is relevant and important. There would be no Amateur Radio as we know it today were it not for the ARRL. We would be happy to welcome you as a member! (An Amateur Radio license is not required for Associate Membership.) For more information about ARRL and answers to any questions you may have about Amateur Radio, write or call:

ARRL
225 Main Street
Newington CT 06111-1494
(860) 594-0200

Prospective new amateurs call:
800-32-NEW HAM (800-326-3942)
E-mail: **newham@arrl.org**
World Wide Web: **http://www.arrl.org/**

INDEX

R

NOTES